TEST BANK

CAMPBELL • REECE • TAYLOR • SIMON • DICKEY

BIOLOGY
CONCEPTS & CONNECTIONS

SIXTH EDITION

Mimi Bres
Prince George's Community College

Jon Hoekstra
Gainesville State College

David Mirman
Mt. San Antonio College

Richard Myers
Missouri State University

David Reid
Blackburn College

Linda Brooke Stabler
University of Central Oklahoma

Arnie Weishaar
Prince George's Community College

PEARSON
Benjamin
Cummings

San Francisco   Boston   New York
Cape Town   Hong Kong   London   Madrid   Mexico City
Montreal   Munich   Paris   Singapore   Sydney   Tokyo   Toronto

Executive Editor: Beth Wilbur
Senior Acquisitions Editor: Chalon Bridges
Project Editor: Rebecca Johnson
Executive Managing Editor: Erin Gregg
Managing Editor: Michael Early
Production Supervisor: Camille Herrera
Production Management and Composition: Progressive Publishing Alternatives
Cover Production: Richard Whitaker
Illustrators: Progressive Publishing Alternatives
Manufacturing Buyer: Michael Penne
Executive Marketing Manager: Lauren Harp
Senior Marketing Manager: Jay Jenkins
Text and Cover printer: Technical Communications Services

Cover Photo Credit: Leopard (*Panthera pardus*) in grass, looking up, in Sabi Sands Conservancy, Mpumalanga Province, South Africa; Heinrich van den Berg, Getty Images

ISBN 10-digit: 0-321-54792-6
13-digit: 978-0-321-54792-7

2 3 4 5 6 7 8 9 10—TCS—11 10 09

www.pearsonhighered.com

Contents

Chapter 1 Introduction: The Scientific Study of Life

Multiple-Choice Questions

1) Which of the following statements about the leopard is *false*?
   A) Leopards are the largest cat in the genus *Panthera*.
   B) Leopards, like lions, can roar.
   C) Leopards prefer to eat their kill in trees.
   D) Leopards are well-adapted for nocturnal hunting.
   E) Leopards are normally solitary animals.

   Answer: A
   Topic: Opening Essay
   Skill: Factual Recall

2) Life is organized in a hierarchical fashion. Which of the following sequences correctly lists that hierarchy as it increases in complexity?
   A) ecosystem, population, organ system, cell, community, molecule, organ, organism, tissue
   B) cell, molecule, organ system, organ, population, tissue, organism, ecosystem, community
   C) organism, organ system, tissue, population, organ, community, cell, ecosystem, molecule
   D) molecule, cell, tissue, organ, organ system, organism, population, community, ecosystem
   E) ecosystem, molecule, cell, tissue, organism, organ system, organ, community

   Answer: D
   Topic: 1.1
   Skill: Factual Recall

3) What is the difference between a tissue and an organ system?
   A) The tissue level of organization is more inclusive than the organ system level.
   B) Tissues are not composed of cells; organ systems are composed of cells.
   C) A tissue cannot exist unless it is a component of an organ system, whereas an organ system can exist independently of tissues.
   D) An organ system includes tissues.
   E) Tissues are not considered to be living; organ systems are considered to be living.

   Answer: D
   Topic: 1.1
   Skill: Factual Recall

4) The tree in your backyard is home to two cardinals, a colony of ants, a wasp's nest, two squirrels, and millions of bacteria. Together, all of these organisms represent
    A) a species.
    B) a community.
    C) a population.
    D) an ecosystem.
    E) the biosphere.
Answer: B
Topic: 1.1
Skill: Application

5) If you eat a hamburger, you are mainly eating ground-up beef muscle. What levels of organization are represented in this ground-up muscle?
    A) organism, population, and community
    B) organ, organ system, and organism
    C) community, ecosystem, and biosphere
    D) organelle, cell, and tissue
    E) tissue, organ, and organ system
Answer: D
Topic: 1.1
Skill: Application

6) Which of the following statements about ecosystems is *false*?
    A) The "web of relationships" within an ecosystem includes the nonliving components of the environment.
    B) Bacteria and fungi recycle energy within an ecosystem.
    C) Plants and other photosynthetic organisms are producers in ecosystems.
    D) Chemical nutrients cycle within an ecosystem's structural web.
    E) In the process of energy conversions within an ecosystem, energy is eventually converted to heat.
Answer: B
Topic: 1.2
Skill: Factual Recall

7) The ultimate source of energy flowing into nearly all ecosystems is
    A) wind.
    B) sunlight.
    C) electricity.
    D) geothermal vents.
    E) radioactivity.
Answer: B
Topic: 1.2
Skill: Conceptual Understanding

8) A consumer eating a producer represents
    A) a transfer of chemical nutrients and energy.
    B) a transfer of chemical nutrients but not a transfer of energy.
    C) a transfer of energy but not a transfer of chemical nutrients.
    D) neither a transfer of chemical nutrients nor a transfer of energy.

Answer: A
Topic: 1.2
Skill: Conceptual Understanding

9) Which of the following statements regarding a common cellular activity is *false*?
    A) Cells respond to the environment.
    B) Cells develop and maintain complex organization.
    C) Cells take in and use energy.
    D) Cells regulate their internal environment.
    E) New cells are derived from cellular components like organelles.

Answer: E
Topic: 1.3
Skill: Factual Recall

10) Your instructor asks you to look into your microscope to see a prokaryotic cell. You will be looking for a cell that
    A) has a nucleus.
    B) has a membrane.
    C) makes up most of the tissues of your body.
    D) is much larger than most cells in your body.
    E) does not use DNA to code genetic information.

Answer: B
Topic: 1.3
Skill: Application

11) Which of the following statements about genetics is *true*?
    A) Genes are proteins that produce DNA.
    B) Each organism has its own unique DNA code.
    C) DNA relies upon five different building blocks as the alphabet of inheritance.
    D) Differences among organisms reflect different nucleotide sequences in their DNA.
    E) Each DNA molecule is a single strand of nucleotides.

Answer: D
Topic: 1.4
Skill: Factual Recall

12) Which of the following statements about the properties of life is *false*?
    A) All organisms have a complex organization.
    B) All organisms have the ability to take in energy and use it.
    C) All organisms have the ability to respond to stimuli from the environment.
    D) All organisms have the ability to reproduce.
    E) All organisms have the ability to maintain a constant internal temperature.

Answer: E
Topic: 1.4
Skill: Factual Recall

13) Which of the following statements about living systems is *false*?
    A) Living systems are composed of two or more cells.
    B) Living systems maintain a relatively consistent internal environment.
    C) Living systems respond to changes in the environment.
    D) Living systems encode their genetic information in DNA.
    E) Living systems grow and develop.

Answer: A
Topic: 1.4
Skill: Conceptual Understanding

14) Organisms that are prokaryotes are in the domains
    A) Bacteria and Archaea.
    B) Plantae and Animalia.
    C) Eukarya and Archaea.
    D) Archaea and Plantae.
    E) Fungi and Bacteria.

Answer: A
Topic: 1.5
Skill: Factual Recall

15) Which of the following statements about the domain Bacteria is *true*?
    A) All bacteria are "animal–like" in that they eat other organisms.
    B) All bacteria have a membrane–bound nucleus.
    C) All bacteria are multicellular organisms.
    D) All bacteria lack a nucleus.
    E) All bacteria are "animal–like" in that they eat other organisms, and all bacteria have a membrane–bound nucleus.

Answer: D
Topic: 1.5
Skill: Factual Recall

16) Members of the kingdom Animalia
    A) can obtain their food either by absorption or by photosynthesis.
    B) are composed of cells that lack a cell membrane.
    C) are composed of cells that are surrounded by a cell wall.
    D) can obtain their food by eating other organisms.
    E) are composed of cells that are surrounded by a cell wall and that lack a cell membrane.

Answer: D
Topic: 1.5
Skill: Factual Recall

17) What feature is common to prokaryotes, fungi, and plants?
    A) a nucleus
    B) single cells
    C) membership in the kingdom Monera
    D) cell walls
    E) photosynthesis

Answer: D
Topic: 1.5
Skill: Factual Recall

18) Which of the following is a kingdom within the domain Eukarya?
  A) Viruses
  B) Monera
  C) Fungi
  D) Archaea
  E) Bacteria

Answer: C
Topic: 1.5
Skill: Factual Recall

19) All organisms belonging to the kingdom Plantae
  A) are photosynthetic.
  B) contain cells that are surrounded by cell walls with cellulose.
  C) are unicellular and lack a nucleus.
  D) lack a nucleus.
  E) are photosynthetic and contain cells that are surrounded by cell walls with cellulose.

Answer: E
Topic: 1.5
Skill: Factual Recall

20) Members of the kingdom Fungi
  A) include the mushrooms.
  B) include the yeasts.
  C) decompose the remains of dead organisms and absorb nutrients from the leftovers.
  D) include the mushrooms and yeasts, and decompose the remains of dead organisms and absorb nutrients from the leftovers.
  E) use photosynthesis to produce their own food.

Answer: D
Topic: 1.5
Skill: Factual Recall

21) A scientist examining a group of cells under the microscope notices the presence of nuclei within these cells. Chemical tests reveal that each cell is surrounded by a wall composed of cellulose. These cells must come from an organism that is a member of the kingdom
  A) Monera.
  B) Protista.
  C) Plantae.
  D) Fungi.
  E) Animalia.

Answer: C
Topic: 1.5
Skill: Application

22) Which of the following observations would provide the strongest evidence that the many different plants we call orchids are actually related to one another?
  A) The flowers have the same shape of petals.
  B) They all produce small seeds.
  C) None of them can grow without the presence of a specific type of fungus.
  D) They all have the same common ancestor.
  E) They all attract insect pollinators.
Answer: D
Topic: 1.6
Skill: Conceptual Understanding

23) The teeth of grain–eating animals (such as horses) are usually broad and ridged. This makes the teeth suitable for grinding and chewing. Meat–eating animals (such as lions) have pointed teeth that are good for puncturing and ripping flesh. This illustrates
  A) a result of natural selection.
  B) the connection between form and function.
  C) a food web.
  D) that natural selection is not necessary in animals.
  E) a result of natural selection and the connection between form and function.
Answer: E
Topic: 1.6
Skill: Application

24) Which of the following statements is *not* consistent with Darwin's theory of natural selection?
  A) Individuals in a population exhibit variations, some of which are heritable.
  B) Individual organisms exhibit genetic change during their life spans to better fit their environment.
  C) Factors in the environment result in some organisms with better reproductive success than others.
  D) Natural selection is based in part on the overproduction of offspring.
  E) Natural selection can lead to the appearance of new species.
Answer: B
Topic: 1.6
Skill: Conceptual Understanding

25) An antibiotic kills 99.9% of a bacterial population. You would expect the next generation of bacteria
  A) to be just as susceptible to that antibiotic as was the previous generation.
  B) to be more resistant to that antibiotic.
  C) to die out due to the drastic decrease in population size.
  D) to be more contagious than the prior generation.
  E) to be less virulent than the previous population.
Answer: B
Topic: 1.6
Skill: Conceptual Understanding

26) Which of the following statements about evolution is *true*?
 A) Individuals evolve within the span of their own lifetimes.
 B) Organisms evolve structures in response to needs.
 C) Evolution is deliberate and purposeful.
 D) Evolution is a passive process.
 E) Evolution is directional.

Answer: D
Topic: 1.6
Skill: Conceptual Understanding

27) Consider the following statement: "If all vertebrates have backbones, and turtles are vertebrates, then turtles have backbones." This statement is an example of
 A) a hypothesis.
 B) discovery science logic.
 C) rationalization.
 D) deductive reasoning.
 E) inductive reasoning.

Answer: D
Topic: 1.7
Skill: Conceptual Understanding

28) A hypothesis is
 A) the same as a theory.
 B) a tentative answer to some question.
 C) an explanatory idea that is broad in scope and supported by a large body of evidence.
 D) a widely accepted idea about a phenomenon.
 E) a widely accepted theory that is broad in scope and supported by a large body of evidence.

Answer: B
Topic: 1.7
Skill: Factual Recall

29) You notice that over the past month, many students on campus have started wearing a new style of school sweatshirt. You think to yourself that perhaps the bookstore has recently started selling this new sweatshirt style. This prediction is an example of
 A) an experimental question.
 B) a type of observation.
 C) a hypothesis.
 D) an experiment.
 E) a type of control.

Answer: C
Topic: 1.7
Skill: Conceptual Understanding

30) A theory is
  A) an idea that has been proven.
  B) a concept in the early stages that still needs to be tested.
  C) a belief that has been accepted by all scientists as fact.
  D) a description of a belief that invokes the supernatural.
  E) an explanation of an idea that is broad in scope with multiple lines of evidence.

Answer: E
Topic: 1.7
Skill: Factual Recall

31) To be scientifically valid, a hypothesis must be
  A) phrased as a question.
  B) based on faith.
  C) controlled.
  D) reasonable.
  E) testable and falsifiable.

Answer: E
Topic: 1.8
Skill: Conceptual Understanding

32) The role of a control in an experiment is to
  A) provide a basis of comparison to the experimental group.
  B) prove that a hypothesis is correct.
  C) ensure repeatability.
  D) prove that a hypothesis is correct and ensure repeatability.
  E) counteract the negative effect of the experiment.

Answer: A
Topic: 1.8
Skill: Conceptual Understanding

33) A scientist performs a controlled experiment. This means that
  A) the experiment is repeated many times to ensure that the results are accurate.
  B) the experiment proceeds at a slow pace to guarantee that the scientist can carefully observe all reactions and process all experimental data.
  C) two experiments are conducted, one differing from the other by only a single variable.
  D) two experiments are conducted, one differing from the other by two or more variables.
  E) one experiment is performed, but the scientist controls the variables.

Answer: C
Topic: 1.8
Skill: Conceptual Understanding

34) Which of the following best represents an example of technology?
    A) figuring out what mountain gorillas eat
    B) sequencing the human genome
    C) testing for genetic diseases
    D) comparing the structure of a human and gorilla arm
    E) identifying the cause of a new contagious disease

Answer: C
Topic: 1.9
Skill: Conceptual Understanding

35) As the environment changes,
    A) populations change with a purpose.
    B) populations will become extinct.
    C) natural selection adapts populations to their environment.
    D) individuals develop new traits to adapt to the environment.
    E) new species will evolve by combining traits from several preexisting species.

Answer: C
Topic: 1.10–Evolution Connection
Skill: Conceptual Understanding

Art Questions

1)

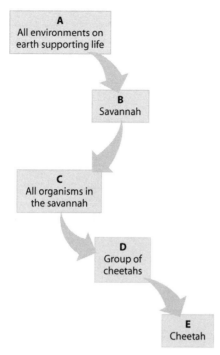

Which level in the hierarchy shown is a community?
A) level A
B) level B
C) level C
D) level D
E) level E

Answer: C
Topic: 1.1
Skill: Factual Recall

2)

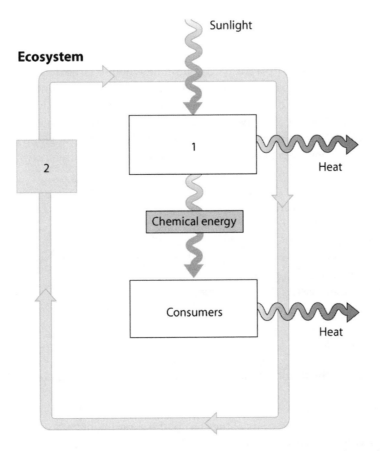

Which of the following organisms belongs to the group represented in Box 1?
    A) giraffe
    B) earthworm
    C) tree
    D) decomposing bacteria
    E) leopard
Answer: C
Topic: 1.2
Skill: Application

Scenario Questions

After reading the following paragraph, answer the question(s) below.

The National Institutes of Health (NIH) set up a study to determine whether large doses of vitamin C would shorten the length of time it takes to recover from a cold. Three thousand volunteers were split into two groups. For two weeks, members of Group A took 3,000 mg of vitamin C daily. Group B received 3,000 mg of a placebo. At the end of the two-week period, the researchers inserted live cold viruses directly into the noses of all the volunteers. The volunteers in both Group A and B continued to take their daily pills. All the volunteers got colds, and there was no significant difference in the length of time the colds lasted.

1) Which was the experimental group?
   A) Group A only
   B) Group B only
   C) all 3,000 volunteers
   D) half of Group A and half of group B
   E) the researchers that inserted the cold virus

   Answer: A
   Topic: 1.7, 1.8
   Skill: Conceptual Understanding

2) To have confidence that the results of the experiment were valid, you'd also want to know
   A) the genders of the volunteers.
   B) whether any volunteers had colds at the start of the experiment.
   C) whether the volunteers exercised daily.
   D) whether the volunteers all worked for the same company.
   E) what the volunteers ate during the experiment.

   Answer: B
   Topic: 1.7, 1.8
   Skill: Application

Chapter 2 The Chemical Basis of Life

Multiple-Choice Questions

1) What phrase best describes the connection between the ants' use of formic acid and the theme of Chapter 2?
   A) Ants are important for the survival of trees.
   B) Ants use the trees as a home.
   C) Other tree species could benefit from the ants.
   D) Chemicals are part of the hierarchical structure of life.
   E) Ants and trees can form symbiotic relationships.

   Answer: D
   Topic: Opening Essay
   Skill: Conceptual Understanding

2) The four most common elements in living organisms are
   A) C, H, O, Fe.
   B) C, H, O, Na.
   C) C, H, O, N.
   D) C, N, O, Na.
   E) Fe, N, O, Ca.

   Answer: C
   Topic: 2.1
   Skill: Factual Recall

3) Which of the following is a trace element in the human body?
   A) carbon
   B) nitrogen
   C) zinc
   D) oxygen
   E) hydrogen

   Answer: C
   Topic: 2.1
   Skill: Factual Recall

4) Which of the following statements regarding matter is *false*?
   A) All life is composed of matter.
   B) Matter occupies space.
   C) Matter has mass.
   D) Matter is composed of elements.
   E) Matter can be created and destroyed.

   Answer: E
   Topic: 2.1
   Skill: Factual Recall

5) Which of the following trace elements is commonly added to table salt to prevent the formation of goiters?
    A) iodine
    B) iron
    C) calcium
    D) magnesium
    E) fluoride

Answer: A
Topic: 2.2
Skill: Factual Recall

6) Which of the following trace elements may be added to bottled water in an effort to prevent tooth decay?
    A) nitrogen
    B) sodium
    C) chlorine
    D) potassium
    E) fluoride

Answer: E
Topic: 2.2
Skill: Factual Recall

7) Which of the following statements best describes a compound?
    A) A compound is a pure element.
    B) A compound is less common than a pure element.
    C) A compound contains two or more different elements in a fixed ratio.
    D) A compound is exemplified by sodium.
    E) A compound is a solution.

Answer: C
Topic: 2.3
Skill: Factual Recall

8) In the equation $2 H_2 + O_2 \rightarrow 2 H_2O$,
    A) H_2, O_2, and H_2O are all compounds.
    B) H_2, O_2, and H_2O are all elements.
    C) only H_2O is a compound.
    D) only H_2 and O_2 are compounds.
    E) H_2, O_2, and H_2O are all trace elements.

Answer: C
Topic: 2.3
Skill: Conceptual Understanding

9) Which of the following particles is found in the nucleus of an atom?
    A) protons and neutrons
    B) protons and electrons
    C) only neutrons
    D) only protons
    E) only electrons
Answer: A
Topic: 2.4
Skill: Factual Recall

10) Electrons move about the nucleus of an atom in the same way that
    A) insects fly around a bright lamp at night.
    B) cars are parked along the sides of a street.
    C) boats cross a lake.
    D) people pass each other along a sidewalk.
    E) birds migrate to a new winter home.
Answer: A
Topic: 2.4
Skill: Conceptual Understanding

11) What is the atomic mass of an atom that has 6 protons, 6 neutrons, and 6 electrons?
    A) 6
    B) 8
    C) +1
    D) 12
    E) 18
Answer: D
Topic: 2.4
Skill: Factual Recall

12) An uncharged atom of boron has an atomic number of 5 and an atomic mass of 11. How many electrons does boron have?
    A) 11
    B) 15
    C) 0
    D) 5
    E) 2
Answer: D
Topic: 2.4
Skill: Application

13) Which of the following is another term used for atomic mass?
    A) roberts
    B) darwin
    C) mendel
    D) dalton
    E) calvin
Answer: D
Topic: 2.4
Skill: Factual Recall

14) The sodium atom contains 11 electrons, 11 protons, and 12 neutrons. What is the mass number of sodium?
    A) 0
    B) 11
    C) 22
    D) 23
    E) 34

Answer: D
Topic: 2.4
Skill: Conceptual Understanding

15) Which of the following best describes the atomic number of an atom?
    A) the number of protons in the atom
    B) the number of electrons in the atom
    C) the number of neutrons in the atom
    D) the number of protons, electrons, and neutrons in the atom
    E) the net electrical charge of the atom

Answer: A
Topic: 2.4
Skill: Factual Recall

16) Typically, nitrogen atoms are composed of electrons, protons, and neutrons. An isotope of nitrogen could
    A) be positively charged.
    B) be negatively charged.
    C) have more than electrons and more than protons.
    D) have more than protons.
    E) have more than neutrons.

Answer: E
Topic: 2.4
Skill: Factual Recall

17) A radioactive isotope is an isotope that
    A) is stable.
    B) decays.
    C) has more protons than the common variant of the element.
    D) has more electrons than the common variant of the element.
    E) has the same atomic mass, but a different atomic number than the common variant of the element.

Answer: B
Topic: 2.4
Skill: Factual Recall

18) If you found a fossilized dinosaur bone, what method could be used to determine the age of the fossil?
    A) electrophoresis
    B) DNA fingerprinting
    C) isotope analysis
    D) radial immunodiffusion
    E) high–pressure liquid chromatography

Answer: C
Topic: 2.4
Skill: Application

19) Which of the following statements about radioactive isotopes is *true*?
    A) The nuclei of radioactive isotopes are unusually stable, but the atoms tend to lose electrons.
    B) When given a choice between radioactive and nonradioactive isotopes of the same atom, living cells are more likely to incorporate the radioactive isotopes into their structures.
    C) The tracers typically used for diagnosing medical problems remain radioactive in the body for a number of years, but give off very low levels of radioactive energy.
    D) The energy emitted by radioactive isotopes can break chemical bonds and cause molecular damage in cells.
    E) Radioactive elements are natural and therefore not harmful.

Answer: D
Topic: 2.5
Skill: Factual Recall

20) Based on your understanding of radioactive isotopes and Alzheimer's disease, what might occur with the use of radioactive isotopes when diagnosing this brain disease?
    A) It would not be very accurate.
    B) It could cause more cellular damage, worsening the condition.
    C) It only works on diseased brains.
    D) It would only work if the isotope was stable.
    E) Naturally occurring radioactive isotopes will provide accurate results.

Answer: B
Topic: 2.5
Skill: Conceptual Understanding

21) Radioactive isotopes
    A) are frequently added to foods as nutritional supplements.
    B) can be used in conjunction with PET scans to diagnose diseases.
    C) have no effect on living tissue.
    D) do not occur naturally.
    E) are never incorporated into organic compounds.

Answer: B
Topic: 2.5
Skill: Factual Recall

22) When full, the innermost electron shell of argon contains _____ electrons, and the outermost shell contains _____ electrons.
   A) 2 . . . 2
   B) 2 . . . 8
   C) 4 . . . 8
   D) 8 . . . 2
   E) 8 . . . 8

Answer: B
Topic: 2.6
Skill: Factual Recall

23) What happens to an atom if the electrons in the outer shell are altered?
   A) The atom becomes radioactive.
   B) The atom will disintegrate.
   C) The properties of the atom will change.
   D) The atom will remain the same.
   E) The atom's characteristics change and it becomes a different element.

Answer: C
Topic: 2.6
Skill: Factual Recall

24) Which particles increase by one as we move from left to right in the elements on the periodic table?
   A) neutrons only
   B) neutrons and protons
   C) electrons only
   D) electrons and protons
   E) electrons and neutrons

Answer: D
Topic: 2.6
Skill: Factual Recall

25) Table salt is formed when
   A) chlorine gives an electron to sodium.
   B) a hydrogen bond forms between sodium and chlorine.
   C) sodium and chlorine share electrons to form a bond.
   D) sodium crystals combine with chlorine crystals.
   E) sodium donates its single outer electron to chlorine

Answer: E
Topic: 2.7
Skill: Factual Recall

26) The body uses atoms in different ways to accomplish different tasks. For example, one portion of the body's calcium supply strengthens bones, whereas another portion combines with proteins to stimulate blood clotting after tissue injury. Which of the statements below provides the most logical chemical explanation of calcium's ability to perform such different functions?
    A) The bone contains calcium salts, which are less reactive than the calcium ions found in the blood.
    B) The calcium in blood is a more reactive form of the atom and therefore has fewer protons than the calcium in bone.
    C) There are many different isotopes of calcium, and the most reactive isotope is found in the bone.
    D) The calcium in blood has a lighter atomic mass than the calcium in bone and is in a more reactive form.
    E) The calcium in blood has fewer protons, is a more reactive form of the atom, and has a lighter atomic mass than the calcium in bone.

Answer: A
Topic: 2.7
Skill: Application

27) Medicines are often administered in pill form. In many cases, the active ingredient of the pill (the drug) is joined to another substance by _____. This forms a(n) _____, which is stable in the dry environment of a pill bottle but dissociates under the wet conditions of the digestive system to release the drug to the body.
    A) ionic bonds . . . salt
    B) hydrogen bonds . . . base
    C) ionic bonds . . . acid
    D) covalent bonds . . . salt
    E) polar covalent bonds . . . acid or base (depending on the drug)

Answer: A
Topic: 2.7
Skill: Application

28) A(n) _____ forms when two atoms share electrons.
    A) ion
    B) element
    C) covalent bond
    D) ionic bond
    E) hydrogen bond

Answer: C
Topic: 2.8
Skill: Factual Recall

29) A hydrogen atom has one electron. How many covalent bonds can hydrogen form?
    A) one covalent bond
    B) four covalent bonds
    C) four covalent bonds
    D) two ionic bonds
    E) two isotonic bonds

Answer: A
Topic: 2.8
Skill: Application

30) What is the fundamental difference between covalent and ionic bonding?
   A) In a covalent bond, the partners have identical electronegativity; in an ionic bond, one of them is more electronegative.
   B) In a covalent bond, the partners share a pair of electrons; in an ionic bond, one partner accepts electrons from the other.
   C) In covalent bonding, both partners end up with filled outer electron shells; in ionic bonding, one partner does and the other does not.
   D) Covalent bonding involves only the outermost electron shell; ionic bonding also involves the next electron shell inside the outermost shell.
   E) Covalent bonds form between atoms of the same element; ionic bonds form between atoms of different elements.

Answer: B
Topic: 2.8
Skill: Conceptual Understanding

31) Which of the following statements regarding the oxygen atom of a water molecule is *true*?
   A) Oxygen is more positively charged than the hydrogen atoms.
   B) Oxygen attracts electrons less strongly than the hydrogen atoms.
   C) Oxygen is more electronegative than the hydrogen atoms.
   D) Oxygen is electrically neutral.
   E) Oxygen is attracted to the negatively charged atoms of other molecules.

Answer: C
Topic: 2.9
Skill: Conceptual Understanding

32) In a water molecule, hydrogen and oxygen are held together by a(n) _____ bond.
   A) double covalent
   B) ionic
   C) nonpolar covalent
   D) hydrogen
   E) polar covalent

Answer: E
Topic: 2.9
Skill: Factual Recall

33) A person shakes up vinegar and oil dressing before pouring it on salads. What is the chemical reason for doing this?
   A) Vinegar contains charged water molecules, while oil is neutral and repels water.
   B) Vinegar and oil must be mixed to decease the viscosity.
   C) Vinegar and oil are oppositely charged, and opposites attract.
   D) Oil is composed of fatty acids, which are too large to dissolve in water.
   E) Vinegar has a basic pH and is neutralized when mixed with oil.

Answer: A
Topic: 2.9
Skill: Application

34) A water molecule (H—O—H) is held together by
    A) an ionic bond.
    B) a single covalent bond.
    C) a double covalent bond.
    D) two polar covalent bonds.
    E) hydrogen bonds.

Answer: D
Topic: 2.9
Skill: Factual Recall

35) The hydrogen atoms of a water molecule are bonded to the oxygen atom by _____
    bonds, whereas neighboring water molecules are held together by _____ bonds.
    A) hydrogen . . . ionic
    B) hydrogen . . . polar covalent
    C) polar covalent . . . hydrogen
    D) ionic . . . covalent
    E) polar covalent . . . ionic

Answer: C
Topic: 2.9, 2.10
Skill: Factual Recall

36) _____ are weak bonds that are not strong enough to hold atoms together to form
    molecules but are strong enough to form bonds within and around large molecules.
    A) Ionic bonds
    B) Covalent bonds
    C) Polar covalent bonds
    D) Hydrogen bonds
    E) Anionic bonds

Answer: D
Topic: 2.10
Skill: Factual Recall

37) Water molecules stick to other water molecules because
    A) water molecules are neutral, and neutral molecules are attracted to each other.
    B) hydrogen bonds form between the hydrogen atoms of one water molecule and the
       oxygen atoms of other water molecules.
    C) covalent bonds form between the hydrogen atoms of one water molecule and the
       oxygen atoms of other water molecules.
    D) the hydrogen atoms of adjacent water molecules are attracted to one another.
    E) the oxygen atoms of adjacent water molecules are attracted to one another.

Answer: B
Topic: 2.10
Skill: Conceptual Understanding

38) The tendency of water molecules to stick together is referred to as
    A) adhesion.
    B) polarity.
    C) cohesion.
    D) transpiration.
    E) evaporation.

Answer: C
Topic: 2.11
Skill: Factual Recall

39) Which of the following is dependent on the ability of water molecules to form hydrogen bonds with other molecules besides water?
    A) the evaporative cooling of skin surfaces
    B) the movement of water from the roots of a tree to its leaves
    C) the milder temperatures of coastal regions compared to inland areas
    D) the ability of certain insects to walk on the surface of water
    E) the universality of water as a solvent

Answer: E
Topic: 2.11, 2.12
Skill: Conceptual Understanding

40) Water's surface tension and heat storage capacity is accounted for by its
    A) orbitals.
    B) weight.
    C) hydrogen bonds.
    D) mass.
    E) size.

Answer: C
Topic: 2.11, 2.12
Skill: Conceptual Understanding

41) As ice melts,
    A) hydrogen bonds are broken.
    B) water molecules become less tightly packed.
    C) the water becomes less dense.
    D) covalent bonds form.
    E) heat is released.

Answer: A
Topic: 2.12, 2.13
Skill: Conceptual Understanding

42) Which of the following will contain more heat but has a lower temperature?
    A) a gas-powered lawnmower engine after it has been used for an hour
    B) an Olympic-sized heated indoor swimming pool
    C) the water used in a dishwasher
    D) the boiling water in a pot for noodles
    E) a hot air balloon

Answer: B
Topic: 2.12
Skill: Conceptual Understanding

43) The temperature of evaporation is much higher for water than for alcohol. Without knowing more about the chemistry of alcohol, which of the following is the most logical chemical explanation for this phenomenon?

   A) Ionic bonds form between alcohol molecules. These are the weakest type of bond and are easier to break than the hydrogen bonds between water molecules.
   B) Alcohol has a higher surface tension than water. This means that alcohol molecules can easily break away from other alcohol molecules and evaporate at a lower temperature.
   C) Alcohol molecules are more cohesive than water molecules. This means that as alcohol molecules evaporate, they pull other alcohol molecules into the air along with them.
   D) Fewer hydrogen bonds form between alcohol molecules. As a result, less heat is needed for alcohol molecules to break away from solution and enter the air.
   E) Water is a better solvent than alcohol. Therefore, alcohol can break covalent bonds easily and will not be restricted from evaporating from its solute.

Answer: D
Topic: 2.12, 2.13
Skill: Application

44) Which of the following statements about water is *false*?

   A) Ice is less dense than liquid water.
   B) The hydrogen bonds in ice are less stable than the hydrogen bonds in liquid water.
   C) Water naturally exists in all three physical states on Earth.
   D) Floating ice on a pond insulates the liquid water below, slowing its rate of freezing.
   E) If ice sank, the oceans would eventually freeze solid.

Answer: B
Topic: 2.13
Skill: Factual Recall

45) You've made a hot drink by dissolving a teaspoon of instant coffee and a teaspoon of sugar in a cup of hot water. Which of the following statements is *true*?

   A) You've just prepared an aqueous solution.
   B) The water is the solute portion of the drink.
   C) The instant coffee and sugar are solvents.
   D) The instant coffee and sugar dissolve because they have no charged regions to repel the partial positive and partial negative regions of the water molecules.
   E) The coffee and sugar would not dissolve in cold water.

Answer: A
Topic: 2.14
Skill: Application

46) Clot formation in our blood can lead to a heart attack or stroke. What was altered in the proteins that made the clot?

   A) The proteins became more polar.
   B) The blood was saturated with proteins.
   C) The proteins were no longer soluble in the blood.
   D) A different solvent other than water was used.
   E) The proteins became more soluble in the blood.

Answer: C
Topic: 2.14
Skill: Conceptual Understanding

47) A pharmaceutical company hires a chemist to analyze the purity of the water being used in its drug preparations. If the water is pure, the chemist would expect to find
  A) only molecules of H_2O.

  B) H_2O molecules and H^+ ions.

  C) H_2O molecules and OH^- ions.

  D) H_2O molecules, H^+ ions, and OH^- ions.

  E) only H^+ ions and OH^- ions.

Answer: D
Topic: 2.15
Skill: Conceptual Understanding

48) A solution with a pH of 7 is
  A) strongly acidic.
  B) weakly acidic.
  C) neutral.
  D) weakly basic.
  E) strongly basic.

Answer: C
Topic: 2.15
Skill: Factual Recall

49) Compared to a solution of pH 3, a solution of pH 1 is
  A) 100 times more acidic.
  B) 10 times more acidic.
  C) neutral.
  D) 10 times more basic.
  E) 100 times more basic.

Answer: A
Topic: 2.15
Skill: Factual Recall

50) Which of the following statements about pH is *true*?
  A) The pH scale is a measure of oxygen ion concentration.
  B) A single unit change on the pH scale is equivalent to a 1% change in hydrogen ion concentration.
  C) An increase in hydrogen ion concentration means a decrease in pH scale units.
  D) Basic pH levels are less than 7.
  E) The pH of solutions inside most cells is close to 9.0.

Answer: C
Topic: 2.15
Skill: Factual Recall

51) Household ammonia has a pH of 12; household bleach has a pH of 13. Which of the following statements about them is *true*?

    A) Both of these substances are strong acids.

    B) The ammonia has 10 times as many OH^- ions as the bleach.

    C) The ammonia has 10 times as many H^+ ions as the bleach.

    D) A solution that could buffer the bleach and ammonia would remove excess OH^- ions.

    E) The ammonia has 10 times as many OH^- ions as the bleach, and a solution that could buffer the bleach and ammonia would remove excess OH^- ions.

Answer: C
Topic: 2.15
Skill: Conceptual Understanding

52) A buffer

    A) is an acid that is used to offset overly basic conditions in the body.

    B) is a base that is used to offset overly acidic conditions in the body.

    C) donates OH^- ions when conditions become too acidic and accepts OH^- ions when conditions become too basic.

    D) donates H^+ ions when conditions become too basic and accepts H^+ ions when conditions become too acidic.

    E) donates OH^- ions when conditions become too basic and accepts OH^- ions when conditions become too acidic.

Answer: D
Topic: 2.15
Skill: Factual Recall

53) A diabetic, who does not utilize insulin properly, will metabolize fats instead of glucose. A condition called diabetic ketoacidosis is a common result of excessive fat metabolism, causing blood pH values of 7.1 or less (normal range = 7.35 — 7.45). What has happened to the blood pH and why?

    A) The pH is above normal (basic) because the ketones are too basic.

    B) The pH is below normal (acidic) because the buffering capacity was exceeded.

    C) The pH is above normal (basic) because the glucose is polar.

    D) The pH is not affected because the blood buffers can absorb the excess H^+.

    E) The pH is below normal because buffers can donate OH^+.

Answer: B
Topic: 2.15
Skill: Application

54) Which of the following statements about acid precipitation is *false*?

    A) Acid precipitation can occur with rain, snow, or fog.

    B) Acid precipitation is defined as having a pH below 5.6.

    C) Acid precipitation damages natural wilderness areas.

    D) Acid precipitation is primarily the result of burning fossil fuels.

    E) Acid precipitation has little or no effect on soil chemistry.

Answer: E
Topic: 2.16
Skill: Factual Recall

55) The emission of _____ and _____ are primarily responsible for acid precipitation.
    A) carbon dioxide . . . methane
    B) CFCs . . . bromides
    C) nitrogen oxides . . . sulfur oxides
    D) halones . . . CFCs
    E) carbon dioxide . . . ozone

Answer: C
Topic: 2.16
Skill: Factual Recall

56) Which of the following would be considered an effective way to decrease the production of acid precipitation?
    A) Drive more full-size SUVs.
    B) Build more coal-generated electricity power plants.
    C) Discourage the use of alternative energy resources such as solar, wind, and geothermal energy.
    D) Whenever possible, walk or ride a bicycle instead of driving a car.
    E) Consume only organically grown foods.

Answer: D
Topic: 2.16
Skill: Application

57) What is likely to happen to wild salmon prices if the burning of fossil fuels continues at the current rate?
    A) Prices will drop to pre-fossil fuel burning levels.
    B) Prices will increase due to decreased salmon harvests.
    C) Prices will stay the same because fossil fuel has nothing to do with salmon.
    D) Prices will fluctuate wildly due to illogical fear in the marketplace.
    E) Prices will initially decline and then stabilize.

Answer: B
Topic: 2.16
Skill: Conceptual Understanding

58) Which of the following statements regarding chemical reactions is *false*?
    A) Chemical reactions involve the making and breaking of chemical bonds.
    B) Some chemical reactions create electrons; others destroy them.
    C) The atoms of the reactants are exactly the same as the atoms of the products.
    D) The reactants contain the same number of atoms as the products.
    E) Although the atoms of a reaction's reactants and products are identical to each other, their molecular formulae differ.

Answer: B
Topic: 2.17
Skill: Factual Recall

59) Which of the following hypotheses would be supported if liquid water were found on Mars and contained evidence of bacteria–like organisms?
    A) Life must evolve in the presence of oxygen.
    B) The chemical evolution of life is possible.
    C) Life on Earth must have originated on Mars.
    D) Life is guided by intelligent design.
    E) Life spontaneously arises from the decaying flesh of organisms.

Answer: B
Topic: 2.17–Evolution Connection
Skill: Conceptual Understanding

60) In the equation $2 H_2 + O_2 \rightarrow 2 H_2O$, the H_2 molecules are _____ and the H_2O molecules are _____.
    A) reactants . . . products
    B) products . . . reactants
    C) created . . . destroyed
    D) used . . . stored
    E) destroyed . . . created

Answer: A
Topic: 2.18
Skill: Factual Recall

61) Photosynthesis requires many steps to make glucose. As a result of the synthesis process,
    A) all the carbons from the six carbon dioxide atoms are found in glucose.
    B) more atoms are present at the beginning than at the end.
    C) more carbon dioxide is released from the plant than is absorbed.
    D) water is synthesized by the plant from H_2 and O_2.
    E) more water is released from the leaves than is absorbed through the roots.

Answer: A
Topic: 2.18
Skill: Conceptual Understanding

Art Questions

1)

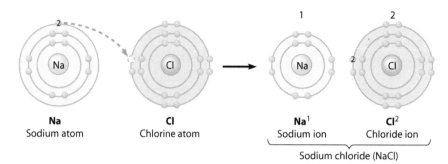

What change is occurring in this figure?
  A) Sodium is gaining an electron.
  B) Chlorine is losing an electron.
  C) Sodium is becoming negatively charged.
  D) Sodium is filling its third electron shell.
  E) Chlorine is filling its third electron shell.

Answer: E
Topic: 2.6, 2.7
Skill: Conceptual Understanding

2)

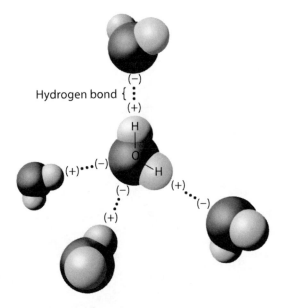

Hydrogen bond {

The hydrogen bonds shown in this figure are each
A) between two hydrogen atoms.
B) between two oxygen atoms.
C) between an oxygen and a hydrogen atom of the same water molecule.
D) between an oxygen and a hydrogen atom of different water molecules.
E) between two atoms with the same charge.

Answer: D
Topic: 2.10
Skill: Application

Scenario Questions

After reading the following paragraph, answer the question(s) below.

You've been experiencing acid indigestion lately, and you'd like a quick fix for the problem. You do a little research on the Internet and discover that your problem is caused by excess stomach acid. In the pharmacy aisles, however, you're having a little trouble deciding what to purchase to address the problem. At the pharmacy counter, the clerk recommends that you purchase Pepcid–AC® or Alka–Seltzer® tablets.

1) If you could check the pH of the recommended tablets, you would expect it to be
A) higher than 7.
B) lower than 7.
C) exactly 7.
D) pH neutral.
E) either C or D.

Answer: A
Topic: 2.15
Skill: Conceptual Understanding

2) If you were able to chemically analyze your stomach fluids 30 minutes after taking two tablets, you would find
   A) more hydrogen ions.
   B) fewer hydrogen ions.
   C) the same number of hydrogen ions.
   D) that the pH in your stomach has decreased.
   E) a greater number of covalent bonds.

Answer: B
Topic: 2.15
Skill: Application

Chapter 3   The Molecules of Cells

Multiple-Choice Questions

1) Lactose intolerance is the inability to
   A) produce milk proteins.
   B) produce lactose.
   C) digest cellulose.
   D) digest lactose.
   E) digest milk fats.

   Answer: D
   Topic: Opening Essay
   Skill: Factual Recall

2) Lactose intolerance
   A) is common in people of all ages, from infancy to adulthood.
   B) is most common in people of European descent.
   C) can currently be treated by gene therapy to treat the underlying cause.
   D) does not affect the consumption of beverages made from soy or rice.
   E) is a fatal disease with no known treatment.

   Answer: D
   Topic: Opening Essay
   Skill: Factual Recall

3) Organic compounds
   A) always contain nitrogen.
   B) are synthesized only by animal cells.
   C) always contain carbon.
   D) can be synthesized only in a laboratory.
   E) always contain oxygen.

   Answer: C
   Topic: 3.1
   Skill: Factual Recall

4) Which of the following statements regarding carbon is *false*?
   A) Carbon has a tendency to form covalent bonds.
   B) Carbon has the ability to bond with up to four other atoms.
   C) Carbon has the capacity to form single and double bonds.
   D) Carbon has the ability to bond together to form extensive, branched, or unbranched "carbon skeletons."
   E) Carbon has the capacity to form polar bonds with hydrogen.

   Answer: E
   Topic: 3.1
   Skill: Factual Recall

5) You now know that the old cliché "oil and water don't mix" is true. Why?
   A) Oil exhibits polarity and water does not.
   B) Water exhibits polarity and oil does not.
   C) Oil is hydrophilic.
   D) Water is hydrophobic.
   E) Oil is an organic compound and water is not.

Answer: B
Topic: 3.1
Skill: Conceptual Understanding

6) Which of the following statements about hydrocarbons is *false*?
   A) Hydrocarbons are inorganic compounds.
   B) Hydrocarbons are composed of a linked chain of carbon atoms, called a carbon skeleton.
   C) Hydrocarbons contain only carbon and hydrogen atoms.
   D) Hydrocarbons consist of atoms linked by single and double bonds.
   E) Hydrocarbons can form straight, branched or ringed structures.

Answer: A
Topic: 3.1
Skill: Factual Recall

7) Propanol and isopropanol are isomers. This means that they have
   A) the same molecular formula, but different chemical properties.
   B) different molecular formulas, but the same chemical properties.
   C) the same molecular formula and the same chemical properties.
   D) the same number of carbon atoms, but different numbers of oxygen and hydrogen atoms.
   E) the same molecular formula, but represent different states of the compound.

Answer: A
Topic: 3.1
Skill: Factual Recall

8) A hydroxyl group is
   A) also called a carbonyl group.
   B) characteristic of proteins.
   C) hydrophobic.
   D) characteristic of alcohols.
   E) basic.

Answer: D
Topic: 3.2
Skill: Factual Recall

9) Which of the following is a carboxyl group?
   A) $-C=O$
   B) $-OH$
   C) $-NH_2$
   D) $-COOH$
   E) $-SH$

Answer: C
Topic: 3.2
Skill: Factual Recall

10) Which of the following is an amino group?
    A) —OH
    B) —NH$_2$
    C) —COOH
    D) —CO
    E) —CH$_3$

Answer: B
Topic: 3.2
Skill: Factual Recall

11) Which of the following statements about the functional groups of organic compounds is
    false?
    A) Functional groups help make organic compounds hydrophilic.
    B) Many biological molecules have two or more functional groups.
    C) Functional groups participate in chemical reactions.
    D) All functional groups include a carbon atom of the organic compound's skeleton.
    E) Functional groups help make organic compounds soluble in water.

Answer: D
Topic: 3.2
Skill: Conceptual Understanding

12) Which of the following contains a carboxyl and an amino group?
    A) amino acids
    B) fats
    C) sugars
    D) ATP
    E) vinegar

Answer: A
Topic: 3.2
Skill: Factual Recall

13) Which of the following functional groups is capable of regulating gene expression?
    A) —OH
    B) —NH$_2$
    C) —COOH
    D) —CO
    E) —CH$_3$

Answer: E
Topic: 3.2
Skill: Factual Recall

14) Which of the following statements about the monomers and polymers found in living organisms is *false*?
    A) Cells typically make all of their macromolecules from a set of 40–50 common monomers and a few other ingredients that are rare.
    B) The monomers used to make polymers are essentially universal.
    C) Monomers serve as building blocks for polymers.
    D) DNA is built from just four kinds of monomers.
    E) Monomers are joined together by the process of hydrolysis.

Answer: E
Topic: 3.3
Skill: Conceptual Understanding

15) Which of the following statements about dehydration synthesis is *false*?
    A) One monomer loses a hydrogen atom, and the other loses a hydroxyl group.
    B) Electrons are shared between atoms of the joined monomers.
    C) H_2O is formed as the monomers are joined.
    D) Covalent bonds are formed between the monomers.
    E) Animal digestive systems utilize this process to break down food.

Answer: E
Topic: 3.3
Skill: Factual Recall

16) The results of dehydration synthesis can be reversed by
    A) condensation.
    B) hydrolysis.
    C) polymerization.
    D) the addition of an amino group.
    E) the addition of a phosphate group.

Answer: B
Topic: 3.3
Skill: Factual Recall

17) Which list below consists of *only* polymers?
    A) sugars, amino acids, nucleic acids, lipids
    B) proteins, lipids, nucleic acids, amino acids
    C) proteins, lipids, nucleic acids, polysaccharides
    D) proteins, lipids, nucleotides, sugars
    E) polysaccharides, lipids, amino acids, nucleic acids

Answer: C
Topic: 3.3
Skill: Conceptual Understanding

18) What is the general function of enzymes within a cell?
    A) to promote the synthesis of monomers
    B) to induce chemical reactions
    C) to stop chemical reactions
    D) to speed up chemical reactions
    E) to reverse the direction of chemical reactions

Answer: D
Topic: 3.3
Skill: Factual Recall

19) The molecular formula of most monosaccharides represents a multiple of
   A) CH_3O.
   B) CH_2O.
   C) CHO.
   D) CHO_2.
   E) CHO_3.

Answer: B
Topic: 3.4
Skill: Factual Recall

20) A molecule with the formula $C_{55}H_{110}O_{55}$ is probably a(n)
   A) oil.
   B) steroid.
   C) wax.
   D) protein.
   E) polysaccharide.

Answer: E
Topic: 3.4
Skill: Application

21) Many names for sugars end in the suffix
   A) –acid.
   B) –ose.
   C) –hyde.
   D) –ase.
   E) –ing.

Answer: B
Topic: 3.4
Skill: Factual Recall

22) Sucrose is formed
   A) from two glucose molecules.
   B) from two monosaccharides through dehydration synthesis.
   C) when ionic bonds link two monosaccharides.
   D) when water molecules are added to two monosaccharides.
   E) when glucose and lactose are combined.

Answer: B
Topic: 3.5
Skill: Factual Recall

23) A disaccharide forms when
   A) two monosaccharides join by dehydration synthesis.
   B) two starches join by dehydration synthesis.
   C) two monosaccharides join by hydrolysis.
   D) two starches join by hydrolysis.
   E) a starch and a monosaccharide join by dehydration synthesis.

Answer: A
Topic: 3.5
Skill: Factual Recall

24) High-fructose corn syrup is composed primarily of a polysaccharide called
    A) sucrose.
    B) starch.
    C) hydrocarbon.
    D) cellulose.
    E) lactose.

Answer: B
Topic: 3.6
Skill: Factual Recall

25) Which of the following lists contains *only* polysaccharides?
    A) sucrose, starch, and cellulose
    B) starch, amino acids, and glycogen
    C) cellulose, starch, and glycogen
    D) nucleotides, glycogen, and cellulose
    E) fructose, cellulose, and glucose

Answer: C
Topic: 3.7
Skill: Factual Recall

26) Cellulose differs from starch in that
    A) the monomers of cellulose are held together by covalent bonds, whereas the monomers of starch are held together by hydrogen bonds.
    B) glycogen is formed by plants and cellulose by animals.
    C) most animals cannot break down cellulose, whereas starch is easily digested.
    D) starch is made of glucose monomers, whereas cellulose is made of fructose monomers.
    E) cellulose is highly branched, whereas starch is unbranched.

Answer: C
Topic: 3.7
Skill: Factual Recall

27) Foods that are high in fiber are most likely derived from
    A) plants.
    B) dairy products.
    C) red meats.
    D) fish.
    E) poultry.

Answer: A
Topic: 3.7
Skill: Conceptual Understanding

28) Cows can derive nutrients from cellulose because
   A) they produce the enzymes that break down cellulose.
   B) they chew their food so thoroughly that cellulose fibers are broken down.
   C) their intestinal tract contains cellulose–hydrolyzing microorganisms.
   D) they convert cellulose into starch, which is easily broken down in the intestinal tract.
   E) their intestinal tract contains termites, which can break down cellulose.

Answer: C
Topic: 3.7
Skill: Factual Recall

29) The storage form of carbohydrates is _____ in animals and _____ in plants.
   A) starch . . . glycogen
   B) glycogen . . . starch
   C) cellulose . . . glycogen
   D) glycogen . . . cellulose
   E) chitin . . . glycogen

Answer: B
Topic: 3.7
Skill: Factual Recall

30) Which of the following organisms contain the polysaccharide chitin?
   A) animals and plants
   B) plants and bacteria
   C) fungi and insects
   D) insects and plants
   E) crustaceans and bacteria

Answer: C
Topic: 3.7
Skill: Factual Recall

31) An oil may be converted into a substance that is solid at room temperature by
   A) adding hydrogens, decreasing the number of double bonds in the molecules.
   B) removing water, causing a dehydration synthesis reaction to occur.
   C) removing hydrogens, increasing the number of double bonds.
   D) cooling it, so that double bonds form and the fats solidify.
   E) adding water and shaking it vigorously.

Answer: A
Topic: 3.8
Skill: Application

32) A diet high in animal products and hydrogenated vegetable margarine may increase the risk for atherosclerosis. This is because
  A) most animal fats are unsaturated and most hydrogenated vegetable margarines contain high levels of steroids.
  B) most hydrogenated vegetable margarines are hydrogenated oils and most animal products contain high levels of phospholipids.
  C) most animal fats are used for energy storage and most hydrogenated vegetable margarines contain high levels of unsaturated fats.
  D) most animal fats are saturated and many hydrogenated vegetable margarines contain high levels of trans fats.
  E) most animal products contain high levels of unsaturated oils and most hydrogenated vegetable margarines contain anabolic steroids.

Answer: D
Topic: 3.8
Skill: Conceptual Understanding

33) Because water and oil don't mix, water is not very effective at washing away oily dirt. The ability of soap to mix with both water and oily dirt allows dirt to be washed away. Which statement provides the most logical chemical explanation for this phenomenon?
  A) Soap molecules have both positively and negatively charged regions. The positively charged regions are attracted to water; the negatively charged regions are attracted to oil.
  B) Soap molecules have both positively and negatively charged regions. The negatively charged regions are attracted to water; the positively charged regions are attracted to oil.
  C) Soap molecules carry no charge. As a result, soap can form an effective bridge between charged water molecules and neutral oil molecules.
  D) Soap molecules have charged regions and neutral regions. The charged regions are attracted to water molecules; the neutral regions are attracted to oils.
  E) Soap molecules have charged regions and neutral regions. The neutral regions are attracted to water molecules; the charged regions are attracted to oils.

Answer: D
Topic: 3.8
Skill: Application

34) Fatty acids are
  A) composed of carbon, hydrogen, and oxygen in a 1:2:1 ratio.
  B) composed of carbon, hydrogen, glycerol, and a phosphate group.
  C) hydrophobic.
  D) composed of four linked rings.
  E) components of DNA.

Answer: C
Topic: 3.8
Skill: Conceptual Understanding

35) Which of the following statements regarding triglyceride molecules is *false*?
    A) Triglycerides consist of three fatty acids attached to a glycerol.
    B) Triglycerides are hydrophobic.
    C) Triglycerides play a role in energy storage.
    D) Triglycerides are a type of fat.
    E) Triglycerides are part of a signal pathway.

Answer: E
Topic: 3.8
Skill: Factual Recall

36) Fatty acids with double bonds between some of their carbons are said to be
    A) unsaturated.
    B) saturated.
    C) completely hydrogenated.
    D) triglycerides.
    E) monoglycerides.

Answer: A
Topic: 3.8
Skill: Factual Recall

37) The development of atherosclerotic disease can result from a diet high in
    A) fiber.
    B) protein.
    C) saturated fats.
    D) sugars.
    E) complex carbohydrates.

Answer: C
Topic: 3.8
Skill: Application

38) If you were to add olive oil to your food as part of a diet to lower your risk of atherosclerotic disease, you would use olive oil that
    A) is liquid at room temperature.
    B) is hydrogenated.
    C) is modified to be solid at room temperature.
    D) has lard added to it.
    E) contains high levels of trans fats.

Answer: A
Topic: 3.8
Skill: Application

39) Which of the following statements about animal cell lipids is *false*?
    A) Fats are a form of lipid that function to store energy.
    B) Phospholipids are important components of cell membranes.
    C) Steroids are lipids that function as signaling molecules.
    D) Many lipids function as enzymes.
    E) Cholesterol is a type of lipid that is a component of cell membranes and steroid hormones.

Answer: D
Topic: 3.8, 3.9
Skill: Factual Recall

40) A phospholipid is composed of
   A) one glycerol molecule linked to three fatty acids.
   B) one fatty acid molecule linked to three glycerol molecules.
   C) one glycerol molecule linked to three phosphate groups.
   D) one fatty acid molecule linked to one glycerol molecule and two phosphate groups.
   E) one glycerol molecule linked to one phosphate group and two fatty acids.

Answer: E
Topic: 3.9
Skill: Factual Recall

41) Which of the following substances is a lipid?
   A) DNA
   B) glucose
   C) cellulose
   D) steroids
   E) enzymes

Answer: C
Topic: 3.9
Skill: Factual Recall

42) A major type of lipid found in cell membranes is
   A) cellulose.
   B) triglycerides.
   C) phospholipids.
   D) glycerol.
   E) waxes.

Answer: C
Topic: 3.9
Skill: Factual Recall

43) Which of the following statements about anabolic steroids is *false*?
   A) They cause a general buildup of muscle mass.
   B) They often cause the body to reduce its normal output of sex hormones.
   C) They chemically resemble testosterone.
   D) They promote bone growth.
   E) They can stimulate mood swings and violent behavior.

Answer: D
Topic: 3.10
Skill: Factual Recall

44) Which of the following statements about enzymes is *false*?
   A) They increase the rate of chemical reactions.
   B) They function as chemical catalysts.
   C) They regulate virtually all chemical reactions in a cell.
   D) They are produced by cells.
   E) They are monomers used to build proteins.

Answer: E
Topic: 3.11
Skill: Factual Recall

45) Which one of the following would be correctly classified as a protein?
    A) cholesterol
    B) starch
    C) enzymes
    D) cellulose
    E) liposaccharide

Answer: C
Topic: 3.11
Skill: Conceptual Understanding

46) Structural proteins
    A) include receptor molecules.
    B) respond to environmental changes.
    C) include hemoglobin.
    D) anchor cell parts.
    E) bond to hormones.

Answer: D
Topic: 3.11
Skill: Application

47) A scientist suspects that the food in an ecosystem may have been contaminated with radioactive nitrogen over a period of months. Which of the following substances could be examined for radioactivity to test the hypothesis?
    A) the cell walls of plants growing in the ecosystem
    B) the hair produced by humans living in the ecosystem
    C) the sugars produced during photosynthesis by plants growing in the ecosystem
    D) the cholesterol in the cell membranes of organisms living in the ecosystem
    E) the adipose tissue from animals living in the ecosystem

Answer: B
Topic: 3.11; 3.12
Skill: Application

48) Amino acids can be distinguished from one another by
    A) the number of R groups found on the amino acid molecules.
    B) the chemical properties of their R groups.
    C) the type of bond between the R group and the rest of the amino acid molecule.
    D) the chemical properties of their amino and carboxyl groups.
    E) the number of alpha carbons present in the amino acid molecules

Answer: B
Topic: 3.12
Skill: Factual Recall

49) Proteins differ from one another because
   A) the peptide bonds linking amino acids differ from protein to protein.
   B) the sequence of amino acids in the polypeptide chain differs from protein to protein.
   C) each protein contains its own unique sequence of sugar molecules.
   D) the number of nucleotides found in each protein varies from molecule to molecule.
   E) the number of nitrogen atoms in each amino acid varies.

Answer: B
Topic: 3.12
Skill: Conceptual Understanding

50) Glucose molecules are to starch as _____ are to proteins.
   A) oils
   B) amino acids
   C) fatty acids
   D) monosaccharides
   E) lards

Answer: B
Topic: 3.12
Skill: Conceptual Understanding

51) Peptide bonds
   A) are used to form amino acids.
   B) form between fatty acids.
   C) are formed by a hydrolysis reaction.
   D) link amino acids.
   E) bind monosaccharides.

Answer: D
Topic: 3.12
Skill: Factual Recall

52) Which of the following characteristics of protein will remain intact if the protein is denatured?
   A) the shape of the protein
   B) the function of the protein
   C) the solubility of the protein in water
   D) the number of amino acids in the protein
   E) the binding properties of the protein

Answer: D
Topic: 3.13
Skill: Conceptual Understanding

53) Proteins cannot be denatured by
   A) heat.
   B) changes in pH.
   C) chemicals that destroy hydrogen bonds.
   D) changes in salt concentration.
   E) freezing.

Answer: E
Topic: 3.13
Skill: Conceptual Understanding

54) The primary structure of a protein is
     A) an α helix or a pleated sheet.
     B) the amino acid sequence of the polypeptide chain.
     C) composed of two or more polypeptide chains.
     D) maintained by hydrogen bonds.
     E) composed of irregular folds.

Answer: B
Topic: 3.14
Skill: Factual Recall

55) Which of the following is an example of secondary structure in a protein?
     A) a particular amino acid sequence
     B) an alpha helix
     C) a globular shape
     D) the joining of two polypeptide chains
     E) a fibrous shape

Answer: B
Topic: 3.14
Skill: Factual Recall

56) The tertiary structure of a polypeptide refers to
     A) its size.
     B) the presence of pleated sheets.
     C) the amino acids of which it is made.
     D) the overall three–dimensional structure.
     E) the number of R groups it contains.

Answer: D
Topic: 3.14
Skill: Factual Recall

57) A protein containing more than one polypeptide chain exhibits the _____ level of
protein structure.
     A) primary
     B) secondary
     C) tertiary
     D) quaternary
     E) infinite

Answer: D
Topic: 3.14
Skill: Factual Recall

58) Mad cow disease serves as an example of how interdependent _____ and _____ are
to protein.
     A) solubility . . . texture
     B) form . . . construction
     C) structure . . . function
     D) adaptability . . . development
     E) validity . . . reliability

Answer: C
Topic: 3.14
Skill: Factual Recall

59) Which of the following statements regarding nucleotides is *false*?
   A) Nucleotides have a nitrogenous base backbone.
   B) Nucleotides contain sugar molecules.
   C) Nucleotides contain phosphate groups.
   D) Nucleotides can be linked together to form nucleic acids.
   E) Nucleotides contain nitrogenous bases.

Answer: A
Topic: 3.16
Skill: Factual Recall

60) Which of the following options correctly pairs a polymer and its monomer?
   A) cellulose, amino acids
   B) triglyceride, steroid
   C) DNA, nucleotides
   D) collagen, nucleic acids
   E) RNA, ribose

Answer: C
Topic: 3.16
Skill: Conceptual Understanding

61) DNA differs from RNA because DNA
   A) contains thymine in place of uracil.
   B) consists of a single rather than a double polynucleotide strand.
   C) contains the sugar ribose rather than the sugar deoxyribose.
   D) contains phosphate groups not found in RNA.
   E) is always double–stranded, while RNA is never double–stranded.

Answer: A
Topic: 3.16
Skill: Factual Recall

62) Genetic information is encoded in the
   A) quaternary structure of a protein.
   B) sequence of nucleotides in DNA.
   C) degree of saturation of fatty acids.
   D) length of glycogen.
   E) linear sequence of amino acids in a polypeptide.

Answer: B
Topic: 3.16
Skill: Conceptual Understanding

63) You work for a company that manufactures food products. A new "wonder food" is being distributed by a rival company. The researchers in your company determine that the "wonder food" contains only carbon, oxygen, and hydrogen. At this point, your researchers can say with certainty that the food

    A) includes proteins.
    B) includes nucleic acids.
    C) could only be made of triglycerides.
    D) could only be made of carbohydrates.
    E) does not include proteins or nucleic acids.

Answer: E
Topic: 3.2, 3.12, 3.16
Skill: Application

64) In what part of the world did the mutation for lactose tolerance first appear?

    A) Eastern Asia
    B) South America
    C) Northern Europe
    D) North America
    E) Western Australia

Answer: C
Topic: 3.17–Evolution Connection
Skill: Factual Recall

65) Why did the lactose tolerance mutation in the East African herders spread so rapidly within the population?

    A) Milk provided calcium for strong bones.
    B) It was a selective advantage for survival during droughts.
    C) Lactose was a better source of energy than glucose.
    D) Milk was a good source of protein during the winter.
    E) Milk from cows could be used to feed infants instead of breast milk.

Answer: B
Topic: 3.17–Evolution Connection
Skill: Conceptual Understanding

Art Questions

1)

H—C(=O) / C / ...

(structural formulas of Glucose and Fructose)

Glucose
(an aldose)

Fructose
(a ketose)

These two molecules are structural isomers. What is the difference between them?
   A) the number of carbon atoms
   B) the number of oxygen atoms
   C) the number of hydrogen atoms
   D) the location of a double-bonded oxygen atom
   E) Only one of them has a double bond between carbon atoms.

Answer: D
Topic: 3.1, 3.4
Skill: Application

2)

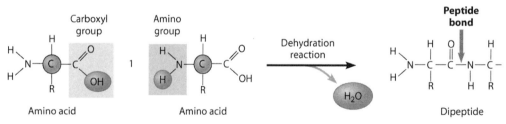

How are these two amino acids attached together?
   A) amino group to amino group
   B) amino group to carboxylic acid group
   C) carboxylic acid group to carboxylic acid group
   D) carbon atom to carbon atom
   E) through a hydrolysis reaction

Answer: B
Topic: 3.12
Skill: Application

Scenario Questions

After reading the following paragraph, answer the question(s) below.

You're the manager of a factory that produces enzyme–washed blue jeans (the enzymes lighten the color of the denim, giving a "faded" appearance). When the most recent batch of fabric came out of the enzyme wash, however, the color wasn't light enough to meet your standards. Your quality control laboratory wants to do some tests to determine why the wash enzymes didn't perform as expected.

1) Which hypothesis is most likely to be productive for their initial investigation?
   A) The nucleotide chain of the enzymes may be incorrectly formed.
   B) The dye in the fabric may have hydrolyzed the fatty acids in the enzymes.
   C) The polysaccharides in the enzymes may have separated in the wash water.
   D) The three–dimensional structure of the proteins may have been altered.
   E) There may not have been enough phospholipids for the volume of fabric.

   Answer: D
   Topic: 3.13
   Skill: Factual Recall

2) Based on your understanding of enzyme structure, which of the following would you recommend that they also investigate?
   A) the temperature of the liquid in the washing vat
   B) the pH of the liquid in the washing vat
   C) the manufacturer of the fabric
   D) how long the fabric has been in storage
   E) the primary structure of the enzyme

   Answer: A
   Topic: 3.13
   Skill: Conceptual Understanding

Chapter 4 A Tour of the Cell

Multiple-Choice Questions

1) Which of the following statements about cells is *true*?
   A) All cells have cell walls.
   B) All cells have internal structures that move.
   C) All cells are attached to other cells.
   D) All cells are motile.
   E) All cells have static organelles.

   Answer: B
   Topic: Opening Essay
   Skill: Factual Recall

2) Light microscopes
   A) can generally magnify objects about 10,000 times without blurring.
   B) typically provide more resolution than an electron microscope.
   C) work by reflecting electrons off the surface of an object being studied.
   D) use light and glass lenses to magnify an image.
   E) are generally not used to view bacteria.

   Answer: D
   Topic: 4.1
   Skill: Factual Recall

3) One centimeter = _____ millimeters.
   A) 0.01
   B) 0.10
   C) 10
   D) 100
   E) 1,000

   Answer: C
   Topic: 4.1
   Skill: Factual Recall

4) Resolution is the
   A) ability of an optical instrument to show two close objects as separate.
   B) size of an image.
   C) ability of an optical instrument to magnify an image.
   D) ability of an optical instrument to estimate the size of an image.
   E) distance between the lenses of a microscope.

   Answer: A
   Topic: 4.1
   Skill: Factual Recall

5) Which of the following statements about electron microscopes is *true*?
   A) Electron microscopes focus electron beams to create a magnified image of an object.
   B) Scanning electron microscopes are used to study the details of internal cell structure.
   C) Electron microscopes use glass lenses to focus and magnify the image.
   D) Transmission electron microscopes are mainly used to study cell surfaces.
   E) Specimens must be sectioned to be viewed under a scanning electron microscope.

Answer: A
Topic: 4.1
Skill: Factual Recall

6) A scientist wants to examine living cells lining the respiratory tract to determine how the cells use tiny hairs to move dirt and mucus away from the lungs. Which of the following instruments would be best, and why?
   A) a light microscope, because it allows observations of whole, live cells
   B) a transmission electron microscope, because it has high resolution
   C) a transmission electron microscope, because it is capable of very high magnification
   D) a scanning electron microscope, because it can reveal structures on cell surfaces
   E) a scanning electron microscope, because it can be used to observe whole cells without slicing them

Answer: A
Topic: 4.1
Skill: Application

7) The idea that all living things are composed of cells and that all cells come from other cells defines
   A) central dogma.
   B) the laws of inheritance.
   C) organelle theory.
   D) cell theory.
   E) inheritance of acquired characteristics.

Answer: D
Topic: 4.1
Skill: Factual Recall

8) A scientist wants to magnify a pollen grain 8,000 times and examine the ridges and pores on its surface. Which one of the following instruments would be best?
   A) a transmission electron microscope
   B) a scanning electron microscope
   C) a fluorescence confocal microscope
   D) a differential interference–contrast microscope
   E) an inverted light microscope

Answer: B
Topic: 4.1
Skill: Application

9) A scanning electron microscope is used to study _____, whereas a transmission electron microscope is used to study _____.
   A) live cells . . . dead cells
   B) cell surfaces . . . internal cell structures
   C) dead cells . . . live cells
   D) internal cell structures . . . cell surfaces
   E) plant tissue . . . animal tissue

Answer: B
Topic: 4.1
Skill: Factual Recall

10) The diameter of most animal and plant cells ranges from
   A) 0.01 to 0.1 micrometers.
   B) 0.1 to 1.0 micrometers.
   C) 1.0 to 10 micrometers.
   D) 10 to 100 micrometers.
   E) 100 to 1000 micrometers.

Answer: D
Topic: 4.2
Skill: Factual Recall

11) As cell size increases, the
   A) volume and surface area decrease.
   B) volume increases faster than the surface area.
   C) surface area increases faster than the volume.
   D) surface area and volume increase at the same rate.
   E) surface area decreases while the volume remains constant.

Answer: B
Topic: 4.2
Skill: Conceptual Understanding

12) Which of the following cells has the greatest surface–to–volume ratio?
   A) bacterium
   B) human red blood cell
   C) human muscle cell
   D) frog egg
   E) ostrich egg

Answer: A
Topic: 4.2
Skill: Conceptual Understanding

13) A cell is exposed to a substance that prevents it from dividing. The cell becomes larger and larger. This situation
    A) should present no problem to the cell, since it can continue to perform all other necessary functions.
    B) should present no problem to the cell, because the surface area of the cell will increase as the volume of the cell increases.
    C) will eventually be problematic, since the cell's ability to absorb nutrients through its outer membrane will not keep increasing as quickly as its cytoplasmic needs.
    D) should be beneficial, since the cell will be able to divert the ATP normally used for cell division to other processes.
    E) will eventually lead to the cell's deterioration, since functional organelles will not proportionally increase with the size of the cell.

Answer: C
Topic: 4.2
Skill: Conceptual Understanding

14) Your throat is dry, and you want the last cough drop in the box to last a long time in your mouth. What should you do?
    A) Break the cough drop into little pieces and put them all in your mouth. Since each little piece must be dissolved separately, the drop will last longer.
    B) Keep the cough drop whole. This maintains the largest surface-to-volume ratio, and slows the dissolution of the cough drop.
    C) Break the cough drop into little pieces and put them all in your mouth. This decreases the surface-to-volume ratio, and slows the dissolution of the cough drop.
    D) It doesn't matter if the cough drop is in one piece or many pieces; the total amount of cough drop is all that matters.
    E) Break the cough drop into little pieces, put them all in your mouth, and drink plenty of water.

Answer: B
Topic: 4.2
Skill: Conceptual Understanding

15) Archaea are composed of _____ cells.
    A) plant
    B) prokaryotic
    C) bacterial
    D) eukaryotic
    E) animal

Answer: B
Topic: 4.3
Skill: Application

16) Which of the following structures is exclusively associated with prokaryotic cells?
    A) a membrane-bound nucleus
    B) nucleoid
    C) a cell wall
    D) membrane-enclosed organelles
    E) ribosomes

Answer: B
Topic: 4.3
Skill: Factual Recall

17) The nucleoid region of a prokaryotic cell
    A) contains the cell's DNA.
    B) separates the RNA from the cytoplasm.
    C) is surrounded by a nucleoid membrane.
    D) contains the cell's nucleoli.
    E) is the site of organelle production.

Answer: A
Topic: 4.3
Skill: Factual Recall

18) _____ cells lack a membrane-enclosed nucleus.
    A) Plant
    B) Animal
    C) Prokaryotic
    D) Eukaryotic
    E) Fungal

Answer: C
Topic: 4.3
Skill: Factual Recall

19) A bacterial cell's DNA is found in its
    A) ribosomes.
    B) nucleus.
    C) peroxisome.
    D) nucleoid region.
    E) capsule.

Answer: D
Topic: 4.3
Skill: Factual Recall

20) Which of the following structures are used by prokaryotes for attaching to surfaces?
    A) pili
    B) flagella
    C) capsules
    D) anchoring junctions
    E) both pili and capsules

Answer: E
Topic: 4.3
Skill: Factual Recall

21) The membranous compartmentalization of a cell
    A) divides the cell into two equal-sized halves.
    B) allows different metabolic processes to occur simultaneously.
    C) requires the presence of a cell wall.
    D) requires the presence of a large central vacuole.
    E) is common in prokaryotes and eukaryotes.

Answer: B
Topic: 4.4
Skill: Factual Recall

22) Which of the following statements about internal membranes in eukaryotic cells is *false*?
   A) In eukaryotic cells, internal membranes greatly increase a cell's total membrane area.
   B) In eukaryotic cells, internal membranes provide an additional area for many metabolic processes occur.
   C) In eukaryotic cells, internal membranes form membranous compartments called organelles.
   D) In eukaryotic cells, internal membranes contain proteins essential for metabolic processes.
   E) In eukaryotic cells, internal membranes standardize the internal environment of all cellular organelles.

Answer: E
Topic: 4.4
Skill: Factual Recall

23) You are told that the cells on a microscope slide are plant, animal, or bacterial. You look at them through a microscope and see cell walls and membrane–bound organelles. You conclude correctly that the cells
   A) are plant cells.
   B) are animal cells.
   C) are bacterial cells.
   D) could be either plant or bacterial cells.
   E) could be plant, animal, or bacterial cells.

Answer: A
Topic: 4.4
Skill: Conceptual Understanding

24) Unlike animal cells, plant cells have _____ and _____. Unlike plant cells, animal cells have _____.
   A) chloroplasts . . . cell walls . . . centrioles
   B) centrioles . . . chloroplasts . . . cell walls
   C) chloroplasts . . . cell walls . . . cell membranes
   D) chloroplasts . . . cell walls . . . a nucleus
   E) centrioles . . . cell walls . . . large central vacuoles

Answer: A
Topic: 4.4
Skill: Factual Recall

25) Which of the following statements about cellular metabolism is *false*?
   A) Cellular metabolism includes different processes that require different conditions.
   B) Cellular metabolism can occur within organelles.
   C) Cellular metabolism can involve the synthesis of steroid hormones.
   D) Cellular metabolism occurs in animal but not plant cells.
   E) Cellular metabolism often occurs on the surfaces of internal membranes.

Answer: D
Topic: 4.4
Skill: Factual Recall

26) Plasma membranes are permeable to
   A) large molecules such as starch.
   B) large molecules such as proteins.
   C) small ions such as Na^+.
   D) nonpolar molecules such as CO_2.
   E) hydrophilic molecules such as glucose.

Answer: D
Topic: 4.5
Skill: Factual Recall

27) What would you expect to find when looking through a SEM at a cell treated with an enzyme that cleaves proteins at their hydrophilic amino acids?
   A) a cell surface that is devoid of any major structures
   B) a cell surface covered with polysaccharides
   C) a cell surface coated with hydrophilic proteins
   D) a cell surface coated with lipids and polysaccharides
   E) a cell surface without its outer phospholipid bilayer

Answer: A
Topic: 4.5
Skill: Conceptual Understanding

28) The nucleus of a cell
   A) is surrounded by a single layer of membrane.
   B) is contained within the nucleolus.
   C) is the region of the cell where ribosomes are degraded.
   D) contains DNA.
   E) is the primary location of protein synthesis.

Answer: D
Topic: 4.6
Skill: Factual Recall

29) Long fibers of DNA and protein are called
   A) chromatin.
   B) a nucleolus.
   C) a ribosome.
   D) a lysosome.
   E) a central vacuole.

Answer: A
Topic: 4.6
Skill: Factual Recall

30) During cell reproduction, chromatin fibers coil up into structures called
   A) ribosomes.
   B) lysosomes.
   C) peroxisomes.
   D) chromosomes.
   E) nucleoli.

Answer: D
Topic: 4.6
Skill: Factual Recall

31) The function of the nucleolus is
    A) to manufacture polypeptides.
    B) to manufacture ribosomal RNA.
    C) intracellular digestion.
    D) to store chromatin.
    E) to produce H_2O_2.

Answer: B
Topic: 4.6
Skill: Factual Recall

32) Protein synthesis requires the use of mRNA, which
    A) is made in the nucleolus.
    B) directs the degradation of DNA.
    C) must be made by the ribosomes.
    D) is translated by the ribosomes into the amino acid sequences of proteins.
    E) carries the message to the nucleus to synthesize new DNA during cell division.

Answer: D
Topic: 4.6
Skill: Factual Recall

33) The plasma cell produces thousands of antibodies per second. What type of intracellular structure would you expect to be very prominent within the cell?
    A) nucleus
    B) endoplasmic reticulum
    C) mitochondria
    D) peroxisome
    E) microtubules

Answer: B
Topic: 4.7
Skill: Conceptual Understanding

34) Which location in the cell is unlikely to contain ribosomes or ribosomal subunits?
    A) nuclear envelope
    B) nucleolus
    C) plasma membrane
    D) endoplasmic reticulum
    E) cytoplasm

Answer: C
Topic: 4.7
Skill: Factual Recall

35) Which of the following statements regarding the endomembrane system is *false*?
   A) The endomembrane system is involved in the synthesis, storage, and export of important molecules.
   B) The endomembrane system includes the rough and smooth endoplasmic reticulum.
   C) The endomembrane system includes the nuclear envelope.
   D) The endomembrane system is a system of interrelated membranes that are all physically connected.
   E) The endomembrane system divides the cell into compartments.

Answer: D
Topic: 4.8
Skill: Factual Recall

36) The endomembrane system includes all of the following organelles *except* the
   A) plasma membrane.
   B) endoplasmic reticulum.
   C) peroxisome.
   D) Golgi apparatus.
   E) lysosome.

Answer: C
Topic: 4.8
Skill: Factual Recall

37) Smooth endoplasmic reticulum
   A) stores calcium ions in muscle cells.
   B) is the major site of carbohydrate synthesis in eukaryotic cells.
   C) produces proteins for cell membranes.
   D) produces antibodies.
   E) helps assemble ribosomes for protein synthesis.

Answer: A
Topic: 4.9
Skill: Factual Recall

38) The two main functions of the rough endoplasmic reticulum are the production of
   A) mitochondria and proteins secreted by the cell.
   B) hydrogen peroxide and steroid hormones secreted by the cell.
   C) ribosomes and steroid hormones.
   D) membrane and proteins secreted by the cell.
   E) chromatin and mitochondria.

Answer: D
Topic: 4.9
Skill: Factual Recall

39) Secretory proteins are
   A) produced by ribosomes on the smooth endoplasmic reticulum.
   B) chemically modified in the nucleus.
   C) produced by the cell for internal use.
   D) released from the cell through the plasma membrane.
   E) incorporated into the mitochondrial membrane.

Answer: D
Topic: 4.9
Skill: Factual Recall

40) The cells that produce hair contain a lot of _____, while the cells that produce the oils that coat the hair contain a lot of _____.

    A) smooth endoplasmic reticulum . . . lysosomes

    B) rough endoplasmic reticulum . . . smooth endoplasmic reticulum

    C) smooth endoplasmic reticulum . . . rough endoplasmic reticulum

    D) microbodies . . . lysosomes

    E) nuclei . . . chromatin

Answer: B
Topic: 4.9
Skill: Conceptual Understanding

41) The Golgi apparatus

    A) is composed of stacks of membranous vesicles that are continuous with one another.

    B) stores, modifies, and packages proteins.

    C) strings together amino acids to produce proteins.

    D) forms fats from glycerols and fatty acids.

    E) is the site of carbohydrate breakdown.

Answer: B
Topic: 4.10
Skill: Factual Recall

42) Which of the following statements regarding the Golgi apparatus is *false*?

    A) The Golgi apparatus works closely with the endoplasmic reticulum.

    B) The Golgi apparatus serves as a molecular warehouse and finishing factory.

    C) The Golgi apparatus decreases in size when a cell increases its protein production.

    D) The Golgi apparatus modifies chemicals received from the endoplasmic reticulum.

    E) The Golgi apparatus sorts molecules according to their destination.

Answer: C
Topic: 4.10
Skill: Factual Recall

43) Which of the following statements about lysosomes is *false*?

    A) Lysosomes help to digest worn-out or damaged organelles.

    B) Lysosomes synthesize proteins from the recycled amino acids.

    C) Lysosomes fuse with food vacuoles to expose nutrients to lysosomal enzymes.

    D) Lysosomes destroy harmful bacteria engulfed by white blood cells.

    E) Lysosomes recycle materials within the cell.

Answer: B
Topic: 4.11
Skill: Factual Recall

44) When a cell is deprived of oxygen, its lysosomes tend to burst and release their contents into the cell. As a result of this, that cell will
   A) recycle damaged organelles.
   B) produce additional ER.
   C) undergo cell division.
   D) produce replacement lysosomes.
   E) undergo self–digestion and die.

Answer: E
Topic: 4.11
Skill: Conceptual Understanding

45) Tay–Sachs disease results from the malfunction of
   A) mitochondria.
   B) lysosomes.
   C) endoplasmic reticulum.
   D) chloroplasts.
   E) nucleoli.

Answer: B
Topic: 4.11
Skill: Factual Recall

46) Tay–Sachs disease
   A) causes an accumulation of lipids in brain cells.
   B) involves damage to liver cells.
   C) is due to the absence of an enzyme that digests polysaccharides.
   D) prevents the breakdown of glycogen.
   E) results in an accumulation of triglycerides in the alveoli of the lungs.

Answer: A
Topic: 4.11
Skill: Factual Recall

47) Which of the following statements about the functions of a plant cell central vacuole is *false*?
   A) The central vacuole of a plant cell may help increase the size of cells by absorbing water.
   B) The central vacuole of a plant cell may store pigments that will help attract pollinating insects.
   C) The central vacuole of a plant cell may store waste products.
   D) The central vacuole of a plant cell may digest chemicals for recycling.
   E) The central vacuole of a plant cell may store poisons.

Answer: D
Topic: 4.12
Skill: Factual Recall

48) Contractile vacuoles
   A) are generally found in protists that inhabit salt water.
   B) help in the excretion of excess salt.
   C) prevent cells from bursting as a result of the influx of excess water.
   D) allow organisms to avoid dehydration by absorbing water from the environment.
   E) stimulate the absorption of salt water.

Answer: C
Topic: 4.12
Skill: Factual Recall

49) A manufacturing company dumps its wastes into a nearby pond. One of the wastes is found to paralyze the contractile vacuoles of certain protists. A biologist looking at individual samples of these organisms taken from the pond would find that they
   A) have lost water and shrunk.
   B) have gained water and burst.
   C) have died of malnutrition.
   D) have died because wastes have built up in the cytoplasm.
   E) are surviving but are unable to reproduce.

Answer: B
Topic: 4.12
Skill: Conceptual Understanding

50) Which organelle is involved in the catabolism of fatty acids and the detoxification of alcohol?
   A) peroxosome
   B) Golgi apparatus
   C) smooth ER
   D) nucleus
   E) ribosomes

Answer: A
Topic: 4.13
Skill: Factual Recall

51) Insulin is a protein that is produced by pancreatic cells and secreted into the bloodstream. Which of the following options correctly lists the order of the structures through which insulin passes from its production to its exit from the cell?
   A) rough ER, transport vesicles, Golgi apparatus, transport vesicles, cell membrane
   B) rough ER, lysosomes, transport vesicles, cell membrane
   C) rough ER, Golgi apparatus, smooth ER, cell membrane
   D) rough ER, transport vesicles, cell membrane
   E) rough ER, transport vesicles, Golgi apparatus, vacuole, cell membrane

Answer: A
Topic: 4.13
Skill: Conceptual Understanding

52) The function of mitochondria is
    A) cellular respiration.
    B) intracellular transport of proteins.
    C) lipid synthesis.
    D) photosynthesis.
    E) intracellular digestion.

Answer: A
Topic: 4.14
Skill: Factual Recall

53) Cyanide inhibits mitochondrial function; as a result, the rate of
    A) ATP synthesis increases.
    B) ATP synthesis decreases.
    C) photosynthesis increases.
    D) lipid synthesis increases.
    E) protein synthesis increases.

Answer: B
Topic: 4.14
Skill: Application

54) The _____ of a mitochondrion is/are an adaptation that increases the surface area and
enhances a mitochondrion's ability to produce ATP.
    A) stroma
    B) grana
    C) intermembrane space
    D) cristae
    E) matrix

Answer: D
Topic: 4.14
Skill: Factual Recall

55) The function of chloroplasts is
    A) cellular respiration.
    B) intracellular transport of proteins.
    C) lipid synthesis.
    D) photosynthesis.
    E) intracellular digestion.

Answer: D
Topic: 4.15
Skill: Factual Recall

56) The stroma is the
    A) thick fluid enclosed by the inner chloroplast membrane.
    B) watery fluid enclosed by the inner membrane of a mitochondrion.
    C) space between the inner and outer membranes of a chloroplast.
    D) space between the inner and outer membranes of a mitochondrion.
    E) fluid within the grana.

Answer: A
Topic: 4.15
Skill: Factual Recall

57) Mitochondria differ from chloroplasts in that mitochondria
  A) convert solar energy to chemical energy, whereas chloroplasts convert one form of chemical energy to another.
  B) contain three different membrane–bound compartments, whereas chloroplasts contain two.
  C) contain membrane folds called cristae, whereas chloroplasts contain disk–like vesicles in stacks called grana.
  D) are not found in plants, whereas chloroplasts are not found in animals.
  E) produce glucose, whereas chloroplasts break glucose down.

Answer: C
Topic: 4.14, 4.15
Skill: Factual Recall

58) The endosymbiosis hypothesis proposes that
  A) two cells were juxtaposed and one benefited from the other.
  B) one cell was dependent on the other for survival.
  C) a small cell lived inside a larger cell to the benefit of both cells.
  D) a large cell engulfed and digested a smaller cell, exposing its enzymes for use by the larger cell.
  E) two cells merged into one cell, improving the enzyme function of the new cell.

Answer: C
Topic: 4.16–Evolution Connection
Skill: Factual Recall

59) The endosymbiosis hypothesis is supported by all of the following pieces of evidence, *except* the fact that
  A) mitochondria have circular DNA like prokaryotes.
  B) mitochondria synthesize glucose like prokaryotes.
  C) chloroplasts have ribosomes like prokaryotes.
  D) mitochondria have a double membrane.
  E) chloroplasts split like prokaryotes.

Answer: B
Topic: 4.16–Evolution Connection
Skill: Factual Recall

60) Microfilaments differ from microtubules in that microfilaments
  A) are larger than microtubules.
  B) are found only in plants, whereas microtubules are found in plants and animal cells.
  C) are mainly composed of actin, whereas microtubules are composed of tubulin.
  D) help to anchor organelles, whereas microtubules primarily function to help cells change shape and move.
  E) form the inner core of cilia and flagella, whereas microtubules regulate metabolism.

Answer: C
Topic: 4.17
Skill: Factual Recall

61) Which of the following statements about the cytoskeleton is *false*?
   A) The cytoskeleton helps to support cells.
   B) Once laid down, the elements of the cytoskeleton are fixed and remain permanently in place.
   C) The cytoskeleton is composed of three types of fibers: microfilaments, microtubules, and intermediate filaments.
   D) The cytoskeleton plays an important role in amoeboid motion.
   E) The cytoskeleton includes fibrous and globular proteins.

Answer: B
Topic: 4.17
Skill: Conceptual Understanding

62) Intermediate filaments
   A) guide the movements of chromosomes.
   B) are found within cilia and flagella.
   C) surround the nucleus.
   D) guide the movements of organelles.
   E) support the inner mitochondrial membrane.

Answer: C
Topic: 4.17
Skill: Factual Recall

63) A drug that interferes with microtubule formation is likely to completely disrupt
   A) the production of ribosomes.
   B) the amoeboid motion of a cell.
   C) the function of lysosomes.
   D) contraction of muscle cells.
   E) the movements of sperm cells.

Answer: E
Topic: 4.17, 4.18
Skill: Conceptual Understanding

64) Cilia differ from flagella in that
   A) cilia are composed of microfilaments and flagella are composed of intermediate filaments.
   B) cilia contain nine microtubule doublets surrounding a central pair of microtubules, while flagella contain only nine microtubule doublets.
   C) the protein filaments of cilia are "naked," while those of flagella are wrapped in an extension of the cell membrane.
   D) cilia are typically more numerous and shorter than flagella.
   E) cilia are anchored only in the proteins of the cell membrane, while flagella are anchored in a special structure called the basal body.

Answer: D
Topic: 4.18
Skill: Factual Recall

65) A basal body is
    A) composed of nine microtubule triplets surrounding a central pair of microtubules.
    B) similar in structure to centrioles.
    C) composed of nine microtubule doublets surrounding a central pair of microtubules.
    D) identical in structure to cilia.
    E) identical in structure to flagella.

Answer: B
Topic: 4.18
Skill: Factual Recall

66) Dynein arms
    A) are present in cilia but not in flagella.
    B) are knobs of carbohydrate that are essential to the movement of cilia and flagella.
    C) are found on microtubules in cilia and flagella and cause movement by grabbing and pulling at adjacent microtubule doublets.
    D) are the anchoring proteins in basal bodies.
    E) join microfilaments to the cell membrane.

Answer: C
Topic: 4.18
Skill: Factual Recall

67) A woman is having trouble becoming pregnant. Examination of her partner's sperm indicates that dynein arms are missing from the flagella in his sperm cells. A physician explains that this could interfere with fertility by
    A) preventing the sperm from attaching to the egg cell.
    B) preventing the sperm from swimming to the egg cell.
    C) preventing the sperm from producing enough energy to power swimming.
    D) interfering with the attachment of the flagella to the sperm.
    E) interfering with the ability of the sperm to tolerate the acid conditions in the vaginal canal.

Answer: B
Topic: 4.18, 4.19
Skill: Conceptual Understanding

68) Decreased fertility in men from developed countries may be related to
    A) increased exposure to hormone–like chemicals in the environment.
    B) decreased flagella motion due to inactivity.
    C) increased sperm motility from multiple flagella.
    D) decreased metabolic levels from overexposure to UV rays.
    E) decreased ATP synthesis from low glucose levels.

Answer: A
Topic: 4.19
Skill: Factual Recall

69) Most animal cells are
    A) surrounded by a cell wall.
    B) attached to each other via plasmodesmata.
    C) embedded in an endomembrane system.
    D) embedded in an extracellular matrix.
    E) embedded in a lipid matrix.

Answer: D
Topic: 4.20
Skill: Factual Recall

70) Most cells from multicellular organisms must be attached to their surroundings via integrins. Failure to maintain this contact will usually result in
    A) the proliferation of the cell.
    B) increased metabolic activity of the cell.
    C) the death of the cell.
    D) increased communication with other cells.
    E) improved autocrine functions.

Answer: C
Topic: 4.20
Skill: Conceptual Understanding

71) Which of the following would be most affected by a mutation that prevented cells from forming tight junctions?
    A) attachment of cells to the surrounding matrix
    B) direct flow of water and small molecules from one cell to another
    C) integrity of the inner lining of the digestive tract
    D) attachment of the cytoskeleton to the inside of the plasma membrane
    E) attachment of the cell wall of one plant cell to the cell wall of another

Answer: C
Topic: 4.21
Skill: Conceptual Understanding

72) Skin cells are attached to the extracellular matrix by
    A) basal bodies.
    B) anchoring junctions.
    C) tight junctions.
    D) communicating junctions.
    E) plasmodesmata.

Answer: B
Topic: 4.21
Skill: Conceptual Understanding

73) It is essential for heart muscle cells to beat in a coordinated fashion. The cell junctions that would best facilitate this are
    A) occluding junctions.
    B) anchoring junctions.
    C) tight junctions.
    D) communicating junctions.
    E) plasmodesmata.

Answer: D
Topic: 4.21
Skill: Factual Recall

74) Which of the following statements about plant cell walls is *false*?
    A) Plant cell walls consist of cellulose fibers embedded in a matrix of polysaccharides and proteins.
    B) The cell wall of one plant cell is separated from the cell wall of another by a layer of sticky polysaccharides.
    C) Plant cell walls are multilayered structures.
    D) Plant cell walls protect plant cells by forming an impermeable layer around the cell.
    E) Wood is primarily composed of plant cell walls.

Answer: D
Topic: 4.22
Skill: Factual Recall

75) Which of the following statements regarding plasmodesmata is *false*?
    A) Plasmodesmata penetrate plant cell walls.
    B) Plasmodesmata are one type of cell junction in plants.
    C) Plasmodesmata carry chemical messages between plant cells.
    D) Plasmodesmata carry nutrients between plant cells.
    E) Plasmodesmata are commonly found in single-celled organisms.

Answer: E
Topic: 4.22
Skill: Factual Recall

76) Which of the following cell structures is associated with the breakdown of harmful substances or substances that are no longer needed by the cell?
    A) chloroplasts
    B) mitochondria
    C) peroxisomes
    D) ribosomes
    E) centrioles

Answer: C
Topic: 4.23
Skill: Factual Recall

77) Which of the following statements regarding cells is *false*?
   A) All cells are enclosed in a membrane that maintains internal conditions different from the surroundings.
   B) All cells have a cell wall.
   C) All cells can interconvert forms of energy.
   D) All cells can interconvert chemical materials.
   E) All cells have DNA as their genetic material.

Answer: B
Topic: 4.23
Skill: Factual Recall

78) A child dies following a series of chronic bacterial infections. At the autopsy, the physicians are startled to see that the child's white blood cells are loaded with vacuoles containing intact bacteria. Which of the following explanations could account for this finding?
   A) A defect in the Golgi apparatus prevented the cells from processing and excreting the bacteria.
   B) A defect in the rough endoplasmic reticulum prevented the synthesis of the antibodies (defensive proteins) that would have inactivated the bacteria.
   C) A defect in the cell walls of the white blood cells permitted bacteria to enter the cells.
   D) A defect in the lysosomes of the white blood cells prevented the cells from destroying engulfed bacteria.
   E) A defect in the surface receptors of the white blood cells permitted bacteria to enter the cells.

Answer: D
Topic: 4.23
Skill: Application

Art Questions

1)

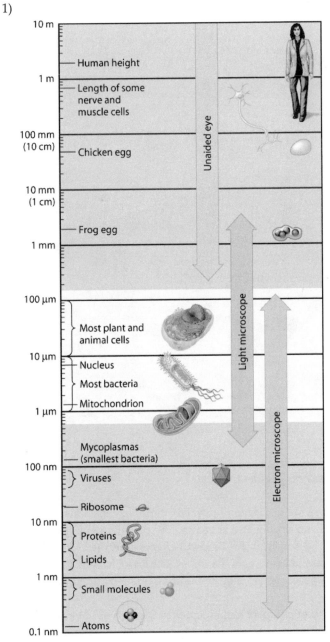

According to this figure, which of the following is large enough to see in the light microscope?
   A) atoms
   B) proteins
   C) ribosome
   D) viruses
   E) mitochondria

Answer: E
Topic: 4.2
Skill: Application

2)

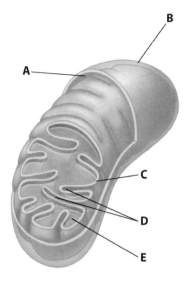

Which part of the mitochondrion shown is its matrix?
A) structure A
B) structure B
C) structure C
D) structure D
E) structure E

Answer: E
Topic: 4.14
Skill: Factual Recall

Scenario Questions

After reading the following paragraph, answer the question(s) below.

The skin is the body's largest organ. It's made up of many different types of cells. Oils, produced by the sebaceous glands, prevent the skin from drying and splitting. The protein melanin, produced by melanocytes in the epidermis, protects the skin from the harmful effects of ultraviolet radiation. Sweat, released through ducts to the skin surface, helps to cool the body. The types of cells that produce these compounds have different numbers of specific organelles, depending on their function.

1) Based on their function, you would expect melanocytes in the skin to have a higher than usual number of
A) lysosomes.
B) chloroplasts.
C) ribosomes.
D) Golgi bodies.
E) microtubules.

Answer: A
Topic: 4.7, 4.9
Skill: Conceptual Understanding

2) The oil from the sebaceous glands is produced by which of the following cell organelles?
   A) ribosomes
   B) rough endoplasmic reticulum
   C) cell membrane
   D) smooth endoplasmic reticulum
   E) central vacuole

Answer: D
Topic: 4.9
Skill: Factual Recall

Chapter 5 The Working Cell

Multiple-Choice Questions

1) Many of the enzymes that control a deep-sea firefly squid's ability to produce light energy from chemical energy are located
   A) in membranes.
   B) in the nucleus.
   C) within chloroplasts.
   D) outside of cells.
   E) within mitochondria.

   Answer: A
   Topic: Opening Essay
   Skill: Factual Recall

2) The fluid mosaic model describes the plasma membrane as consisting of
   A) a phospholipid bilayer with embedded carbohydrates.
   B) two layers of phospholipids with protein sandwiched between them.
   C) a protein bilayer with embedded phospholipids.
   D) carbohydrates, proteins, and phospholipids that can drift in the membrane.
   E) individual proteins and phospholipids that can drift in a phospholipid bilayer.

   Answer: E
   Topic: 5.1
   Skill: Factual Recall

3) Membrane phospholipids
   A) have hydrophobic heads that face the center of the membrane and are shielded from water.
   B) have hydrophilic tails that face outward and are exposed to water.
   C) often have "kinks" in their tails caused by the presence of a double bond between carbons.
   D) remain fluid because they are tightly packed against one another.
   E) form impermeable layers for cells .

   Answer: C
   Topic: 5.1
   Skill: Factual Recall

4) The cholesterol associated with animal cell membranes
   A) is attached to membrane proteins and extends into the watery environment surrounding the cell.
   B) helps to stabilize the cell membrane at body temperature.
   C) makes the cell membrane fluid at room temperature.
   D) is an abnormality resulting from a diet high in cholesterol.
   E) helps solidify the membranes when the room temperature is below freezing.

   Answer: B
   Topic: 5.1
   Skill: Factual Recall

5) A major function of glycoproteins and glycolipids in the cell membrane is to
    A) glue cells together to form tissues.
    B) allow the cells of an embryo to sort themselves into tissues and organs.
    C) attach the cell membrane to the cytoskeleton.
    D) help the cell resist swelling.
    E) help the cell retain its shape.

Answer: B
Topic: 5.1
Skill: Factual Recall

6) When physicians perform an organ transplant, they choose a donor whose tissues match those of the recipient as closely as possible. Which of the following cell components are being matched?
    A) plasma membrane phospholipids
    B) plasma membrane proteins
    C) cell–surface carbohydrates
    D) plasma membrane cholesterols
    E) cytoskeletal elements

Answer: C
Topic: 5.1
Skill: Application

7) Most of the functions of a cell membrane are performed by
    A) glycolipids.
    B) proteins.
    C) phospholipids.
    D) cholesterol.
    E) nucleotides.

Answer: B
Topic: 5.1
Skill: Factual Recall

8) Which of the following statements regarding membrane protein function is *false*?
    A) Membrane proteins serve as enzymes.
    B) Membrane proteins act as receptors to molecules like hormones.
    C) Membrane proteins provide cellular identification tags.
    D) Membrane proteins form junctions between cells.
    E) Membrane proteins transfer genetic information to the cytoplasm.

Answer: E
Topic: 5.1
Skill: Factual Recall

9) Relaying a message from a membrane receptor to a molecule that performs a specific function within a cell is called
　　A) signal transduction.
　　B) inhibition.
　　C) competition.
　　D) self–recognition.
　　E) selective permeability.

Answer: A
Topic: 5.1
Skill: Factual Recall

10) Plasma membranes are selectively permeable. This means that
　　A) anything can pass into or out of a cell as long as the membrane is intact and the cell is healthy.
　　B) the plasma membrane allows some substances to enter or leave a cell more easily than others.
　　C) glucose cannot enter the cell.
　　D) cholesterol cannot enter the cell.
　　E) plasma membranes must be very thick.

Answer: B
Topic: 5.1
Skill: Factual Recall

11) Which of the following statements regarding membrane function is *false*?
　　A) The plasma membrane forms a selective barrier around the cell.
　　B) The plasma membrane plays a role in signal transduction.
　　C) The plasma membrane has receptors for chemical messages.
　　D) The plasma membrane is the control center of the cell.
　　E) The plasma membrane is involved in self–recognition.

Answer: D
Topic: 5.1
Skill: Factual Recall

12) Small, nonpolar, hydrophobic molecules such as fatty acids
　　A) easily pass through a membrane's lipid bilayer.
　　B) very slowly diffuse through a membrane's lipid bilayer.
　　C) require transport proteins to pass through a membrane's lipid bilayer.
　　D) are actively transported across cell membranes.
　　E) usually enter the cell via endocytosis.

Answer: A
Topic: 5.1
Skill: Factual Recall

13) Which characteristic promoted the utilization of lipids as the first cell membrane?
   A) spontaneous degradation of the intracellular environment
   B) self–assembly into a simple membrane
   C) ability to form an impermeable membrane
   D) formation of a semi–solid membrane
   E) utilization of the hydrophilic nature of lipids

Answer: B
Topic: 5.2–Evolution Connection
Skill: Conceptual Understanding

14) All cells are enclosed by a plasma membrane that is similar in _____ and _____.
   A) thickness . . . composition
   B) permeability . . . content
   C) proteins . . . lipids
   D) lucidity . . . texture
   E) structure . . . function

Answer: E
Topic: 5.2–Evolution Connection
Skill: Factual Recall

15) Which of the following substances would have the most trouble crossing a biological membrane by diffusing through the lipid bilayer?
   A) H_2O
   B) O_2
   C) CO_2
   D) Na^+
   E) a small, nonpolar molecule such as butane (C_4H_{10})

Answer: D
Topic: 5.3
Skill: Factual Recall

16) Oxygen crosses a plasma membrane by
   A) osmosis.
   B) phagocytosis.
   C) active transport.
   D) pinocytosis.
   E) passive transport.

Answer: E
Topic: 5.3
Skill: Factual Recall

17) Which of the following statements regarding diffusion is *false*?
    A) Diffusion is a result of the kinetic energy of atoms and molecules.
    B) Diffusion is driven by concentration gradients.
    C) Diffusion requires no input of energy into the system.
    D) Diffusion occurs when particles spread from areas where they are less concentrated to areas where they are more concentrated.
    E) Diffusion occurs even after equilibrium is reached and no net change is apparent.

Answer: D
Topic: 5.3
Skill: Conceptual Understanding

18) Diffusion does not require the cell to expend ATP. Therefore, diffusion is considered a type of
    A) exocytosis.
    B) phagocytosis.
    C) passive transport.
    D) active transport.
    E) endocytosis.

Answer: C
Topic: 5.3
Skill: Conceptual Understanding

19) Osmosis can be defined as
    A) the diffusion of water.
    B) the diffusion of nonpolar molecules.
    C) active transport.
    D) the diffusion of a solute.
    E) endocytosis.

Answer: A
Topic: 5.4
Skill: Factual Recall

20) When two aqueous solutions that differ in solute concentration are placed on either side of a semipermeable membrane and osmosis is allowed to take place, the water will
    A) exhibit a net movement to the side with lower water concentration.
    B) exhibit a net movement to the side with higher water concentration.
    C) exhibit a net movement to the side with lower solute concentration.
    D) exhibit an equal movement in both directions across the membrane.
    E) not cross the membrane.

Answer: A
Topic: 5.4
Skill: Factual Recall

21) In the lab, you use a special balloon that is permeable to water, but not sucrose, to make an "artificial cell." The balloon is filled with a solution of 20% sucrose and 80% water and is immersed in a beaker containing a solution of 40% sucrose and 60% water. Which of the following will occur?
    A) Water will leave the balloon.
    B) Water will enter the balloon.
    C) Sucrose will leave the balloon.
    D) Sucrose will enter the balloon.
    E) Sucrose and water will pass across the balloon simultaneously.

Answer: A
Topic: 5.4
Skill: Application

22) Some protozoans have special organelles called contractile vacuoles that continually eliminate excess water from the cell. The presence of these organelles tells you that the environment
    A) is isotonic to the protozoan.
    B) is hypotonic to the protozoan.
    C) is contaminated with pollutants.
    D) contains a higher concentration of solutes than the protozoan.
    E) is hypertonic to the protozoan.

Answer: B
Topic: 5.4
Skill: Application

23) A cell that neither gains nor loses water when it is immersed in a solution is
    A) isotonic to its environment.
    B) hypertonic to its environment.
    C) hypotonic to its environment.
    D) metabolically inactive.
    E) dead.

Answer: A
Topic: 5.5
Skill: Factual Recall

24) In a hypotonic solution, an animal cell will
    A) lyse.
    B) experience turgor.
    C) neither gain nor lose water.
    D) shrivel.
    E) lose water.

Answer: A
Topic: 5.5
Skill: Application

25) If placed in tap water, an animal cell will undergo lysis, whereas a plant cell will not. What accounts for this difference?
    A) the expulsion of water by the plant cell's central vacuole
    B) the relative impermeability of the plant cell membrane to water
    C) the relative impermeability of the plant cell wall to water
    D) the fact that plant cells are isotonic to tap water
    E) the relative inelasticity and strength of the plant cell wall

Answer: E
Topic: 5.5
Skill: Factual Recall

26) In the lab, you use a special balloon that is permeable to water but not sucrose to make an "artificial cell." The balloon is filled with a solution of 20% sucrose and 80% water and is immersed in a beaker containing a solution of 40% sucrose and 60% water. The solution in the balloon is _____ relative to the solution in the beaker.
    A) isotonic
    B) hypotonic
    C) hypertonic
    D) hydrophobic
    E) hydrophilic

Answer: B
Topic: 5.5
Skill: Application

27) White blood cells (WBCs) are more resistant to lysis than red blood cells (RBCs). When looking at a sample of blood for WBCs, would could you do to reduce interference from RBCs?
    A) Mix the blood in a salty solution to cause the RBCs to lyse.
    B) Mix the blood in an isotonic solution and allow the WBCs to float to the top.
    C) Mix the blood with a dye that stains the proteins in the cytoplasm.
    D) Mix the blood in a hypotonic solution, which will cause the RBCs to lyse.
    E) Mix the blood in a hypertonic solution, which will cause the RBCs to lyse.

Answer: D
Topic: 5.5
Skill: Application

28) A plant cell in a hypotonic solution
    A) is turgid.
    B) lyses.
    C) shrivels.
    D) wilts.
    E) is flaccid.

Answer: A
Topic: 5.5
Skill: Factual Recall

29) You are adrift in the Atlantic Ocean, and, being thirsty, drink the surrounding seawater. As a result,
   A) you quench your thirst.
   B) your cells lyse, due to the excessive intake of salt.
   C) your cells become turgid.
   D) you dehydrate yourself.
   E) your cells lyse from excessive water intake.

Answer: D
Topic: 5.5
Skill: Application

30) Facilitated diffusion across a biological membrane requires _____ and moves a substance _____ its concentration gradient.
   A) energy and transport proteins . . . down
   B) energy . . . down
   C) transport proteins . . . down
   D) energy and transport proteins . . . against
   E) transport proteins . . . against

Answer: C
Topic: 5.6
Skill: Factual Recall

31) The molecules responsible for membrane transport are
   A) steroids.
   B) ATP.
   C) phospholipids.
   D) carbohydrates.
   E) proteins.

Answer: E
Topic: 5.6
Skill: Factual Recall

32) Which of the following statements is *true* among all types of passive diffusion?
   A) Proteins are needed to transport molecules across the membrane.
   B) The concentration gradient is the driving force.
   C) Only small polar molecules are able to cross the plasma membrane.
   D) Only small nonpolar molecules are able to cross the plasma membrane.
   E) Ions never cross the plasma membrane by passive transport.

Answer: B
Topic: 5.4, 5.5, 5.6
Skill: Factual Recall

33) Which of the following processes can move a solute against its concentration gradient?
   A) osmosis
   B) passive transport
   C) diffusion
   D) facilitated diffusion
   E) active transport

Answer: E
Topic: 5.7
Skill: Factual Recall

42) Glucose molecules provide energy to power the swimming motion of sperm. In this example, the sperm are changing
    A) chemical energy into kinetic energy.
    B) chemical energy into potential energy.
    C) kinetic energy into potential energy.
    D) kinetic energy into chemical energy.
    E) kinetic energy into thermal energy.

Answer: A
Topic: 5.10
Skill: Application

43) In the reaction A → B + C + heat,
    A) there is a net input of energy.
    B) the potential energy of the products is greater than that of the reactant.
    C) the potential energy of the products is the same as that of the reactant.
    D) the potential energy of the products is less than that of the reactant.
    E) entropy has decreased.

Answer: D
Topic: 5.10
Skill: Application

44) Which of the following statements regarding thermodynamics is *false*?
    A) Thermodynamics is the study of energy transformations that occur in a collection of matter.
    B) The collection of matter under study is called the system.
    C) A single cell or the planet Earth could be a thermodynamic system.
    D) An open system exchanges both energy and matter with its surroundings.
    E) An automobile engine is an example of a closed system.

Answer: E
Topic: 5.11
Skill: Factual Recall

45) According to _____, energy cannot be created or destroyed.
    A) Aristotle's first principle
    B) the first law of thermodynamics
    C) the second law of thermodynamics
    D) the third law of thermodynamics
    E) Einstein's law of relativity

Answer: B
Topic: 5.11
Skill: Factual Recall

46) A steer must eat at least 100 pounds of grain to gain less than 10 pounds of muscle tissue. This illustrates
  A) the first law of thermodynamics.
  B) the second law of thermodynamics.
  C) that some energy is destroyed in every energy conversion.
  D) that energy transformations are typically 100% efficient.
  E) that thermal energy can be transformed into chemical energy.

Answer: B
Topic: 5.11
Skill: Application

47) Which of the following energy transfers is impossible in living systems?
  A) light energy to chemical energy
  B) chemical energy to kinetic energy
  C) potential energy to kinetic energy
  D) light energy to potential energy
  E) heat to light energy.

Answer: E
Topic: 5.11
Skill: Conceptual Understanding

48) Living systems
  A) violate the first law of thermodynamics.
  B) violate the second law of thermodynamics.
  C) decrease their entropy while increasing the entropy of the universe.
  D) are examples of a closed system.
  E) are only compelled to follow the first law of thermodynamics.

Answer: C
Topic: 5.11
Skill: Conceptual Understanding

49) Which of the following processes is endergonic?
  A) the burning of wood
  B) the release of heat from the breakdown of glucose
  C) the synthesis of glucose from carbon dioxide and water
  D) the breakdown of glucose
  E) cellular respiration

Answer: C
Topic: 5.12
Skill: Conceptual Understanding

50) What is the basic difference between exergonic and endergonic reactions?
- A) Exergonic reactions involve ionic bonds; endergonic reactions involve covalent bonds.
- B) Exergonic reactions involve the breaking of bonds; endergonic reactions involve the formation of bonds.
- C) Exergonic reactions involve the formation of bonds; endergonic reactions involve the breaking of bonds.
- D) Exergonic reactions release energy; endergonic reactions absorb it.
- E) In exergonic reactions, the reactants have less chemical energy than the products; in endergonic reactions, the opposite is true.

Answer: D
Topic: 5.12
Skill: Conceptual Understanding

51) Which of the following statements concerning energy is *false*?
- A) Fireflies are able to take potential energy in the form of food and convert that energy into kinetic energy in the form of heat and light.
- B) A gasoline engine converts chemical energy into kinetic energy.
- C) Living systems convert heat energy into chemical energy to reduce entropy.
- D) Energy transformations in cells are accompanied by the release of heat energy.
- E) During photosynthesis, plants convert kinetic energy into chemical energy.

Answer: C
Topic: 5.12
Skill: Conceptual Understanding

52) Which of the following examples is classified as a metabolic pathway?
- A) protein synthesis
- B) osmosis
- C) cell lysis
- D) spontaneous combustions
- E) passive diffusion

Answer: A
Topic: 5.12
Skill: Conceptual Understanding

53) When a cell uses chemical energy to perform work, it couples a(n) _____ reaction with a(n) _____ reaction.
- A) exergonic . . . endergonic
- B) endergonic . . . exergonic
- C) exergonic . . . spontaneous
- D) spontaneous . . . exergonic
- E) endergonic . . . spontaneous

Answer: A
Topic: 5.12
Skill: Factual Recall

54) Which of the following statements about the ATP molecule is *true*?
    A) It contains two phosphate groups.
    B) Extremely stable bonds link the second and third phosphate groups.
    C) It contains the six-carbon sugar hexose.
    D) It contains a nitrogenous base molecule called adenine.
    E) It can be coupled with an exergonic reaction.

Answer: D
Topic: 5.13
Skill: Factual Recall

55) The transfer of a phosphate group to a molecule or compound is called
    A) carboxylation.
    B) ionization.
    C) phosphorylation.
    D) hydrogen bonding.
    E) hydrogenation.

Answer: C
Topic: 5.13
Skill: Factual Recall

56) Anything that prevents ATP formation will most likely
    A) result in cell death.
    B) force the cell to rely on lipids for energy.
    C) result in the conversion of kinetic energy to potential energy.
    D) force the cell to rely on ADP for energy.
    E) have no effect on the cell.

Answer: A
Topic: 5.13
Skill: Conceptual Understanding

57) ATP can be used as the cell's energy exchange mechanism because
    A) endergonic reactions can be fueled by coupling them with the formation of ATP from ADP.
    B) ATP is the most energy-rich small molecule in the cell.
    C) endergonic reactions can be fueled by coupling them with the hydrolysis of high-energy phosphate bonds in ATP.
    D) the regeneration of ATP from ADP can be fueled by coupling it with endergonic reactions.
    E) ATP is a disposable form of chemical energy, used once and then discarded by the cell.

Answer: C
Topic: 5.13
Skill: Factual Recall

58) An energy barrier
   A) is the amount of energy that must be produced by the reactants to start a chemical reaction.
   B) is higher than the energy of activation of a reaction.
   C) is lower than the energy of activation of a reaction.
   D) prevents the spontaneous decomposition of molecules in the cell.
   E) can only be overcome with the use of enzymes.

Answer: D
Topic: 5.14
Skill: Factual Recall

59) The energy required to initiate an exergonic reaction is called
   A) exergonic energy.
   B) endergonic energy.
   C) input energy.
   D) hydrolytic energy.
   E) the energy of activation.

Answer: E
Topic: 5.14
Skill: Factual Recall

60) Most of a cell's enzymes are
   A) lipids.
   B) proteins.
   C) amino acids.
   D) nucleic acids.
   E) carbohydrates.

Answer: B
Topic: 5.14
Skill: Factual Recall

61) When an enzyme catalyzes a reaction,
   A) it lowers the activation energy of the reaction.
   B) it raises the activation energy of the reaction.
   C) it becomes a product.
   D) it acts as a reactant.
   E) it is used once and discarded.

Answer: A
Topic: 5.14, 5.15
Skill: Factual Recall

62) Substrates bind to an enzyme's _____ site.
   A) reactant
   B) allosteric
   C) regulatory
   D) phosphate
   E) active

Answer: E
Topic: 5.15
Skill: Factual Recall

63) The active site of an enzyme is
    A) the region of a substrate that is changed by an enzyme.
    B) the highly changeable portion of an enzyme that adapts to fit the substrates of various reactions.
    C) the region of an enzyme that attaches to a substrate.
    D) the region of a product that detaches from the enzyme.
    E) the region of the enzyme composed of only a few specific nucleic acids.

Answer: C
Topic: 5.15
Skill: Factual Recall

64) Which of the following statements regarding enzyme function is *false*?
    A) An enzyme's function depends on its three-dimensional shape.
    B) Enzymes are very specific for certain substrates.
    C) Enzymes are used up in chemical reactions.
    D) Enzymes emerge unchanged from the reactions they catalyze.
    E) An enzyme binds to its substrate at the enzyme's active site.

Answer: C
Topic: 5.14, 5.15
Skill: Factual Recall

65) Which of the following statements regarding enzymes is *true*?
    A) Enzymes are inorganic.
    B) An enzyme's function is unaffected by changes in pH.
    C) Enzymes are the reactants in a chemical reaction.
    D) Enzymes catalyze specific reactions.
    E) All enzymes depend on protein cofactors to function.

Answer: D
Topic: 5.15
Skill: Factual Recall

66) A child is brought to the hospital with a fever of 107°F. Doctors immediately order an ice bath to lower the child's temperature. Which of the following statements offers the most logical explanation for this action?
    A) Elevated body temperature will increase reaction rates in the child's cells and overload the limited number of enzymes found in the cell.
    B) Elevated body temperatures may denature enzymes. This would interfere with the cell's abilities to catalyze various reactions.
    C) Elevated body temperatures will increase the energy of activation needed to start various chemical reactions in the body. This will interfere with the ability of enzymes to catalyze vital chemical reactions.
    D) Elevated body temperatures cause molecules to vibrate more quickly and prevent enzymes from easily attaching to reactants. This would slow vital body reactions.
    E) Elevated body temperatures easily break the covalent bonds linking biologically important molecules. This will cause a general breakdown of cell structures.

Answer: B
Topic: 5.15
Skill: Application

Art Questions

1)

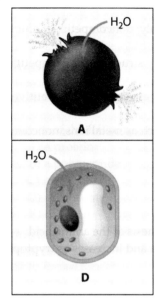 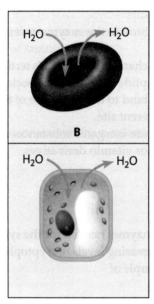 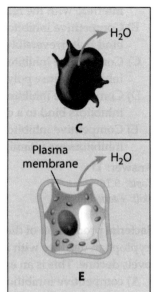

Which figure depicts an animal cell placed in a solution hypotonic to the cell?

A) cell A

B) cell B

C) cell C

D) cell D

E) cell E

Answer: A

Topic: 5.4, 5.5

Skill: Conceptual Understanding

2)

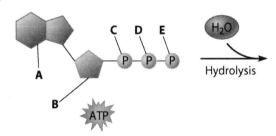

Which part of the ATP molecule breaks free of the rest when an ATP molecule is used for energy?

A) part A

B) part B

C) part C

D) part D

E) part E

Answer: E

Topic: 5.13

Skill: Factual Recall

Scenario Questions

After reading the following paragraph, answer the question(s) below.

Americans spend up to $100 billion annually for bottled water (41 billion gallons). The only beverages with higher sales are carbonated soft drinks. Recent news stories have highlighted the fact that most bottled water comes from municipal water supplies (the same source as your tap water), although it may undergo an extra purification step called reverse osmosis.

Imagine two tanks that are separated by a membrane that's permeable to water, but not to the dissolved minerals present in the water. Tank A contains tap water and Tank B contains the purified water. Under normal conditions, the purified water would cross the membrane to dilute the more concentrated tap water solution. In the reverse osmosis process, pressure is applied to the tap water tank to force the water molecules across the membrane into the pure water tank.

1) After the reverse osmosis system has been operating for 30 minutes, the solution in Tank A would
  A) be hypotonic to Tank B.
  B) be isotonic to Tank B.
  C) be hypertonic to Tank B.
  D) contain more minerals than Tank B.
  E) move by passive transport to Tank B.

Answer: C
Topic: 5.3, 5.4, 5.5, 5.8
Skill: Conceptual Understanding

2) If you shut the system off and pressure was no longer applied to Tank A, you would expect
  A) the water movement to follow the concentration gradient.
  B) the water to reverse flow from B to A.
  C) the water to flow in equal amounts in both directions.
  D) the water to flow against the concentration gradient.
  E) both a and b above to occur.

Answer: E
Topic: 5.3, 5.4, 5.5, 5.8
Skill: Application

Chapter 6 How Cells Harvest Chemical Energy

Multiple–Choice Questions

1) Which of the following statements regarding muscle fibers is *false*?
   A) All human muscles contain fast and slow muscle fibers.
   B) The proportion of fast and slow fibers is genetically determined.
   C) Training usually converts one type of muscle fiber into another.
   D) The percentage of each fiber type varies from person to person.
   E) Fast fibers are better able to produce ATP anaerobically.

   Answer: C
   Topic: Opening Essay
   Skill: Factual Recall

2) The term anaerobic means
   A) without bacteria.
   B) without ATP.
   C) without CO_2.
   D) with O_2.
   E) without O_2.

   Answer: E
   Topic: Opening Essay
   Skill: Factual Recall

3) Which of the following statements regarding fast-twitch muscles is *false*?
   A) Fast–twitch muscles are thicker than slow-twitch muscles.
   B) Fast-twitch muscles have fewer mitochondria than slow-twitch muscles.
   C) Fast-twitch muscles have less myoglobin than slow-twitch muscles.
   D) Fast-twitch muscles are better at generating short bursts of power than slow-twitch muscles.
   E) Fast-twitch muscles produce more ATP per glucose than slow-twitch muscles.

   Answer: E
   Topic: Opening Essay
   Skill: Factual Recall

4) Which of the following statements regarding photosynthesis and cellular respiration is *true*?
   A) Photosynthesis occurs in chloroplasts, and cellular respiration occurs in mitochondria.
   B) Photosynthesis occurs in mitochondria, and cellular respiration occurs in chloroplasts.
   C) Photosynthesis occurs in mitochondria and in chloroplasts.
   D) Cellular respiration occurs in mitochondria and in chloroplasts.
   E) Neither cellular respiration nor photosynthesis occurs in either mitochondria or chloroplasts.

   Answer: A
   Topic: 6.1
   Skill: Factual Recall

5) How do cells capture the energy released by cellular respiration?
   A) They produce ATP.
   B) They produce glucose.
   C) They store it in molecules of carbon dioxide.
   D) The energy is coupled to oxygen.
   E) They store it as thermal energy.

Answer: A
Topic: 6.1
Skill: Conceptual Understanding

6) The processes of photosynthesis and cellular respiration are complementary. During these energy conversions, some energy is
   A) lost in the form of heat.
   B) created in the form of heat.
   C) used to create light.
   D) destroyed when the chemical bonds of glucose are made.
   E) saved in the chemical bonds of water, CO_2 and O_2.

Answer: A
Topic: 6.1
Skill: Factual Recall

7) Respiration _____, and cellular respiration _____.
   A) produces ATP . . . is gas exchange
   B) is gas exchange . . . produces ATP
   C) produces glucose . . . produces oxygen
   D) uses glucose . . . produces glucose
   E) produces glucose . . . is gas exchange

Answer: B
Topic: 6.2
Skill: Conceptual Understanding

8) Which of the following are products of cellular respiration?
   A) oxygen and carbon dioxide
   B) energy to make ATP and carbon dioxide
   C) oxygen and glucose
   D) oxygen and energy to make ATP
   E) glucose and carbon dioxide

Answer: B
Topic: 6.2
Skill: Factual Recall

9) Which of the following statements regarding cellular respiration is *false*?
   A) Cellular respiration consumes glucose.
   B) Cellular respiration is a single chemical reaction with just one step.
   C) Cellular respiration produces water.
   D) Cellular respiration produces carbon dioxide.
   E) Cellular respiration releases heat.

Answer: B
Topic: 6.3
Skill: Conceptual Understanding

10) The overall equation for the cellular respiration of glucose is
   A) $C_5H_{12}O_6 + 6 O_2 \rightarrow 5 CO_2 + 6 H_2O$ + energy.
   B) $5 CO_2 + 6 H_2O \rightarrow C_5H_{12}O_6 + 6 O_2$ + energy.
   C) $C_6H_{12}O_{12} + 3 O_2 \rightarrow 6 CO_2 + 6 H_2O$ + energy.
   D) $C_6H_{12}O_6 + 6 O_2 \rightarrow 6 CO_2 + 6 H_2O$ + energy.
   E) $C_6H_{12}O_6$ + energy $\rightarrow 6 CO_2 + 6 H_2O + 6 O_2$.

Answer: D
Topic: 6.3
Skill: Factual Recall

11) Which of the following statements about the energy yields from cellular respiration is
   true?
   A) Cellular respiration is more efficient at harnessing energy from glucose than car
      engines are at harnessing energy from gasoline.
   B) Cellular respiration converts all of the energy in glucose into high–energy ATP
      bonds.
   C) Cellular respiration converts the kinetic energy of glucose into chemical energy.
   D) The heat produced during cellular respiration is only a tiny fraction of the chemical
      energy available in a glucose molecule.
   E) Most energy conversion systems are more efficient than cellular respiration.

Answer: A
Topic: 6.3
Skill: Conceptual Understanding

12) Humans use the calories they obtain from _____ as their source of energy.
   A) food
   B) water
   C) sunlight
   D) minerals
   E) carbon dioxide

Answer: A
Topic: 6.4
Skill: Factual Recall

13) Humans use about _____ of their daily calories for involuntary life–sustaining
   activities such as digestion, circulation, and breathing.
   A) 10%
   B) 25%
   C) 50%
   D) 75%
   E) 90%

Answer: D
Topic: 6.4
Skill: Factual Recall

14) A kilocalorie is defined as
  A) the quantity of glucose needed to increase the body temperature by 1°C.
  B) the quantity of water heat needed to solubilize 1 g of glucose.
  C) the quantity of heat needed to raise the temperature of 1 kg of water by 1°C.
  D) the quantity of food used to maintain normal bodily functions.
  E) the quantity of food consumed during a given type of exercise.

Answer: C
Topic: 6.4
Skill: Factual Recall

15) The label on the box of breakfast cereal lists one serving as containing 200 calories per serving. How many calories are actually in one serving?
  A) 20
  B) 2,000
  C) 20,000
  D) 200,000
  E) 2,000,000

Answer: D
Topic: 6.4
Skill: Application

16) During cellular respiration, the energy in glucose
  A) becomes stored in molecules of ammonia.
  B) is used to manufacture glucose.
  C) is released all at once.
  D) is carried by electrons.
  E) can be used to oxidize NADH.

Answer: D
Topic: 6.5
Skill: Factual Recall

17) During redox reactions,
  A) the loss of electrons from one substance is called reduction.
  B) a substance that gains electrons is said to be oxidized.
  C) electrons are lost from one substance and added to another substance.
  D) protons from one molecule replace the electrons lost from another molecule.
  E) the reduction of a substance does not need to be coupled to the oxidation of another substance.

Answer: C
Topic: 6.5
Skill: Factual Recall

18) Oxidation is the _____, and reduction is the _____.
  A) gain of electrons . . . loss of electrons
  B) loss of electrons . . . gain of electrons
  C) loss of oxygen . . . gain of oxygen
  D) gain of oxygen . . . loss of oxygen
  E) gain of protons . . . loss of protons

Answer: B
Topic: 6.5
Skill: Factual Recall

19) In biological systems, an important enzyme involved in the regulation of redox reactions is
    A) glucose.
    B) dehydrogenase.
    C) oxygen.
    D) water.
    E) ATP.

Answer: B
Topic: 6.5
Skill: Factual Recall

20) During cellular respiration, NADH
    A) is converted to NAD^+ by an enzyme called dehydrogenase.
    B) is chemically converted into ATP.
    C) is reduced to form NAD^+.
    D) delivers its electron load to the first electron carrier molecule.
    E) is the final electron acceptor.

Answer: D
Topic: 6.5
Skill: Conceptual Understanding

21) During cellular respiration, electrons move through a series of electron carrier molecules. Which of the following statements about this process is *true*?
    A) The electrons move from carriers that have more affinity for them to carriers that have less affinity for them.
    B) Molecular oxygen is eventually oxidized by the electrons to form water.
    C) The electrons release large amounts of energy each time they are transferred from one carrier to another.
    D) The carrier molecules are found in the cytoplasm of eukaryotic and prokaryotic cells.
    E) Molecular oxygen is reduced when it accepts electrons and forms water.

Answer: E
Topic: 6.5
Skill: Factual Recall

22) The functioning of an electron transport chain is analogous to
    A) a Slinky toy going down a flight of stairs.
    B) a canoe going over a waterfall.
    C) a person climbing a flight of stairs one step at a time.
    D) a person leaping from the top to the bottom of a flight of stairs in one jump.
    E) playing Ping–Pong.

Answer: A
Topic: 6.5
Skill: Conceptual Understanding

23) Which of the following options lists the stages in cellular respiration in the correct order?
    A) glycolysis, the citric acid cycle, and oxidative phosphorylation
    B) glycolysis, oxidative phosphorylation, and the citric acid cycle
    C) the citric acid cycle, oxidative phosphorylation, and glycolysis
    D) oxidative phosphorylation, glycolysis, and the citric acid cycle
    E) oxidative phosphorylation, the citric acid cycle, and glycolysis

Answer: A
Topic: 6.6
Skill: Factual Recall

24) A drug is tested in the laboratory and is found to create holes in both mitochondrial membranes. Scientists suspect that the drug will be harmful to human cells because it will inhibit
    A) the citric acid cycle.
    B) oxidative phosphorylation.
    C) glycolysis.
    D) the formation of alcohol.
    E) the citric acid cycle and oxidative phosphorylation.

Answer: E
Topic: 6.6
Skill: Application

25) During which of the following phases of cellular respiration does substrate–level phosphorylation take place?
    A) glycolysis
    B) the citric acid cycle
    C) "grooming" of pyruvate
    D) oxidative phosphorylation
    E) glycolysis and the citric acid cycle

Answer: E
Topic: 6.6
Skill: Factual Recall

26) Which of the following metabolic pathways is common in aerobic and anaerobic metabolism?
    A) the citric acid cycle
    B) oxidative phosphorylation
    C) chemiosmosis
    D) glycolysis
    E) electron transport chain

Answer: D
Topic: 6.7
Skill: Conceptual Understanding

27) As a result of glycolysis there is a net gain of _____ ATPs.
    A) 0
    B) 1
    C) 2
    D) 4
    E) 36

Answer: C
Topic: 6.7
Skill: Factual Recall

28) How many molecules of NADH are produced during glycolysis?
    A) 2
    B) 3
    C) 4
    D) 6
    E) 8

Answer: A
Topic: 6.7
Skill: Factual Recall

29) Which of the following is a result of glycolysis?
    A) conversion of FAD to $FADH_2$

    B) production of CO_2

    C) conversion of glucose to two three–carbon compounds

    D) a net loss of two ATPs per glucose molecule

    E) conversion of NADH to NAD^+

Answer: C
Topic: 6.7
Skill: Factual Recall

30) A culture of bacteria growing aerobically is fed glucose containing radioactive carbon and is then examined. As the bacteria metabolize the glucose, radioactivity will appear first in
    A) carbon dioxide.
    B) NADH.
    C) glucose–6–phosphate.
    D) pyruvate.
    E) ATP.

Answer: C
Topic: 6.7
Skill: Conceptual Understanding

31) The end products of glycolysis include
   A) $FADH_2$.
   B) NADH.
   C) acetyl CoA.
   D) citric acid.
   E) O_2.

Answer: B
Topic: 6.7
Skill: Factual Recall

32) Pyruvate
   A) forms at the end of glycolysis.
   B) is the molecule that starts the citric acid cycle.
   C) is the end product of oxidative phosphorylation.
   D) is the end product of chemiosmosis.
   E) is a six-carbon molecule.

Answer: A
Topic: 6.8
Skill: Factual Recall

33) Between glycolysis and the citric acid cycle,
   A) pyruvate is oxidized while a molecule of NAD^+ is reduced to NADH.
   B) a carbon atom is added to make a four-carbon compound.
   C) coenzyme A is cleaved off the four-carbon compound.
   D) coenzyme A is removed from pyruvate.
   E) a CO_2 molecule is added to pyruvate.

Answer: A
Topic: 6.8
Skill: Factual Recall

34) Which of the following statements regarding the chemical grooming of pyruvate is *false*?
   A) Two molecules of pyruvate are each converted into two-carbon molecules joined to a coenzyme A molecule.
   B) Each pyruvate loses a carbon atom, which is released as CO_2.
   C) Two pyruvate molecules together contain less chemical energy than was found in the original glucose molecule.
   D) The pyruvate molecules are oxidized and two NAD^+ are reduced.
   E) Each pyruvate molecule has a CO_2 added and then joins with an NADH.

Answer: E
Topic: 6.8
Skill: Factual Recall

35) Pyruvate is considered a(n) _____ aerobic cellular respiration.
   A) source of O_2 for
   B) end product of
   C) intermediate in
   D) cofactor in
   E) enzyme in

Answer: C
Topic: 6.8
Skill: Factual Recall

36) The enzymes of the citric acid cycle are located in the
   A) intermembrane space of the mitochondrion.
   B) outer mitochondrial membrane.
   C) mitochondrial matrix.
   D) inner mitochondrial membrane.
   E) matrix and inner mitochondrial membrane.

Answer: E
Topic: 6.9
Skill: Factual Recall

37) The end products of the citric acid cycle include all of the following *except*
   A) CO_2.
   B) pyruvate.
   C) ATP.
   D) NADH.
   E) $FADH_2$.

Answer: B
Topic: 6.9
Skill: Factual Recall

38) The function of coenzyme A in the citric acid cycle is most like
   A) a limousine driver dropping off a couple at the school prom.
   B) a recycling company, collecting paper and using it to manufacture new products.
   C) a hamster in its exercise wheel, running quickly but not getting anywhere.
   D) a kid jumping up and down on a trampoline.
   E) throwing a baited hook into a lake and catching a fish.

Answer: A
Topic: 6.9
Skill: Conceptual Understanding

39) A culture of bacteria growing aerobically is fed glucose containing radioactive carbon and is then examined. During the citric acid cycle, radioactivity would first appear in
   A) NADH.
   B) citrate.
   C) $FADH_2$.
   D) oxaloacetic acid.
   E) CoA.

Answer: B
Topic: 6.9
Skill: Application

40) At the end of the citric acid cycle, most of the energy remaining from the original glucose is stored in
   A) CO_2.
   B) pyruvate.
   C) ATP.
   D) NADH.
   E) $FADH_2$.

Answer: D
Topic: 6.9
Skill: Conceptual Understanding

41) During chemiosmosis,
   A) energy is released as H^+ ions move freely across mitochondrial membranes.
   B) ATP is synthesized when H^+ ions move through a protein port provided by ATP synthase.
   C) energy is generated by coupling exergonic reactions with other exergonic reactions.
   D) a concentration gradient is generated when large numbers of H^+ ions are passively transported from the matrix of the mitochondrion to the mitochondrion's intermembrane space.
   E) H^+ ions serve as the final electron acceptor.

Answer: B
Topic: 6.10
Skill: Factual Recall

42) Which of the following statements about the inner mitochondrial membrane is *false*?
   A) ATP synthase is associated with the inner mitochondrial membrane.
   B) The inner mitochondrial membrane plays a role in the production of pyruvate.
   C) Electron carriers are associated with the inner mitochondrial membrane.
   D) The inner mitochondrial membrane is involved in chemiosmosis.
   E) A gradient of H^+ exists across the inner mitochondrial membrane.

Answer: B
Topic: 6.10
Skill: Factual Recall

43) The mitochondrial cristae are an adaptation that
   A) permits the expansion of mitochondria as oxygen accumulates in the mitochondrial matrix.
   B) helps mitochondria divide during times of greatest cellular respiration.
   C) increases the space for more copies of the electron transport chain and ATP synthase complexes.
   D) carefully encloses the DNA housed within the mitochondrial matrix.
   E) allows other ions (like Na^+) to build up when H^+ ions are not available.

Answer: C
Topic: 6.10
Skill: Conceptual Understanding

44) A mutant protist is found in which some mitochondria lack an inner mitochondrial membrane. Which of the following pathways would be completely disrupted in these mitochondria?
    A) oxidative phosphorylation
    B) alcoholic fermentation
    C) the citric acid cycle
    D) glycolysis
    E) biosynthesis

Answer: A
Topic: 6.10
Skill: Application

45) If you were able to stop the process of cellular respiration after completing electron transport but prior to chemiosmosis, you would find the pH of a mitochondrion to be at its lowest
    A) on the outer membrane.
    B) on the inner membrane.
    C) in the cytoplasm.
    D) in the mitochondrial matrix.
    E) in the intermembrane space.

Answer: E
Topic: 6.10
Skill: Conceptual Understanding

46) By-products of cellular respiration include
    A) oxygen and heat.
    B) carbon dioxide and water.
    C) carbon dioxide and ATP.
    D) $FADH_2$ and NADH.
    E) NADH and ATP.

Answer: B
Topic: 6.10
Skill: Factual Recall

47) In the electron transport chain, the final electron acceptor is
    A) an oxygen atom.
    B) a molecule of carbon dioxide.
    C) a molecule of water.
    D) ADP.
    E) ATP.

Answer: A
Topic: 6.10
Skill: Factual Recall

48) Rotenone is a poison commonly added to insecticides. Insects exposed to rotenone will die because
    A) they will no longer be able to perform anaerobic respiration.
    B) high levels of fermentation products will build up in their bodies.
    C) they will no longer be able to produce adequate amounts of ATP.
    D) they will no longer be able to absorb water and will become dehydrated.
    E) they will no longer be able to perform chemiosmosis.

Answer: C
Topic: 6.11
Skill: Application

49) Cyanide differs from dinitrophenol in that
    A) cyanide is highly toxic to human cells, while dinitrophenol is nontoxic.
    B) cyanide is an electron transport blocker, while dinitrophenol is a reaction uncoupler.
    C) cyanide makes the membrane of mitochondria leaky to H^+ ions and prevents a concentration gradient from building up, while dinitrophenol blocks the passage of electrons through electron carriers.
    D) cyanide inhibits the production of ATP by inhibiting ATP synthase, while dinitrophenol causes mitochondrial membranes to become less permeable to H^+ ions.
    E) cyanide increases the rate of H^+ crossing to the intermembrane beyond the capacity to synthesize ATP, while dinitrophenol blocks the transfer electrons from NADH.

Answer: B
Topic: 6.11
Skill: Factual Recall

50) Which of the following statements about the energy yield of aerobic respiration is *false*?
    A) Less than 50% of the chemical energy available in glucose is converted to ATP energy.
    B) Each $FADH_2$ molecule yields 2 ATP molecules and each NADH molecule generates 3 ATP molecules.
    C) Most of the ATP derived during aerobic respiration results from oxidative phosphorylation.
    D) Oxidative phosphorylation resulting from 1 glucose molecule may yield 32−34 ATP molecules.
    E) Glycolysis and the "grooming" of pyruvate together produce more NADH per glucose molecule than does the citric acid cycle.

Answer: E
Topic: 6.12
Skill: Factual Recall

51) Each $FADH_2$ yields a maximum of _____ ATP, and each NADH yields a maximum of _____ ATP as a result of transferring pairs of electrons to the electron transport chain.

    A) 3 . . . 2
    B) 2 . . . 3
    C) 3 . . . 3
    D) 1 . . . 3
    E) 3 . . . 1

Answer: B
Topic: 6.12
Skill: Factual Recall

52) Glycolysis and the citric acid cycle must occur _____ time(s) per glucose molecule.

    A) 1
    B) 2
    C) 3
    D) 4
    E) 5

Answer: B
Topic: 6.12
Skill: Factual Recall

53) The energy yield from the complete aerobic breakdown of a single molecule of glucose

    A) is equivalent to the yield from alcoholic fermentation.
    B) is always 38 ATP.
    C) increases as the supply of oxygen increases.
    D) can vary with the mechanism used to shuttle NADH electrons into the mitochondrion.
    E) is less than the yield from anaerobic respiration.

Answer: D
Topic: 6.12
Skill: Conceptual Understanding

54) Which of the following processes produces the most ATP per molecule of glucose oxidized?

    A) aerobic respiration
    B) anaerobic respiration
    C) alcoholic fermentation
    D) lactic acid fermentation
    E) All produce approximately the same amount of ATP per molecule of glucose.

Answer: A
Topic: 6.13
Skill: Factual Recall

55) In fermentation, _____ is _____.
   A) NADH . . . reduced
   B) NAD$^+$ . . . oxidized
   C) NADH . . . oxidized
   D) pyruvate . . . oxidized
   E) ethanol . . . oxidized

Answer: C
Topic: 6.13
Skill: Factual Recall

56) When an organism such as a yeast lives by fermentation, it converts the pyruvate from glycolysis into a different compound, such as alcohol. Why doesn't it secrete the pyruvate directly?
   A) The conversion yields one ATP per pyruvate molecule.
   B) The conversion yields one NADH per pyruvate molecule.
   C) The conversion yields one FADH$_2$ per pyruvate molecule.
   D) The conversion is needed to regenerate the NAD$^+$ consumed during glycolysis.
   E) A buildup of pyruvate in the surrounding environment would be too toxic.

Answer: D
Topic: 6.13
Skill: Factual Recall

57) Muscle soreness associated with strenuous exercise is at least partly due to
   A) an excess of ATP that builds up during vigorous exercise.
   B) the presence of lactate produced during fermentation in muscle cells.
   C) the large amount of carbon dioxide that builds up in the muscle.
   D) the accumulation of alcohol from anaerobic respiration.
   E) the excess buildup of carbon monoxide due to inefficient respiration.

Answer: B
Topic: 6.13
Skill: Factual Recall

58) A child is born with a rare disease in which mitochondria are missing from skeletal muscle cells. However, the muscles still function. Physicians find that
   A) the muscles contain large amounts of lactate following even mild physical exercise.
   B) the muscles contain large amounts of carbon dioxide following even mild physical exercise.
   C) the muscles require extremely high levels of oxygen to function.
   D) the muscle cells cannot split glucose to pyruvate.
   E) the muscles require extremely large amounts of carbon dioxide to function.

Answer: A
Topic: 6.13
Skill: Application

59) Some friends are trying to make wine in their basement. They've added yeast to a sweet grape juice mixture and have allowed the yeast to grow. After several days they find that sugar levels in the grape juice have dropped, but there's no alcohol in the mixture. The most likely explanation is that
   A) the mixture needs more sugar, because yeast need a lot of energy before they can begin to produce alcohol.
   B) the mixture needs less oxygen, because yeast only produce alcohol in the absence of oxygen.
   C) the mixture needs more oxygen, because yeast need oxygen to break down sugar and get enough energy to produce alcohol.
   D) the mixture needs less sugar, because high sugar concentrations stimulate cellular respiration, and alcohol is not a by-product of cellular respiration.
   E) the yeast used the alcohol as a carbon source.

Answer: B
Topic: 6.13
Skill: Application

60) In yeast cells,
   A) lactic acid is produced during anaerobic respiration.
   B) lactic acid is produced during glycolysis.
   C) alcohol is produced during the citric acid cycle.
   D) alcohol is produced after glycolysis.
   E) glucose is produced during photosynthesis.

Answer: D
Topic: 6.13
Skill: Factual Recall

61) Bacteria that are unable to survive in the presence of oxygen are called
   A) obligate anaerobes.
   B) obligate aerobes.
   C) facultative anaerobes.
   D) aerotolerant anaerobes.
   E) microaerophiles.

Answer: A
Topic: 6.13
Skill: Factual Recall

62) Yeasts can produce ATP by either fermentation or oxidative phosphorylation; thus, they are
   A) strict anaerobes.
   B) strict aerobes.
   C) facultative anaerobes.
   D) facultative aerobes.
   E) producers of lactic acid.

Answer: C
Topic: 6.13
Skill: Factual Recall

63) When did the level of oxygen in Earth's atmosphere become high enough to sustain aerobic respiration?
    A) 1.0 billion years ago
    B) 1.5 billion years ago
    C) 2.5 billion years ago
    D) 2.7 billion years ago
    E) 3.5 billion years ago

Answer: D
Topic: 6.14–Evolution Connection
Skill: Factual Recall

64) Which of the following statements regarding glycolysis is *false*?
    A) Glycolysis is considered to be an ancient metabolic system because it does not require oxygen.
    B) Glycolysis is considered to be an ancient metabolic system because it is not located in a membrane–bound organelle.
    C) Glycolysis is considered to be an ancient metabolic system because it occurs universally.
    D) Glycolysis is considered to be an ancient metabolic system because it is the most efficient metabolic pathway for ATP synthesis.
    E) Glycolysis is considered to be an ancient metabolic system because glucose is the universal substrate for glycolysis.

Answer: D
Topic: 6.14–Evolution Connection
Skill: Conceptual Understanding

65) To obtain energy from starch and glycogen, the body must begin by
    A) hydrolyzing the starch to glucose and the glycogen to amino acids.
    B) hydrolyzing both starch and glycogen to glucose.
    C) converting both starch and glycogen to fatty acids.
    D) removing nitrogen atoms from both molecules.
    E) removing one glucose at a time with a condensation reaction.

Answer: B
Topic: 6.15
Skill: Conceptual Understanding

66) When proteins are used as a source of energy for the body, the proteins
    A) are converted into glucose molecules, which are fed into glycolysis.
    B) are converted mainly into intermediates of glycolysis or the citric acid cycle.
    C) are hydrolyzed to their constituent amino acids; electrons are stripped from the amino acids and passed to the electron transport chain.
    D) are hydrolyzed to glycerols and then converted to glyceraldehyde–3–phosphate, which is fed into glycolysis.
    E) are hydrolyzed to fatty acids and converted to acetyl CoA, which enters the citric acid cycle.

Answer: B
Topic: 6.15
Skill: Factual Recall

67) When a cell uses fatty acid for aerobic respiration, it first hydrolyzes fats to
    A) glycerol and amino acids.
    B) glycerol and fatty acids.
    C) fatty acids and sugars.
    D) sugars and amino acids.
    E) sugars and glycerol.

Answer: B
Topic: 6.15
Skill: Factual Recall

68) If you consume 1 g of each of the following, which will yield the most ATP?
    A) fat
    B) glucose
    C) sucrose
    D) protein
    E) starch

Answer: A
Topic: 6.15
Skill: Conceptual Understanding

69) Which of the following statements regarding food is *false*?
    A) Food provides the raw materials for biosynthetic pathways that make molecules for cellular repair and growth.
    B) Food provides the raw materials for biosynthetic pathways that can produce molecules that are not actually present in the original food.
    C) Food provides the raw materials for biosynthetic pathways that can use "intermediate" compounds from glycolysis and the citric acid cycle to make food.
    D) Food provides the raw materials for biosynthetic pathways that can produce sugar by a process that is the exact opposite of glycolysis.
    E) Food provides the raw materials for biosynthetic pathways that consume ATP.

Answer: D
Topic: 6.16
Skill: Factual Recall

70) Which of the following organisms can make organic molecules from water and carbon dioxide?
    A) bear
    B) mushroom
    C) wheat
    D) crayfish
    E) honeybee

Answer: C
Topic: 6.16
Skill: Application

71) The conversion of CO_2 and H_2O into organic compounds using energy from light is called
   A) glycolysis.
   B) photosynthesis.
   C) fermentation.
   D) cellular respiration.
   E) photorespiration.

Answer: B
Topic: 6.16
Skill: Factual Recall

72) The glycolytic pathway will _____ after a large meal and _____ during a long period of exercise.
   A) speed up . . . speed up
   B) slow down . . . slow down
   C) slow down . . . speed up
   D) speed up . . . slow down
   E) not change . . . not change

Answer: C
Topic: 6.16
Skill: Application

Art Questions

1)

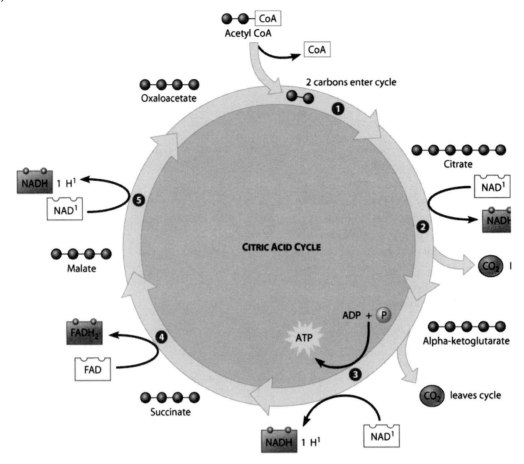

Which step of the Krebs cycle requires both NAD$^+$ and ADP as reactants?
   A) step 1
   B) step 2
   C) step 3
   D) step 4
   E) step 5
Answer: C
Topic: 6.9
Skill: Application

2)

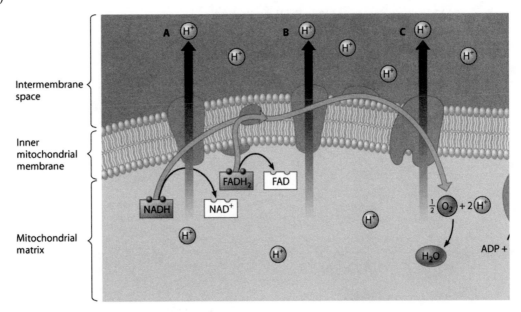

Which H$^+$ ion has just passed through the inner mitochondrial membrane by diffusion?
   A) hydrogen ion A
   B) hydrogen ion B
   C) hydrogen ion C
   D) hydrogen ion D
   E) hydrogen ion E

Answer: E
Topic: 6.14
Skill: Application

Scenario Questions

After reading the following paragraph, answer the question(s) below.

As a scientist employed by the FDA, you've been asked to sit on a panel to evaluate a pharmaceutical company's application for approval of a new weight loss drug called Fat Away. The company has submitted a report summarizing the results of their animal and human testing. In the report, it was noted that Fat Away works by affecting the electron transport chain. It decreases the synthesis of ATP by making the mitochondrial membrane permeable to H$^+$ which allows H$^+$ to leak from the mitochondrial matrix to the intermembrane space. This effect leads to weight loss.

1) The method of weight loss described for Fat Away shows that the drug is acting as a metabolic
   A) coenzyme.
   B) feedback inhibitor.
   C) oxygen carrier.
   D) redox promoter.
   E) uncoupler.

Answer: E
Topic: 6.10, 6.11
Skill: Factual Recall

2) Fat Away prevents ATP from being made by
    A) blocking access of H^+ to ATP synthetase.
    B) glycolysis from occurring.
    C) preventing the conversion of NADH to NAD^+.
    D) lowering body temperature.
    E) slowing down the Krebs cycle.

Answer: A
Topic: 6.10, 6.11
Skill: Conceptual Understanding

Chapter 7 Photosynthesis: Using Light to Make Food

Multiple-Choice Questions

1) The summary equation for photosynthesis is
   A) $6 CO_2 + 6 H_2O + sunlight \rightarrow C_6H_{12}O_6 + 6 O_2$.
   B) $C_5H_{12}O_6 + 6 O_2 + sunlight \rightarrow 5 CO_2 + 6 H_2O$.
   C) $C_6H_{12}O_6 + 6 O_2 + sunlight \rightarrow 6 CO_2 + 6 H_2O$.
   D) the same as the equation for glycolysis written in reverse.
   E) $6 CH_2O + 5 O_2 + sunlight \rightarrow CO_2 + 2 H_2O$.

   Answer: A
   Topic: Opening Essay
   Skill: Factual Recall

2) Which of the following statements regarding photosynthesis and carbon dioxide is *false*?
   A) Plants require carbon dioxide, water, and sunlight to make glucose.
   B) Burning fossil fuels release carbon dioxide that was removed from the atmosphere millions of years ago.
   C) Because of their short growth period and self–regeneration, willows are more viable as a source of potential power than the trees in most natural forests.
   D) Most of the food humans eat can be traced back to photosynthetic plants.
   E) Burning wood contributes more to acid rain than burning fossil fuels.

   Answer: E
   Topic: Opening Essay
   Skill: Factual Recall

3) What is the name given to organisms that can make their own food and the food for the biosphere?
   A) chemotrophs
   B) heterotrophs
   C) manufacturers
   D) synthesizers
   E) producers

   Answer: E
   Topic: 7.1
   Skill: Factual Recall

4) Photoautotrophs
   A) make sugar by using organic raw materials.
   B) produce organic molecules from inorganic molecules.
   C) eat other organisms that use light energy to make food molecules.
   D) include only the green plants.
   E) are only found on land.

   Answer: B
   Topic: 7.1
   Skill: Factual Recall

5) Which of the following is an example of a photoautotroph?
   A) cyanobacteria in freshwater and marine ecosystems
   B) grizzly bears in Alaska
   C) bacteria in our mouth
   D) fungi growing in the refrigerator
   E) mushrooms growing on the side of a dead tree

Answer: A
Topic: 7.1
Skill: Factual Recall

6) Autotrophs that utilize light as their energy source are
   A) chemosynthetic autotrophs.
   B) photoautotrophs.
   C) consumers.
   D) fungi.
   E) heterotrophs.

Answer: B
Topic: 7.1
Skill: Factual Recall

7) What is the likely origin of chloroplasts?
   A) mitochondria that had a mutation for photosynthesis
   B) photosynthetic prokaryotes that lived inside eukaryotic cells
   C) a combination of mitochondria and Golgi bodies
   D) prokaryotes with photosynthetic mitochondria
   E) eukaryotes that engulfed photosynthetic fungi

Answer: B
Topic: 7.1
Skill: Conceptual Understanding

8) In most green plants, chloroplasts are
   A) concentrated in a zone of leaf tissue called the mesophyll.
   B) concentrated in the stomata.
   C) concentrated in a portion of the leaf called the stroma.
   D) found throughout the leaf tissue.
   E) found throughout the plant.

Answer: A
Topic: 7.2
Skill: Factual Recall

9) _____ cells in leaves are specialized for photosynthesis.
   A) Companion
   B) Mesophyll
   C) Sclerenchyma
   D) Tracheid
   E) Collenchyma

Answer: B
Topic: 7.2
Skill: Factual Recall

10) CO_2 enters and O_2 escapes from a leaf via
   A) stomata.
   B) thylakoids.
   C) grana.
   D) stroma.
   E) central vacuoles.

Answer: A
Topic: 7.2
Skill: Factual Recall

11) In the chloroplast, sugars are made in a compartment that is filled with a thick fluid called the
   A) stomata.
   B) thylakoid.
   C) matrix.
   D) stroma.
   E) mesophyll.

Answer: D
Topic: 7.2
Skill: Factual Recall

12) Chloroplasts contain disklike membranous sacs arranged in stacks called
   A) cristae.
   B) thylakoids.
   C) grana.
   D) vacuoles.
   E) stroma.

Answer: C
Topic: 7.2
Skill: Factual Recall

13) Where is chlorophyll found in a plant cell?
   A) stroma
   B) thylakoid membranes
   C) matrix
   D) cytoplasm
   E) cristae

Answer: B
Topic: 7.2
Skill: Factual Recall

14) The oxygen released into the air as a product of photosynthesis comes from
   A) water.
   B) glucose.
   C) carbon dioxide.
   D) chlorophyll.
   E) mitochondria.

Answer: A
Topic: 7.3
Skill: Factual Recall

15) Which of the following molecules is both a reactant and a product of photosynthesis?
   A) H_2O
   B) glucose
   C) O_2
   D) CO_2
   E) chlorophyll

Answer: A
Topic: 7.3
Skill: Conceptual Understanding

16) If you expose a photosynthesizing plant to water that contains both radioactive H and radioactive O, in which of the products of photosynthesis will the radioactive H and O show up?
   A) H and O both in glucose
   B) H in glucose; O in water
   C) H in water; O in glucose
   D) H in glucose and water; O in O_2
   E) H in glucose and water; O in water and O_2

Answer: D
Topic: 7.3
Skill: Application

17) A redox reaction involves the transfer of
   A) a hydrogen ion.
   B) oxygen.
   C) water.
   D) an electron.
   E) carbon dioxide.

Answer: D
Topic: 7.4
Skill: Application

18) Which of the following statements concerning the role of redox reactions in photosynthesis and cellular respiration is *true*?
   A) Photosynthesis involves only reductions, while respiration involves only oxidations.
   B) Photosynthesis involves only oxidations, while respiration involves only reductions.
   C) In photosynthesis, carbon dioxide is oxidized to form sugar, while in respiration, sugar is reduced to form carbon dioxide.
   D) In photosynthesis, carbon dioxide is reduced to form sugar, while in respiration, sugar is oxidized to form carbon dioxide.
   E) Photosynthesis involves both reduction and oxidation, while respiration involves only oxidation.

Answer: D
Topic: 7.4
Skill: Conceptual Understanding

19) What is the source of energy that provides the boost for electrons during photosynthesis?
   A) light
   B) electromagnetism
   C) cellular respiration
   D) ATP
   E) glucose

Answer: A
Topic: 7.4
Skill: Conceptual Understanding

20) Which of the following statements regarding photosynthesis is *false*?
   A) ATP is not produced during photosynthesis, but only during respiration.
   B) Photosynthesis is ultimately powered by light energy and respiration by the chemical energy of fuel molecules.
   C) Photosynthesis consumes CO_2; respiration consumes O_2.
   D) Photosynthesis produces O_2; respiration produces CO_2.
   E) The principal electron carrier in photosynthesis is NADPH; the principal electron carrier in respiration is NADH.

Answer: A
Topic: 7.4, 7.5
Skill: Conceptual Understanding

21) The light reactions occur in the _____, while the Calvin cycle occurs in the _____.
   A) stroma . . . thylakoid membranes
   B) stroma . . . nucleus
   C) cytoplasm . . . stroma
   D) cytoplasm . . . thylakoid membrane
   E) thylakoid membranes . . . stroma

Answer: E
Topic: 7.5
Skill: Factual Recall

22) Which of the following are produced during the light reactions of photosynthesis?
   A) glucose, ADP, $NADP^+$
   B) glucose, ADP, $NADP^+$, CO_2
   C) ADP, $NADP^+$, O_2
   D) ATP, NADPH, O_2
   E) ATP, NADPH, CO_2

Answer: D
Topic: 7.5
Skill: Factual Recall

23) Which of the following is part of the light reaction?
    A) carbon fixation
    B) reduction of carbon
    C) addition of electrons and protons to carbon
    D) regeneration of NADP+
    E) formation of waste products in the form of O_2

Answer: E
Topic: 7.5
Skill: Conceptual Understanding

24) Which of the following are produced during the Calvin cycle?
    A) glucose, ADP, NADP+
    B) glucose, ADP, NADP+, CO_2
    C) ADP, NADP+, O_2
    D) ATP, NADPH, O_2
    E) ATP, NADPH, CO_2

Answer: A
Topic: 7.5
Skill: Factual Recall

25) Carbon fixation
    A) occurs when carbon and oxygen from CO_2 are incorporated into an organic molecule.
    B) powers the process of glucose synthesis by supplying the cell with ATP.
    C) occurs during the light reactions.
    D) provides the cell with a supply of NADPH molecules.
    E) uses noncyclic electron flow to capture energy in glucose.

Answer: A
Topic: 7.5
Skill: Factual Recall

26) Sunlight is a type of _____ energy.
    A) electromagnetic
    B) potential
    C) stored
    D) kinetic
    E) nuclear

Answer: A
Topic: 7.6
Skill: Factual Recall

27) The full range of electromagnetic energy is called the _____ spectrum.
    A) wavelength
    B) visible
    C) electromagnetic
    D) energy
    E) ultraviolet
Answer: C
Topic: 7.6
Skill: Factual Recall

28) Why are most plants green?
    A) Chlorophyll *a* reflects green light.
    B) Chlorophyll *a* absorbs green light.
    C) Chlorophyll *b* primarily uses green light as the source of energy for photosynthesis.
    D) Green helps plants blend into their environment as a sort of camouflage.
    E) All photosynthetic pigments are colored green.
Answer: A
Topic: 7.6
Skill: Conceptual Understanding

29) Which of the following colors contributes the *least* energy to photosynthesis?
    A) blue
    B) red
    C) violet
    D) orange
    E) green
Answer: E
Topic: 7.6
Skill: Application

30) Of the following wavelengths of light, which would you expect to be reflected or transmitted by chlorophyll *a*?
    A) blue
    B) green
    C) yellow
    D) orange
    E) red
Answer: B
Topic: 7.6
Skill: Conceptual Understanding

31) Chlorophyll *b* and carotenoids
    A) are best at absorbing the energy of green light.
    B) are found at the reaction center.
    C) are located on the inner membrane of the chloroplast.
    D) pass absorbed energy to chlorophyll *a*.
    E) catalyze the incorporation of carbon atoms into RuBP.
Answer: D
Topic: 7.6
Skill: Factual Recall

32) Plant cells are protected from the harmful effects of oxygen radicals with
   A) NADPH.
   B) mitochondria.
   C) chlorophyll.
   D) carotenoids.
   E) ATP.

Answer: D
Topic: 7.6
Skill: Conceptual Understanding

33) A packet of light energy is called a
   A) quantum.
   B) pigment.
   C) photon.
   D) phaser.
   E) wavelength.

Answer: C
Topic: 7.6
Skill: Factual Recall

34) Which of the following statements about the absorption of photons by pigment molecules is true?
   A) It takes several minutes for the pigment electrons to become excited.
   B) Photons raise electrons in pigments to the ground state.
   C) Pigments only lose energy in the excitation process.
   D) Excitation of the electrons is a very stable state.
   E) The release of energy by the excited electron can be as heat, light, or fluorescence.

Answer: E
Topic: 7.7
Skill: Factual Recall

35) Which of the following photosynthetic pigments can be found at the photosystem reaction center?
   A) chlorophyll *b*
   B) chlorophyll *a*
   C) a carotenoid
   D) phycocyanin
   E) eosinophyll

Answer: B
Topic: 7.7
Skill: Factual Recall

36) Which of the following is a normal process of photosynthesis that could not occur if all reaction centers were inactivated by a toxin?
    A) donation of excited electrons by chlorophyll *a* to a primary electron acceptor
    B) donation of excited electrons by chlorophyll *b* to a primary electron acceptor
    C) absorption of photons by chlorophyll *b*
    D) reduction of chlorophyll *b* by a primary electron acceptor
    E) absorption of photons by carotenoids

Answer: A
Topic: 7.7
Skill: Conceptual Understanding

37) How do the reaction centers of photosystem I and II differ?
    A) Chlorophyll *a* is found in photosystem I and chlorophyll *b* in photosystem II.
    B) Each preferentially absorbs slightly different wavelengths of light.
    C) Photosystem I functions first in the sequence of steps that make up the light reactions.
    D) Only photosystem I is found in the thylakoid membranes.
    E) Photosystem II does not transfer electrons from photons.

Answer: B
Topic: 7.7
Skill: Conceptual Understanding

38) Clusters of light–gathering pigments in a photosystem
    A) pass energy to the reaction center.
    B) are found in the roots of plants.
    C) absorb electrons.
    D) do not absorb photons.
    E) break down H_2O.

Answer: A
Topic: 7.7
Skill: Factual Recall

39) In a photosystem, clusters of chlorophyll *a*, chlorophyll *b*, and carotenoid pigments function most like
    A) an electrical generator.
    B) an antenna.
    C) a propeller on a motorboat.
    D) a windmill.
    E) a spring.

Answer: B
Topic: 7.7
Skill: Conceptual Understanding

40) The energy that excites P680 and P700 is supplied by
   A) electrons passing down the electron transport chain.
   B) the breaking of glucose bonds.
   C) ATP.
   D) photons.
   E) NADPH.

Answer: D
Topic: 7.8
Skill: Factual Recall

41) The electron transport chains of the light reactions
   A) are located in the stroma.
   B) are very different from those of cellular respiration.
   C) shuttle electrons along in a series of redox reactions.
   D) provide energy for the Krebs cycle.
   E) are found on the inner membrane of chloroplasts.

Answer: C
Topic: 7.8
Skill: Factual Recall

42) As a result of the cascade of electrons down the electron transport chains of the light reactions,
   A) NADPH is reduced to $NADP^+$.
   B) NADPH is oxidized to $NADP^+$.
   C) $NADP^+$ is reduced to NADPH.
   D) $NADP^+$ is oxidized to NADPH.
   E) water is formed.

Answer: C
Topic: 7.8
Skill: Factual Recall

43) The electrons lost from the reaction center of photosystem I are replaced by electrons from
   A) CO_2.
   B) ATP.
   C) H_2O.
   D) the top of the electron transport chain.
   E) the bottom of the electron transport chain.

Answer: E
Topic: 7.8
Skill: Factual Recall

44) The electrons lost from the reaction center of photosystem II are replaced by electrons from
   A) CO_2.
   B) ATP.
   C) H_2O.
   D) NADPH.
   E) photosystem I.

Answer: C
Topic: 7.8
Skill: Factual Recall

45) Photosystem II
   A) has P700 at its reaction center.
   B) is reduced by NADPH.
   C) passes electrons to photosystem I.
   D) does not have a reaction center.
   E) releases CO_2 as a by–product.

Answer: C
Topic: 7.8
Skill: Factual Recall

46) Photophosphorylation differs from oxidative phosphorylation in that
   A) it involves an electron transport chain.
   B) energy is stored in the form of a proton concentration difference.
   C) regeneration of ATP is driven by a flow of protons through an ATP synthase.
   D) the final electron acceptor is $NADP^+$ and not oxygen.
   E) its enzymes are membrane–bound.

Answer: D
Topic: 7.9
Skill: Conceptual Understanding

47) In photophosphorylation, energy from electron flow is used to transport _____ from the _____ to the thylakoid compartment, generating a concentration gradient of _____.
   A) electrons . . . grana . . . H^+
   B) H^+ . . . grana . . . electrons
   C) H^+ . . . stroma . . . H^+
   D) electrons . . . stroma . . . H^+
   E) H^+ . . . stroma . . . ATP

Answer: C
Topic: 7.9
Skill: Factual Recall

48) A concentration gradient is a form of
    A) kinetic energy.
    B) life.
    C) an exergonic reaction.
    D) potential energy.
    E) entropy.

Answer: D
Topic: 7.9
Skill: Conceptual Understanding

49) The chloroplast ATP synthase
    A) is a nucleic acid complex.

    B) transports H^+ ions from the stroma to the thylakoid space.

    C) couples the flow of H^+ to the phosphorylation of $NADP^+$.

    D) is embedded in the inner membrane of the chloroplast.

    E) helps transport H^+ against the concentration gradient.

Answer: B
Topic: 7.9
Skill: Factual Recall

50) In photosynthesis, the chemiosmotic production of ATP
    A) requires oxygen.
    B) is analogous to the production of ATP in mitochondria.
    C) is done by the Calvin cycle.
    D) requires the input of NADPH.
    E) is a result of the oxidation of glucose.

Answer: B
Topic: 7.9
Skill: Factual Recall

51) Mitochondria transfer _____ energy from _____ to ATP; chloroplasts transform _____ energy into the chemical energy of ATP.
    A) chemical . . . food . . . light
    B) food . . . light . . . chemical
    C) light . . . food . . . kinetic
    D) nuclear . . . light . . . food
    E) food . . . light . . . nuclear

Answer: A
Topic: 7.9
Skill: Conceptual Understanding

52) Photosynthetic organisms derive their carbon from
    A) carbon monoxide.
    B) carbon dioxide.
    C) hydrocarbons.
    D) methane.
    E) ribose.

Answer: B
Topic: 7.10
Skill: Factual Recall

53) ATP and NADPH
  A) play a role in glucose synthesis by plants.
  B) are products of the Calvin cycle.
  C) are inputs to the photosystems.
  D) production is associated with events taking place on the inner mitochondrial membrane.
  E) are used in the electron transport chain to pump H^+ into the thylakoid space.

Answer: A
Topic: 7.10
Skill: Factual Recall

54) To produce one glucose, the Calvin cycle needs to be run through _____ time(s).
  A) one
  B) two
  C) four
  D) six
  E) eight

Answer: D
Topic: 7.10
Skill: Conceptual Understanding

55) The Calvin cycle constructs _____, an energy-rich molecule that a plant cell can then use to make glucose or other organic molecules.
  A) G3P
  B) ATP
  C) NADH
  D) NADPH
  E) carbon dioxide

Answer: A
Topic: 7.10
Skill: Factual Recall

56) The ultimate source of all the food we eat and the oxygen we breathe is
  A) cellular respiration.
  B) chemiosmosis.
  C) photosynthesis.
  D) glycolysis.
  E) anaerobic metabolism.

Answer: C
Topic: 7.11
Skill: Conceptual Understanding

57) Plants use sugars as
   A) a fuel for photophosphorylation.
   B) a fuel for photosynthesis.
   C) a starting material for the Calvin cycle.
   D) a source of electrons for chemiosmosis.
   E) a fuel for cellular respiration and a starting material for making other organic molecules.

Answer: E
Topic: 7.11
Skill: Application

58) Plant cells
   A) lack mitochondria and chloroplasts.
   B) lack mitochondria but have chloroplasts.
   C) have mitochondria but do not have chloroplasts.
   D) have mitochondria and chloroplasts.
   E) have chloroplasts and vestigial mitochondria.

Answer: D
Topic: 7.11
Skill: Conceptual Understanding

59) The addition of oxygen to RuBP by rubisco to form a two-carbon product that is then broken down by the cell to carbon dioxide and water defines
   A) cellular respiration.
   B) photorespiration.
   C) chemiosmosis.
   D) photophosphorylation.
   E) aerobic respiration.

Answer: B
Topic: 7.12–Evolution Connection
Skill: Factual Recall

60) Photorespiration
   A) is an evolutionary relic from when atmospheric O_2 levels were low and did not interfere with rubisco.
   B) is of benefit to the plant since it breaks down rubisco.
   C) is attributable to high CO_2 levels.
   D) produces glucose.
   E) produces ATP.

Answer: A
Topic: 7.12–Evolution Connection
Skill: Factual Recall

61) What is the main adaptive advantage of the C_4 and CAM photosynthesis strategies over the C_3 strategy?
   A) They help the plant conserve water and synthesize glucose efficiently under hot, dry conditions.
   B) They allow the plant to fix carbon more efficiently under conditions of low atmospheric CO_2.
   C) They allow the plant to fix carbon more efficiently in dim or cool conditions.
   D) They make it possible for the plant to use the Calvin cycle at night.
   E) They allow the plant to avoid photorespiration by producing a four-carbon sugar in place of glucose.

Answer: A
Topic: 7.12–Evolution Connection
Skill: Conceptual Understanding

62) The greenhouse effect is
   A) reduced by photosynthesis, which removes carbon dioxide from the atmosphere.
   B) made worse by photosynthesis, which adds carbon dioxide to the atmosphere.
   C) reduced by the burning of fossil fuels, which removes oxygen from the atmosphere.
   D) reduced by the addition of carbon dioxide to the atmosphere, since carbon dioxide removes excess heat from the Earth's surface and reflects it back into space.
   E) of little concern, since it is part of the normal cycle for the planet.

Answer: A
Topic: 7.13
Skill: Conceptual Understanding

63) Which of the following statements about the greenhouse effect is *true*?
   A) The greenhouse effect is reduced by deforestation.
   B) The greenhouse effect is exacerbated by the use of fossil fuels.
   C) The greenhouse effect is inversely related to increasing levels of atmospheric CO_2.
   D) The greenhouse effect will decrease the average temperature of the planet.
   E) The greenhouse effect has no direct relationship with the Industrial Revolution of the 1800s.

Answer: B
Topic: 7.13
Skill: Factual Recall

64) It has been argued that cutting old-growth forests and replacing them with plantations of young trees would help to alleviate the threat of global greenhouse warming. What important fact does this argument ignore?
   A) Forests play too minor a role in global CO_2 dynamics, which are affected far more by marine algae.
   B) Young trees fix carbon at a lower rate per unit mass than old trees.
   C) Most of the biomass of the cut trees would be added to the atmosphere as CO_2 within a few years.
   D) Most of the young trees would die within a few years.
   E) Young trees emit ozone-destroying gases at a higher rate than old trees and would thus worsen the ozone-hole problem while alleviating global warming.

Answer: C
Topic: 7.13
Skill: Conceptual Understanding

65) Ozone
   A) formation is promoted by CFCs.
   B) is broken down by carbon dioxide.
   C) is a source of oxygen for cellular respiration.
   D) levels in the atmosphere have been steadily increasing in the past century.
   E) protects Earth from UV radiation.

Answer: E
Topic: 7.14
Skill: Factual Recall

66) Ozone consists of _____ oxygen atom(s).
   A) zero
   B) one
   C) two
   D) three
   E) four

Answer: D
Topic: 7.14
Skill: Factual Recall

67) Which of the following has been a major source of ozone destruction over the past 50 years?
   A) chlorofluorocarbons
   B) ethylene glycol
   C) carbon dioxide
   D) chemiosmosis
   E) cellular respiration

Answer: A
Topic: 7.14
Skill: Factual Recall

Art Questions

1)

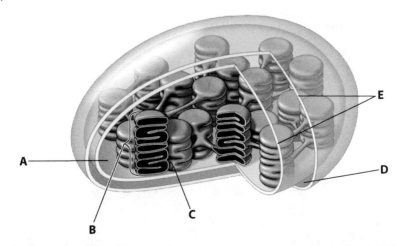

In this drawing of a chloroplast, which structure represents the thylakoid membrane?
   A) structure A
   B) structure B
   C) structure C
   D) structure D
   E) structure E

Answer: C
Topic: 7.2
Skill: Factual Recall

2)

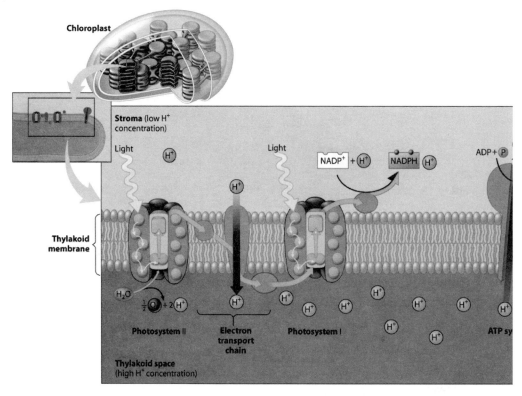

According to this figure, how do H+ ions make their way from the stroma to the thylakoid interior?
- A) through photosystem I
- B) through photosystem II
- C) through an electron transport chain molecule
- D) through the ATP synthase
- E) directly through the phospholipids of the thylakoid membrane

Answer: C
Topic: 7.9
Skill: Application

Scenario Questions

After reading the following paragraph, answer the question(s) below.

You're conducting an experiment to determine the effect of different wavelengths of light on the absorption of carbon dioxide as an indicator of the rate of photosynthesis in aquatic ecosystems. If the rate of photosynthesis increases, the amount of carbon dioxide in the environment will decrease and vice versa. You've added an indicator to each solution. When the carbon dioxide concentration decreases, the color of the indicator solution also changes.

Small aquatic plants are placed into three containers of water mixed with carbon dioxide and indicator solution. Container A is placed under normal sunlight, B under green light, and C under red light. The containers are observed for a 24–hour period.

1) Based on your knowledge of the process of photosynthesis, the plant in the container placed under red light would probably
   A) absorb no CO_2.
   B) absorb the same amount of CO_2 as the plants under both the green light and normal sunlight.
   C) absorb the same amount of CO_2 as the plants under the green light.
   D) absorb less CO_2 than the plants under green light.
   E) absorb more CO_2 than the plants under the green light.

   Answer: E
   Topic: 7.6
   Skill: Application

2) Carbon dioxide absorption is an appropriate indicator of photosynthesis because
   A) CO_2 is needed to produce sugars in the Calvin cycle.
   B) CO_2 is needed to complete the light reactions.
   C) plants produce oxygen gas by splitting CO_2.
   D) the energy in CO_2 is used to produce ATP and NADPH.
   E) CO_2 energizes electrons in the electron transport system.

   Answer: A
   Topic: 7.3–7.5, 7.11
   Skill: Factual Recall

Chapter 8 The Cellular Basis of Reproduction and Inheritance

Multiple-Choice Questions

1) The creation of offspring carrying genetic information from a single parent is called
   A) asexual reproduction.
   B) sexual reproduction.
   C) a life cycle.
   D) regeneration.
   E) spontaneous generation.

Answer: A
Topic: Opening Essay
Skill: Factual Recall

2) Which of the following statements regarding sexual and asexual reproduction is *true*?
   A) Cell division only occurs after sexual reproduction.
   B) Only offspring from asexual reproduction inherit traits from two parents.
   C) Sexual reproduction typically includes the development of unfertilized eggs.
   D) Sexual reproduction is more likely to increase genetic variation than is asexual reproduction.
   E) Only asexual reproduction results from the union of a sperm and an egg.

Answer: D
Topic: Opening Essay, 8.1
Skill: Conceptual Understanding

3) Strictly speaking, the phrase "like begets like" refers to
   A) all forms of reproduction.
   B) sexual reproduction only.
   C) asexual reproduction only.
   D) production of gametes from a premeiotic cell.
   E) sexual reproduction between different species.

Answer: C
Topic: 8.1
Skill: Factual Recall

4) Asexual reproduction requires _____ individual(s).
   A) 0
   B) 1
   C) 2
   D) 3
   E) 4

Answer: B
Topic: 8.1
Skill: Factual Recall

5) With the exception of identical twins, siblings who have the same two biological parents are likely to look similar, but not identical, to each other because they have
A) identical chromosomes, but different genes.
B) identical genes but different chromosomes.
C) the same combination of traits, but different genes.
D) only a 20% chance of sharing the same combination of genes.
E) a similar but not identical combination of genes.

Answer: E
Topic: 8.1
Skill: Conceptual Understanding

6) Virchow's principle, stated formally in 1858, was that
A) animals must always reproduce.
B) photosynthesis is the center of all life.
C) animals must develop.
D) every cell comes from a cell.
E) all life evolves.

Answer: D
Topic: 8.2
Skill: Factual Recall

7) Which of the following statements regarding cell division is *false*?
A) Cell division can reproduce an entire organism.
B) Cell division is necessary for development to occur.
C) Cell division ensures the continuity of life from generation to generation.
D) Cell division is the basis of both sexual and asexual reproduction.
E) Cell division is common in eukaryotes but rare in prokaryotes.

Answer: E
Topic: 8.2
Skill: Factual Recall

8) Which of the following statements regarding prokaryotes is *false*?
A) Prokaryotic chromosomes are more complex than those of eukaryotes.
B) Most prokaryotes reproduce by binary fission.
C) Prokaryotic cells are generally smaller and simpler than eukaryotic cells.
D) In prokaryotes, daughter chromosomes are separated by an active movement away from each other and the growth of a new plasma membrane between them.
E) Daughter prokaryotic chromosomes are separated by some sort of active movement away from each other and the growth of new plasma membrane between them.

Answer: A
Topic: 8.3, 8.4
Skill: Factual Recall

9) Eukaryotic chromosomes differ from prokaryotic chromosomes in that they
  A) are simpler.
  B) are circular in structure.
  C) include fewer proteins.
  D) are copied immediately after cell division.
  E) are housed in a membrane–enclosed nucleus.

Answer: E
Topic: 8.4
Skill: Factual Recall

10) Which of the following helps maintain the structure of chromosomes and control the activity of genes?
  A) the nuclear membrane
  B) proteins
  C) centromeres
  D) ribosomes
  E) lipids

Answer: B
Topic: 8.4
Skill: Factual Recall

11) Sister chromatids are
  A) found right after a cell divides.
  B) tightly linked together at a centromere.
  C) formed when chromatids separate during cell division.
  D) made only of DNA.
  E) unique to prokaryotes.

Answer: B
Topic: 8.4
Skill: Factual Recall

12) Prior to mitosis, each chromosome of a eukaryotic cell consists of a pair of identical structures called
  A) chromatin.
  B) sister chromosomes.
  C) DNA transcripts.
  D) nucleoli.
  E) sister chromatids.

Answer: E
Topic: 8.4
Skill: Factual Recall

13) Eukaryotic cells spend most of their cell cycle in which phase?
  A) interphase
  B) prophase
  C) metaphase
  D) anaphase
  E) telophase

Answer: A
Topic: 8.5
Skill: Factual Recall

14) Which of the following occurs during interphase?
   A) a reduction in the size of the nuclear membrane
   B) duplication of the chromosomes
   C) cytokinesis
   D) cell growth and duplication of the chromosomes
   E) separation of newly formed DNA to opposite ends of the cell

Answer: D
Topic: 8.5
Skill: Conceptual Understanding

15) The genetic material is duplicated during
   A) the mitotic phase.
   B) G_1.
   C) the S phase.
   D) G_2.
   E) mitosis.

Answer: C
Topic: 8.5
Skill: Application

16) If the S phase were eliminated from the cell cycle, the daughter cells would
   A) have half the genetic material found in the parent cell.
   B) be genetically identical to each other.
   C) be genetically identical to the parent cell.
   D) synthesize the missing genetic material on their own.
   E) continue to function without the normal amount of DNA.

Answer: A
Topic: 8.5
Skill: Conceptual Understanding

17) The process by which the cytoplasm of a eukaryotic cell divides to produce two cells is called
   A) mitosis.
   B) cytokinesis.
   C) binary fission.
   D) telophase.
   E) spindle formation.

Answer: B
Topic: 8.5
Skill: Factual Recall

18) Looking into your microscope, you spot an unusual cell. Instead of the typical rounded cell shape, the cell has a very narrow middle separating two bulging ends. It sort of looks like the number 8! Then you realize that this cell is
    A) undergoing cytokinesis.
    B) in the S phase of interphase.
    C) in the G1 phase of interphase.
    D) in the G2 phase of interphase.
    E) about to undergo mitosis.

Answer: A
Topic: 8.5
Skill: Application

19) The phase of mitosis during which the nuclear envelope fragments and the nucleoli disappear is called
    A) interphase.
    B) prophase.
    C) metaphase.
    D) anaphase.
    E) telophase.

Answer: B
Topic: 8.6
Skill: Factual Recall

20) During which phase of mitosis do the chromosomes line up on a plane equidistant from the two spindle poles?
    A) interphase
    B) prophase
    C) metaphase
    D) anaphase
    E) telophase

Answer: C
Topic: 8.6
Skill: Factual Recall

21) At the start of mitotic anaphase,
    A) the centromeres of each chromosome come apart.
    B) sister chromatids separate.
    C) the chromatid DNA replicates.
    D) daughter chromosomes begin to move toward opposite poles of the cell.
    E) equivalent and complete collections of chromosomes have reached the two poles.

Answer: A
Topic: 8.6
Skill: Conceptual Understanding

22) During which phase of mitosis does the nuclear envelope re-form and the nucleoli reappear?
   A) anaphase
   B) metaphase
   C) prophase
   D) interphase
   E) telophase

Answer: E
Topic: 8.6
Skill: Factual Recall

23) Which of the following is a feature of plant cell division that distinguishes it from animal cell division?
   A) formation of a cell plate
   B) formation of a cleavage furrow
   C) lack of cytokinesis
   D) production of four (rather than two) new cells per mitotic division
   E) disappearance and subsequent reappearance of the nucleolus

Answer: A
Topic: 8.7
Skill: Factual Recall

24) Which of the following features likely accounts for the difference between plant and animal cell cytokinesis?
   A) Animal cells lack the microfilaments required for forming a cleavage furrow.
   B) Animal cells lack chloroplasts.
   C) Plant cell division must maintain the integrity of the cell wall.
   D) Plant cells have two sets of chromosomes; animal cells have one set of chromosomes.
   E) Plant and animal cells do not have a common ancestor.

Answer: C
Topic: 8.7
Skill: Conceptual Understanding

25) Which of the following must occur for a plant or animal to grow and develop normally?
   A) The organism must receive a supply of the appropriate hormones from its parents.
   B) The organism must be able to control the timing and rate of cell division in different parts of its body.
   C) Sufficient light must be available to stimulate cell division.
   D) Sufficient oxygen must be available to stimulate cell division.
   E) Dividing cells must be freed from attachment sites.

Answer: B
Topic: 8.8
Skill: Conceptual Understanding

26) When animal cells are grown in a petri dish, they typically stop dividing once they have formed a single, unbroken layer on the bottom of the dish. This arrest of division is an example of
    A) cancer.
    B) cell constraint.
    C) density–dependent inhibition.
    D) cell division repression.
    E) growth factor desensitization.

Answer: C
Topic: 8.8
Skill: Factual Recall

27) As a patch of scraped skin heals, the cells fill in the injured area but do not grow beyond that. This is an example of
    A) density–independent inhibition.
    B) density–dependent inhibition.
    C) anchorage independence.
    D) growth factor inhibition.
    E) anchorage–dependent inhibition.

Answer: B
Topic: 8.8
Skill: Application

28) Which of the following is probably the main factor responsible for the phenomenon of density–dependent inhibition?
    A) a local accumulation of growth–inhibiting factors
    B) availability of growth factors
    C) cells' innate ability to "sense" when the organ of which they are a part has no need for additional cells
    D) a local deficiency of nutrients
    E) physical contact of cell-surface proteins between adjacent cells.

Answer: B
Topic: 8.8
Skill: Conceptual Understanding

29) Mature human nerve cells and muscle cells
    A) remain undifferentiated unless an injury occurs.
    B) become cancerous more easily than other cell types.
    C) continue to divide throughout their lifetime.
    D) are permanently in a state of nondivision.
    E) cease dividing after a predetermined number of cell generations.

Answer: D
Topic: 8.9
Skill: Factual Recall

30) Which of the following statements regarding the cell-cycle control system is *false*?
    A) The cell–cycle control system receives messages from outside the cell that influence cell division.
    B) The cell–cycle control system triggers and controls major events in the cell cycle.
    C) The cell–cycle control system is influenced by growth factors that bind to cell receptors.
    D) The cell–cycle control system includes three key checkpoints to complete a cell cycle.
    E) The cell–cycle control system operates independently of the growth factors.

Answer: E
Topic: 8.9
Skill: Factual Recall

31) The cell cycle control system is most like
    A) a row of dominoes falling down, each one triggering the fall of the next.
    B) the control device of an automatic washing machine.
    C) an orchestra directed by a conductor.
    D) a light switch turning on a set of room lights.
    E) a video game controller.

Answer: B
Topic: 8.9
Skill: Conceptual Understanding

32) You are asked to culture an unidentified sample of animal tissue. You notice that the cells seem to fail to exhibit density–dependent inhibition. The source of this tissue sample is most likely
    A) a scar.
    B) a cancer.
    C) skin.
    D) a fetal liver.
    E) the sperm–producing tissue of the testis.

Answer: B
Topic: 8.10
Skill: Application

33) A benign tumor differs from a malignant tumor in that a benign tumor
    A) is cancerous.
    B) spreads from the original site.
    C) does not metastasize.
    D) never causes health problems.
    E) can only arise in the brain, whereas a malignant tumor can arise anywhere in the body.

Answer: C
Topic: 8.10
Skill: Factual Recall

34) Which of the following shows the greatest promise as a cancer chemotherapy agent?
   A) a drug that causes cells to divide at a right angle from their usual orientation
   B) a drug that interferes with cellular respiration
   C) a drug that prevents sister chromatids from separating at anaphase
   D) a drug that prevents crossing over
   E) a drug that prevents tetrad formation

Answer: C
Topic: 8.10
Skill: Application

35) Which of the following statements regarding the function of mitosis is *false*?
   A) Mitosis allows organisms to grow.
   B) Mitosis allows organisms to generate genetic diversity.
   C) Mitosis allows organisms to reproduce asexually.
   D) Mitosis allows organisms to repair tissues.
   E) Mitosis allows organisms to regenerate lost parts.

Answer: B
Topic: 8.11
Skill: Factual Recall

36) Two chromosomes in a nucleus that carry loci for the same traits in the same positions on the chromosome but specify different versions of some traits constitute a pair of
   A) homologous chromosomes.
   B) heterologous chromosomes.
   C) complementary chromosomes.
   D) polyploid chromosomes.
   E) parallel chromosomes.

Answer: A
Topic: 8.12
Skill: Factual Recall

37) A pair of male human sex chromosomes is most like
   A) a pair of blue jeans.
   B) a bride and groom.
   C) a knife, fork, and spoon.
   D) identical twins.
   E) the letters of the alphabet.

Answer: B
Topic: 8.12
Skill: Application

38) Which of the following statements regarding mitosis and meiosis is *false*?
   A) Meiosis only occurs in the ovaries and testes.
   B) All sexual life cycles involve an alternation of diploid and haploid stages.
   C) Mitosis produces daughter cells with half the number of chromosomes as the parent cell.
   D) A normal human zygote has 46 chromosomes.
   E) A haploid cell has half the chromosomes of a diploid cell.

Answer: C
Topic: 8.13
Skill: Conceptual Understanding

39) Which of the following statements is *false*?
   A) A typical body cell is called a somatic cell.
   B) Gametes are haploid cells.
   C) Somatic cells are diploid.
   D) Gametes are made by mitosis.
   E) A zygote is a fertilized egg.

Answer: D
Topic: 8.12, 8.13
Skill: Factual Recall

40) During which stage of meiosis does synapsis and the formation of tetrads occur?
   A) interphase I
   B) prophase I
   C) interphase II
   D) prophase II
   E) metaphase I

Answer: B
Topic: 8.14
Skill: Factual Recall

41) Which of the following options correctly describes the behavior of a tetrad during anaphase I of meiosis?
   A) It goes intact to one pole of the dividing cell.
   B) It splits into two pairs of sister chromatids, and one pair goes to each pole of the dividing cell.
   C) It splits into two pairs of homologous, nonsister chromatids, and one pair goes to each pole of the dividing cell.
   D) It splits into four chromosomes, which distribute in random pairs to the two poles of the dividing cell.
   E) It splits into four chromosomes, which distribute in sister–chromosome pairs to the two poles of the dividing cell.

Answer: B
Topic: 8.14
Skill: Conceptual Understanding

42) Which of the following statements regarding the differences between mitosis and meiosis is *false*?
   A) In meiosis four daughter cells are produced, whereas in mitosis two daughter cells are produced.
   B) Cells produced by mitosis are diploid, whereas cells produced by meiosis are haploid.
   C) In mitosis cytokinesis occurs once, whereas in meiosis cytokinesis occurs twice.
   D) Crossing over is a phenomenon that creates genetic diversity during mitosis.
   E) Mitosis, but not meiosis, occurs in somatic cells.

Answer: D
Topic: 8.14, 8.15
Skill: Conceptual Understanding

43) Which of the following statements regarding mitosis and meiosis is *false*?
    A) Mitosis provides for growth and tissue repair.
    B) Meiosis provides for asexual reproduction.
    C) In mitosis, the chromosomes replicate only once in the preceding interphase.
    D) In meiosis, the chromosomes replicate only once in the preceding interphase.
    E) All the events unique to meiosis occur during meiosis I.

Answer: B
Topic: 8.15
Skill: Factual Recall

44) Both mitosis and meiosis are preceded by
    A) prometaphase.
    B) interphase.
    C) prophase.
    D) telophase.
    E) anaphase.

Answer: B
Topic: 8.15
Skill: Factual Recall

45) Independent orientation of chromosomes at metaphase I and random fertilization are most like
    A) shuffling cards and dealing out hands of poker.
    B) cutting up a pie into eight even-sized slices.
    C) alphabetizing files in a filing cabinet.
    D) pairing up similar socks after washing your clothes.
    E) stringing beads onto a string to make a necklace.

Answer: A
Topic: 8.16
Skill: Conceptual Understanding

46) Independent orientation of chromosomes at metaphase I results in an increase in the number of
    A) gametes.
    B) homologous chromosomes.
    C) possible combinations of characteristics.
    D) sex chromosomes.
    E) points of crossing over.

Answer: C
Topic: 8.17
Skill: Conceptual Understanding

47) Which of the following statements regarding genetic diversity is *false*?
A) Genetic diversity is enhanced by random fertilization.
B) Genetic diversity is enhanced by independent orientation of chromosomes at metaphase I.
C) Genetic diversity is enhanced by mitosis of somatic cells.
D) Genetic diversity is enhanced by crossing over during prophase I of meiosis.
E) Genetic diversity is enhanced by random mutations of the DNA.

Answer: C
Topic: 8.16–8.18
Skill: Factual Recall

48) Karyotyping
A) shows chromosomes as they appear in metaphase of meiosis II.
B) can reveal alterations in chromosome number.
C) examines points of crossing over.
D) reveals the results of independent orientation of chromosomes during meiosis I.
E) reveals the presence of cancerous genes.

Answer: B
Topic: 8.19
Skill: Factual Recall

49) A karyotype is most like
A) a map showing the hidden location of buried treasure.
B) a movie showing the stages of the reproductive cycle of a beetle.
C) a necklace formed by stringing beads onto a string.
D) photographs of every couple at a high school prom.
E) the answer key to a multiple–choice exam.

Answer: D
Topic: 8.19
Skill: Conceptual Understanding

50) Which of the following statements regarding Down syndrome is *false*?
A) Trisomy 21 usually leads to Down syndrome.
B) A human embryo with an abnormal number of chromosomes is usually spontaneously aborted.
C) Down syndrome is the most common serious birth defect in the United States.
D) People with Down syndrome usually have a life span much shorter than normal.
E) Women with Down syndrome cannot reproduce.

Answer: E
Topic: 8.20
Skill: Factual Recall

51) Nondisjunction occurs when
A) a portion of a chromosome breaks off and is lost.
B) chromosomes replicate too many times.
C) two chromosomes fuse into one.
D) members of a chromosome pair fail to separate.
E) an entire pair of chromosomes is lost during meiosis I.

Answer: D
Topic: 8.21
Skill: Factual Recall

52) Which of the following statements about nondisjunction is *false*?
   A) Nondisjunction in meiosis can affect autosomes and sex chromosomes.
   B) In mammals, extra copies of the Y chromosome are typically inactivated.
   C) The absence of a Y chromosome results in "femaleness."
   D) In general, a single Y chromosome is enough to produce "maleness."
   E) Women with a single X chromosome have Turner syndrome and are sterile.

Answer: B
Topic: 8.22
Skill: Factual Recall

53) Which of the following types of organisms commonly demonstrates polyploidy?
   A) mammals
   B) reptiles
   C) flowering plants
   D) amphibians
   E) fish

Answer: C
Topic: 8.23–Evolution Connection
Skill: Factual Recall

54) How many generations does it take to develop a new plant species by nondisjunction?
   A) one
   B) two
   C) ten
   D) twenty
   E) fifty

Answer: A
Topic: 8.23–Evolution Connection
Skill: Factual Recall

55) Which of the following variations of the sentence "Where is the cat" is most like a chromosomal deletion?
   A) Where is cat?
   B) Where is the the cat?
   C) Where the is cat?
   D) Where is cat the the cat?
   E) Where is is is is the cat?

Answer: A
Topic: 8.24
Skill: Factual Recall

56) If a chromosome fragment breaks off and then reattaches to the original chromosome, but in the reverse direction, the resulting chromosomal abnormality is called a(n)
   A) deletion.
   B) inversion.
   C) translocation.
   D) nondisjunction.
   E) reciprocal translocation.

Answer: B
Topic: 8.24
Skill: Factual Recall

57) Cancer is not usually inherited because
   A) the chromosomal changes in cancer are usually confined to somatic cells.
   B) people with cancer usually die before reproducing.
   C) cancer typically causes disruptions of meiosis.
   D) the causes of cancer are not usually genetic.
   E) the cancerous cells usually interfere with the ability to produce gametes.

Answer: A
Topic: 8.24
Skill: Conceptual Understanding

Art Questions

1)

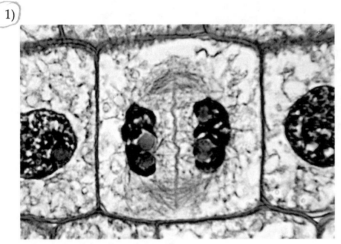

What type of cell is shown?
   A) animal cell in metaphase
   B) animal cell in telophase
   C) plant cell in metaphase
   D) plant cell in telophase
   E) plant cell in interphase

Answer: D
Topic: 8.6, 8.7
Skill: Application

2)

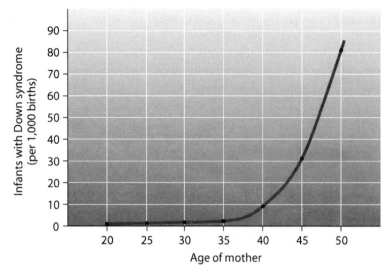

According to the graph, at what maternal age does the incidence of Down syndrome begin to increase substantially?

A) about 26 or 27
B) about 31 or 32
C) about 37 or 38
D) about 42 or 43
E) about 45 or 46

Answer: C
Topic: 8.20
Skill: Application

3)

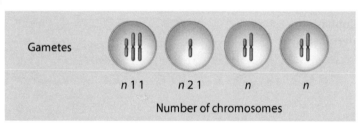

If these four cells resulted from cell division of a single cell with diploid chromosome number $2n = 4$, what best describes what just occurred?

A) normal binary fission
B) normal mitosis
C) normal meiosis
D) meiosis with nondisjunction in meiosis I
E) meiosis with nondisjunction in meiosis II

Answer: E
Topic: 8.3, 8.6, 8.14, 8.21
Skill: Conceptual Understanding

Scenario Questions

After reading the following paragraph, answer the question(s) below.

Mr. and Mrs. Smith have three sons in elementary school. Two of their children are progressing normally, but their last son, Charles, has been much slower than his siblings at developing speech and language skills. His parents are concerned that he has a learning disability and decide to investigate further. Since some learning disabilities can be genetically based, their pediatrician recommends a chromosomal analysis.

The results show that Charles has a trisomy of the sex chromosomes, diagnosed as XYY, which is caused by nondisjunction in the formation of the father's sperm. The nondisjunction resulted in an extra copy of the Y chromosome. The extra copy was passed on to Charles during fertilization. Most often, this chromosomal change causes no unusual physical features or medical problems, but those with trisomy of the sex chromosomes do have a higher than normal risk of delays in learning development.

1) During which stage of meiosis must this nondisjunction have occurred?
   A) anaphase I
   B) metaphase I
   C) metaphase II
   D) anaphase II
   E) prophase II

Answer: C
Topic: 8.16, 8.19, 8.20–8.22
Skill: Conceptual Understanding

2) If Charles gets married and starts a family, which of the following chromosomal abnormalities might be found in his children?
   A) XY
   B) XX
   C) XYY
   D) XO
   E) XXY

Answer: E
Topic: 8.16, 8.19, 8.20–8.22
Skill: Application

Chapter 9 Patterns of Inheritance

Multiple-Choice Questions

1) Which of the following statements regarding domestic dogs is *false*?
   A) Dogs originated in East Asia.
   B) Dogs of different breeds can be identified through genetic analysis.
   C) Shar-pei and Akita are genetically very similar to the wolf.
   D) All dogs are descended from wolves.
   E) Humans have bred dogs for thousands of years.

   Answer: D
   Topic: Opening Essay
   Skill: Factual Recall

2) Which of the following statements best represents the theory of pangenesis developed by Hippocrates?
   A) Pregnancy is a spontaneous event, and the characteristics of the offspring are determined by the gods.
   B) Particles called pangenes, which originate in each part of an organism's body, collect in the sperm or eggs and are passed on to the next generation.
   C) Offspring inherit the traits of either the mother or the father, but not both.
   D) Fertilization of plants is dependent on an animal.
   E) Heritable traits are influenced by the environment and the behaviors of the parents.

   Answer: B
   Topic: 9.1
   Skill: Conceptual Understanding

3) Which of the following statements regarding hypotheses about inheritance is *false*?
   A) The theory of pangenesis incorrectly suggests that reproductive cells receive particles from somatic cells.
   B) Contrary to the theory of pangenesis, somatic cells do not influence eggs or sperm.
   C) The blending hypothesis does not explain how traits that disappear in one generation can reappear in later generations.
   D) The blending hypothesis suggests that all of the traits of the offspring come from either the mother or the father.
   E) Aristotle suggested that inheritance is the potential to produce body features.

   Answer: D
   Topic: 9.1
   Skill: Conceptual Understanding

4) Mendel conducted his most memorable experiments on
   A) peas.
   B) roses.
   C) guinea pigs.
   D) fruit flies.
   E) clones.

   Answer: A
   Topic: 9.2
   Skill: Factual Recall

5) Varieties of plants in which self–fertilization produces offspring that are identical to the parents are referred to as
   A) hybrids.
   B) the F_2 generation.
   C) monohybrid crosses.
   D) independent crosses.
   E) true–breeding.

Answer: E
Topic: 9.2
Skill: Conceptual Understanding

6) Which of the following statements regarding cross–breeding and hybridization is *false*?
   A) The offspring of two different varieties are called hybrids.
   B) Hybridization is also called a cross.
   C) The parental plants of a cross are the P generation.
   D) The hybrid offspring of a cross are the P_1 generation.
   E) The hybrid offspring of an F_1 cross are the F_2 generation.

Answer: D
Topic: 9.2
Skill: Factual Recall

7) A monohybrid cross is
   A) the second generation of a self–fertilized plant.
   B) a breeding experiment in which the parental varieties have only one trait in common.
   C) a breeding experiment in which the parental varieties differ in only one character.
   D) a triploid plant that results from breeding two very different plants.
   E) a breeding experiment in which the parental varieties have only one prominent trait.

Answer: C
Topic: 9.3
Skill: Conceptual Understanding

8) Which of the following statements regarding genotypes and phenotypes is *false*?
   A) The genetic makeup of an organism constitutes its genotype.
   B) An organism with two different alleles for a single trait is said to be heterozygous for that trait.
   C) Alleles are alternate forms of a gene.
   D) An allele that is fully expressed is referred to as recessive. *should be dominent*
   E) The expressed physical traits of an organism are called its phenotype.

Answer: D
Topic: 9.3
Skill: Factual Recall

9) Research since Mendel's time has established that the law of the segregation of genes during gamete formation
  A) applies to all forms of life.
  B) applies to all sexually reproducing organisms.
  C) applies to all asexually reproducing organisms.
  D) applies only to unicellular organisms.
  E) is invalid.

Answer: B
Topic: 9.3
Skill: Conceptual Understanding

10) All the offspring of a cross between a black-eyed mendelien and an orange-eyed mendelien have black eyes. This means that the allele for black eyes is _____ the allele for orange eyes.
  A) codominant to
  B) recessive to
  C) more aggressive than
  D) dominant to
  E) better than

Answer: D
Topic: 9.3
Skill: Conceptual Understanding

11) All the offspring of a cross between a black-eyed mendelien and an orange-eyed mendelien have black eyes. What is the expected phenotypic ratio of a cross between two orange-eyed mendeliens?
  A) 3 black-eyed:1 orange-eyed
  B) 0 black-eyed:1 orange-eyed
  C) 1 black-eyed:3 orange-eyed
  D) 1 black-eyed:0 orange-eyed
  E) 1 black-eyed:1 orange-eyed

Answer: B
Topic: 9.3
Skill: Application

12) The alleles of a gene are found at _____ chromosomes.
  A) the same locus on homologous mitochondrial
  B) the same locus on heterologous
  C) different loci on homologous
  D) different loci on heterologous
  E) the same locus on homologous

Answer: E
Topic: 9.4
Skill: Factual Recall

13) The phenotypic ratio resulting from a dihybrid cross showing independent assortment is expected to be
   A) 1:2:1.
   B) 3:1.
   C) 9:1:1:3.
   D) 3:9:9:1.
   E) 9:3:3:1.

Answer: E
Topic: 9.5
Skill: Factual Recall

14) If *A* is dominant to *a* and *B* is dominant to *b*, what is the expected phenotypic ratio of the cross: *AaBb* × *AaBb*?
   A) 16:0:0:0
   B) 8:4:2:2
   C) 4:4:4:4
   D) 1:1:1:1
   E) 9:3:3:1

Answer: E
Topic: 9.5
Skill: Application

15) Mendel's law of independent assortment states that
   A) chromosomes sort independently of each other during mitosis and meiosis.
   B) genes sort independently of each other in animals but not in plants.
   C) independent sorting of genes produces polyploid plants under some circumstances.
   D) each pair of alleles segregates independently of the other pairs of alleles during gamete formation.
   E) genes are sorted concurrently during gamete formation.

Answer: D
Topic: 9.5
Skill: Conceptual Understanding

16) Imagine that we mate two black Labrador dogs with normal vision and find that three of the puppies are like the parents, but one puppy is chocolate with normal vision and another is black with PRA (progressive retinal atrophy, a serious disease of vision). We can conclude that
   A) both of the parents are homozygous for both traits.
   B) one of the parents is homozygous for both traits.
   C) the same alleles that control coat color can also cause PRA.
   D) the alleles for color and vision segregate independently during gamete formation.
   E) the alleles for color and vision segregate dependently during gamete formation.

Answer: D
Topic: 9.5, 9.6
Skill: Conceptual Understanding

17) A testcross is
   A) a mating between an individual of unknown genotype and an individual homozygous recessive for the trait of interest.
   B) a mating between an individual of unknown genotype and an individual heterozygous for the trait of interest.
   C) a mating between an individual of unknown genotype and an individual homozygous dominant for the trait of interest.
   D) a mating between two individuals heterozygous for the trait of interest.
   E) a mating between two individuals of unknown genotype.

Answer: A
Topic: 9.6
Skill: Conceptual Understanding

18) Using a six-sided die, what is the probability of rolling either a 5 or a 6?
   A) 1/6 × 1/6 = 1/36
   B) 1/6 + 1/6 = 1/3
   C) 1/6 + 1/6 = 2/3
   D) 1/6 + 1/6 = 1/12
   E) 1/6

Answer: B
Topic: 9.7
Skill: Application

19) Assuming that the probability of having a female child is 50% and the probability of having a male child is also 50%, what is the probability that a couple's first-born child will be female and that their second-born child will be male?
   A) 20%
   B) 25%
   C) 50%
   D) 75%
   E) 100%

Answer: B
Topic: 9.7
Skill: Application

20) A carrier of a genetic disorder who does not show symptoms is most likely to be _____ to transmit it to offspring.
   A) heterozygous for the trait and able
   B) heterozygous for the trait and unable
   C) homozygous for the trait and able
   D) homozygous for the trait and unable
   E) heterozygous for the trait and unlikely

Answer: A
Topic: 9.8
Skill: Conceptual Understanding

21) Dr. Smith's parents have normal hearing. However, Dr. Smith has an inherited form of deafness. Deafness is a recessive trait that is associated with the abnormal allele *d*. The normal allele at this locus, associated with normal hearing, is *D*. Dr. Smith's parents could have which of the following genotypes?

A) *DD* and *dd*

B) *dd* and *dd*

C) *Dd* and *Dd*

D) *DD* and *DD*

E) *Dd* and *DD*

Answer: C
Topic: 9.8
Skill: Application

22) Most genetic disorders of humans are caused by

A) multiple alleles.

B) recessive alleles.

C) drinking during pregnancy.

D) a mutation that occurs in the egg, sperm, or zygote.

E) dominant alleles.

Answer: B
Topic: 9.9
Skill: Factual Recall

23) The vast majority of people afflicted with recessive disorders are born to parents who were

A) both affected by the disease.

B) not affected at all by the disease.

C) slightly affected by the disease, showing some but not all of the symptoms.

D) subjected to some environmental toxin that caused the disease in their children.

E) affected by the disease but had subclinical symptoms.

Answer: B
Topic: 9.9
Skill: Conceptual Understanding

24) Which of the following statements best explains why dominant alleles that cause lethal disorders are less common than recessive alleles that cause lethal disorders?

A) Lethal disorders caused by dominant alleles are usually more severe than lethal disorders caused by recessive alleles.

B) Unlike lethal disorders caused by recessive alleles, lethal disorders caused by dominant alleles usually cause the death of the embryo.

C) Most individuals carrying a lethal dominant allele have the disorder and die before they reproduce, whereas individuals carrying a lethal recessive allele are more likely to be healthy and reproduce.

D) The presence of a lethal dominant allele causes sterility.

E) Many lethal recessive alleles cause enhanced disease resistance when they are present in the heterozygous state, and carriers of these alleles have more children, on average, than other people.

Answer: C
Topic: 9.9
Skill: Conceptual Understanding

25) Amniocentesis and chorionic villus sampling allow for _____ and _____ of the fetus so that it can be tested for abnormalities.
    A) imaging . . . biochemical testing
    B) imaging . . . karyotyping
    C) sexing . . . imaging
    D) karyotyping . . . biochemical testing
    E) direct observation . . . biochemical testing

Answer: D
Topic: 9.10
Skill: Factual Recall

26) Which of the following statements regarding prenatal testing is *false*?
    A) Results from chorionic villus sampling come faster than from amniocentesis.
    B) Chorionic villus sampling is typically performed later in the pregnancy than amniocentesis.
    C) Ultrasound imaging has no known risk.
    D) The complication rate for chorionic villus sampling is about 2% and for amniocentesis is about 1%.
    E) Chorionic villus sampling and amniocentesis are usually reserved for pregnancies with higher than usual risks of complications.

Answer: B
Topic: 9.10
Skill: Factual Recall

27) Which of the following statements regarding genetic testing is *false*?
    A) Genetic testing before birth requires the collection of fetal cells.
    B) Carrier testing helps determine if a person carries a potentially harmful disorder.
    C) Most children with recessive disorders are born to healthy parents.
    D) The screening of newborns can catch inherited disorders right after birth.
    E) Most human genetic diseases are treatable if caught early.

Answer: E
Topic: 9.10
Skill: Factual Recall

28) For most sexually reproducing organisms, Mendel's laws
    A) cannot strictly account for most patterns of inheritance.
    B) explain the reasons why certain genes are dominant.
    C) help us understand the global geographic patterns of genetic disease.
    D) indicate if a particular genotype will cause a certain phenotype.
    E) clarify the phenomenon of incomplete dominance.

Answer: A
Topic: 9.11
Skill: Conceptual Understanding

29) Which of the following statements is *false*?
  A) Incomplete dominance supports the blending hypothesis.
  B) Heterozygotes for hypercholesterolemia have blood cholesterols about twice normal.
  C) The four blood types result from various combinations of the three different ABO alleles.
  D) ABO blood groups can provide evidence of paternity.
  E) The impact of a single gene on more than one character is called pleiotropy.

Answer: A
Topic: 9.11, 9.13
Skill: Factual Recall

30) All the offspring of a cross between a red-flowered plant and a white-flowered plant have pink flowers. This means that the allele for red flowers is _____ to the allele for white flowers.
  A) dominant
  B) codominant
  C) pleiotropic
  D) incompletely dominant
  E) recessive

Answer: D
Topic: 9.11
Skill: Conceptual Understanding

31) Imagine that beak color in a finch species is controlled by a single gene. You mate a finch homozygous for orange (pigmented) beak with a finch homozygous for ivory (unpigmented) beak and get numerous offspring, all of which have a pale, ivory-orange beak. This pattern of color expression is most likely to be an example of
  A) incomplete dominance.
  B) codominance.
  C) pleiotropy.
  D) polygenic inheritance.
  E) crossing over.

Answer: A
Topic: 9.11
Skill: Application

32) Which of the following is an example of incomplete dominance in humans?
  A) sickle-cell disease
  B) hypercholesterolemia
  C) skin color
  D) ABO blood groups
  E) phenylketonuria

Answer: B
Topic: 9.11
Skill: Factual Recall

33) The expression of both alleles for a trait in a heterozygous individual illustrates
    A) incomplete dominance.
    B) codominance.
    C) pleiotropy.
    D) polygenic inheritance.
    E) blending inheritance.

Answer: B
Topic: 9.12
Skill: Factual Recall

34) A person with AB blood illustrates the principle of
    A) incomplete dominance.
    B) codominance.
    C) pleiotropy.
    D) polygenic inheritance.
    E) blending inheritance.

Answer: B
Topic: 9.12
Skill: Factual Recall

35) Which of the following statements regarding sickle-cell disease is *false*?
    A) Sickle-cell disease is common in tropical Africa.
    B) Persons who are heterozygous for sickle-cell disease are also resistant to malaria.
    C) Sickle-cell disease causes white blood cells to be sickle-shaped.
    D) All of the symptoms of sickle-cell disease result from the actions of just one allele.
    E) About one in ten African-Americans is a carrier of sickle-cell disease.

Answer: C
Topic: 9.13
Skill: Factual Recall

36) Sickle-cell disease is an example of
    A) codominance and pleiotropy.
    B) codominance and blended inheritance.
    C) multiple alleles, pleiotropy, and blended inheritance.
    D) codominance and multiple alleles.
    E) multiple alleles and pleiotropy.

Answer: A
Topic: 9.13
Skill: Conceptual Understanding

37) Which of the following terms refers to a situation where a single phenotypic character is determined by the additive effects of two or more genes?
    A) incomplete dominance
    B) codominance
    C) pleiotropy
    D) polygenic inheritance
    E) blending inheritance

Answer: D
Topic: 9.14
Skill: Factual Recall

38) Which of the following is essentially the opposite of pleiotropy?
    A) incomplete dominance
    B) codominance
    C) multiple alleles
    D) polygenic inheritance
    E) blending inheritance

Answer: D
Topic: 9.14
Skill: Factual Recall

39) The individual features of all organisms are the result of
    A) genetics.
    B) the environment.
    C) genetics and cytoplasmic determinants.
    D) the environment and individual needs.
    E) genetics and the environment.

Answer: E
Topic: 9.15
Skill: Conceptual Understanding

40) The chromosome theory of inheritance states that
    A) chromosomes that exhibit mutations are the source of genetic variation.
    B) the behavior of chromosomes during meiosis and fertilization accounts for patterns
       of inheritance.
    C) the behavior of chromosomes during mitosis accounts for inheritance patterns.
    D) humans have 46 chromosomes.
    E) the inheritance pattern of humans is predetermined from chromosomes.

Answer: B
Topic: 9.16
Skill: Conceptual Understanding

41) Genes located close together on the same chromosomes are referred to as _____ genes
    and generally _____.
    A) associated . . . sort independently during meiosis
    B) linked . . . sort independently during meiosis
    C) homologous . . . are inherited together
    D) linked . . . do not sort independently during meiosis
    E) codependent . . . do not sort independently during meiosis

Answer: D
Topic: 9.17
Skill: Conceptual Understanding

42) Linked genes generally
    A) follow the laws of independent assortment.
    B) do not follow the laws of independent assortment.
    C) show incomplete dominance.
    D) reflect a pattern of codominance.
    E) show pleiotropy.

Answer: B
Topic: 9.17
Skill: Factual Recall

43) You conduct a dihybrid cross and then testcross the generation. A _____ ratio would make you suspect that the genes are linked.
    A) 3:1
    B) 1:2:1
    C) 1:1:1:1
    D) 7:7:1:1
    E) 9:3:3:1

Answer: D
Topic: 9.17
Skill: Conceptual Understanding

44) Crossing over _____ genes into assortments of _____ not found in the parents.
    A) recombines unlinked . . . genes
    B) recombines linked . . . alleles
    C) combines unlinked . . . alleles
    D) combines linked . . . genes
    E) recombines unlinked . . . chromosomes

Answer: B
Topic: 9.18
Skill: Factual Recall

45) The mechanism that "breaks" the linkage between linked genes is
    A) incomplete dominance.
    B) pleiotropy.
    C) codominance.
    D) independent assortment.
    E) crossing over.

Answer: E
Topic: 9.18
Skill: Factual Recall

46) Which of the following kinds of data could be used to map the relative position of three genes on a chromosome?
    A) the frequencies with which the genes exhibit incomplete dominance over each other
    B) the frequencies of mutations in the genes
    C) the frequencies with which the genes are inherited from the mother and from the father
    D) the frequencies with which the genes are heterozygous
    E) the frequencies with which the corresponding traits occur together in offspring

Answer: E
Topic: 9.19
Skill: Conceptual Understanding

47) What is the normal complement of sex chromosomes in a human male?
   A) two X chromosomes
   B) two Y chromosomes
   C) two X chromosomes and one Y chromosome
   D) one X chromosome and one Y chromosome
   E) one Y chromosome

Answer: D
Topic: 9.20
Skill: Factual Recall

48) The sex chromosome complement of a normal human male is
   A) XO.
   B) XX.
   C) XY.
   D) YY.
   E) YO.

Answer: C
Topic: 9.20
Skill: Application

49) How many sex chromosomes are in a human gamete?
   A) one
   B) two
   C) three
   D) four
   E) five

Answer: A
Topic: 9.20
Skill: Conceptual Understanding

50) How is sex determined in most ants and bees?
   A) by the X–Y system
   B) by the Z–W system
   C) by the number of chromosomes
   D) by the size of the sex chromosome
   E) by the X–O system

Answer: C
Topic: 9.20
Skill: Factual Recall

51) Given the sex determination system in bees, we can expect that
   A) female bees will produce eggs by meiosis, while male bees will produce sperm by mitosis.
   B) female bees will produce eggs by mitosis, while male bees will produce sperm by meiosis.
   C) male and female bees will produce sperm and eggs by meiosis.
   D) male and female bees will produce sperm and eggs by mitosis.
   E) female bees will produce eggs by meiosis, but male bees will not produce sperm.

Answer: A
Topic: 9.20
Skill: Application

52) What is meant by the statement that "male bees are fatherless"?
   A) Male bees don't play a role in the rearing of bee young.
   B) Male bees are produced by budding.
   C) Male bees develop from fertilized eggs.
   D) Male bees develop from unfertilized eggs.
   E) The queen bee's mate dies before the male eggs hatch.

Answer: D
Topic: 9.20
Skill: Factual Recall

53) Any gene located on a sex chromosome
   A) is called a recessive gene.
   B) is called a sex-linked gene.
   C) is called a dominant allele.
   D) will exhibit pleiotropy.
   E) will exhibit codominance.

Answer: B
Topic: 9.21
Skill: Factual Recall

54) Recessive X-linked traits are more likely to be expressed in a male fruit fly than a female fruit fly because
   A) males are haploid.
   B) the male's SRY gene doubles the chances that sex-linked genes are expressed.
   C) the male's phenotype results entirely from his single X-linked gene.
   D) the male chromosome is more fragile than the female chromosome.
   E) the male chromosome is more susceptible to mutations.

Answer: C
Topic: 9.21
Skill: Conceptual Understanding

55) A color-blind woman marries a man who is not color-blind. All of their sons, but none of their daughters, are color-blind. Which of the following statements correctly explains these results?
   A) The gene for color vision is incompletely dominant to the gene for sex determination.
   B) The gene for color vision is completely dominant to the gene for sex determination.
   C) The gene for color vision is codominant with the gene for sex determination.
   D) The gene for color vision is linked to the X chromosome.
   E) The gene for color vision is linked to the Y chromosome.

Answer: D
Topic: 9.22
Skill: Application

56) Sex-linked conditions are more common in men than in women because
  A) men acquire two copies of the defective gene during fertilization.
  B) men need to inherit only one copy of the recessive allele for the condition to be fully expressed.
  C) women simply do not develop the disease regardless of their genetic composition.
  D) the sex chromosomes are more active in men than in women.
  E) the genes associated with the sex-linked conditions are linked to the Y chromosome, which determines maleness.

Answer: B
Topic: 9.22
Skill: Factual Recall

57) According to scientists, about what percentage of men currently living in Central Asia may be descended from the Mongolian ruler Genghis Khan?
  A) 4%
  B) 8%
  C) 12%
  D) 25%
  E) 40%

Answer: B
Topic: 9.23-Evolution Connection
Skill: Factual Recall

58) Female inheritance patterns cannot be analyzed by simply studying the X chromosome because
  A) the X chromosome is too fragile for long-term analysis.
  B) the X chromosome is too susceptible to mutations.
  C) the X chromosome is obtained from both father and mother.
  D) the X chromosome is too difficult to isolate from the other chromosomes.
  E) the X chromosome is physically too large to analyze accurately.

Answer: C
Topic: 9.23-Evolution Connection
Skill: Conceptual Understanding

Art Questions

1)

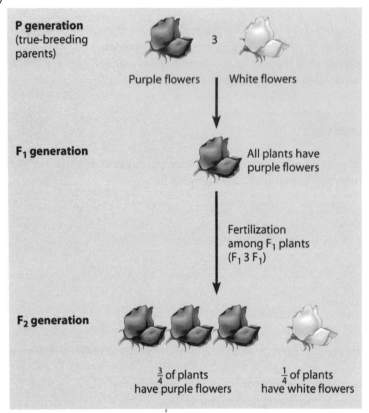

Which plants in this figure must all be heterozygous?
   A) purple–flowered plants in the P generation
   B) white–flowered plants in the P generation
   C) purple–flowered plants in the F1 generation
   D) purple–flowered plants in the F2 generation
   E) white–flowered plants in the F2 generation

Answer: C
Topic: 9.3
Skill: Application

2)

Genotypes:

HH
Homozygous
for ability to make
LDL receptors

Hh
Heterozygous

hh
Homozygous
for inability to make
LDL receptors

Phenotypes:

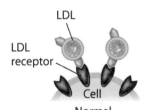

LDL

LDL
receptor

Cell

Normal

Mild disease

Severe disease

According to this figure, heterozygotes for this form of hypercholesterolemia suffer from the disease because they
- A) produce an abnormally shaped LDL receptor.
- B) don't produce any HDL receptors.
- C) don't produce any LDL receptors.
- D) produce too many LDL receptors.
- E) don't produce enough LDL receptors.

Answer: E
Topic: 9.11
Skill: Application

Scenario Questions

After reading the following paragraph, answer the question(s) below.

A woman has been trying to conceive for several years, unsuccessfully. At a fertility clinic, they discover that she has blocked fallopian tubes. Using modern technologies, some of her eggs are removed, fertilized with her husband's sperm, and implanted into her uterus. The procedure is successful, but the couple discovers that their new son is color–blind and has blood type O. The woman claims that the child can't be theirs since she has blood type A and her husband has type B. Also, neither parent is color–blind, although one grandparent (the woman's father) is also color–blind.

1) As a genetic counselor, you would explain to the parents that
- A) the eggs must have been accidentally switched, since the baby's blood type has to match one of his parents.
- B) each parent could have contributed one recessive allele, resulting in type O blood.
- C) the eggs must have been accidentally switched, since a type A parent and a type B parent can have any type children except O.
- D) it is possible for the baby to have type O blood, since type O is inherited through a dominant allele.
- E) the baby is theirs, since the blood types of parents have no relation to their children's blood types.

Answer: B
Topic: 9.12
Skill: Application

2) In regard to the baby's color blindness, a sex-linked recessive trait, you explain that
   A) color blindness often appears randomly, even if neither parent is color-blind.
   B) the baby's father must have a recessive allele for color blindness.
   C) since color blindness is sex-linked, a son can inherit color blindness if his mother has the recessive color blindness allele.
   D) the eggs must have been accidentally switched, since males inherit sex-linked traits only from their fathers.
   E) since color blindness is recessive, both parents can pass it on, even if neither is color-blind.

Answer: C
Topic: 9.21
Skill: Conceptual Understanding

Chapter 10 Molecular Biology of the Gene

Multiple-Choice Questions

1) Which of the following statements regarding viruses is *false*?
   A) A virus is generally considered to be alive because it is cellular and can reproduce on its own.
   B) The host cell provides most of the tools and raw materials for viral multiplication.
   C) Once a person is infected with the herpesvirus, the virus remains permanently latent in the body.
   D) Viruses can enter a host cell when the protein molecules on the outside of the virus fit into receptor molecules on the outside of the cell.
   E) Herpesviruses and the virus that causes AIDS can remain latent inside our cells for long periods of time.

   Answer: A
   Topic: Opening Essay
   Skill: Factual Recall

2) Which of the following people conducted the experiments that demonstrated that DNA is the genetic material of bacteriophages?
   A) Watson and Crick
   B) Hershey and Chase
   C) Franklin
   D) Griffith
   E) Pauling

   Answer: B
   Topic: 10.1
   Skill: Factual Recall

3) One type of virus that infects bacteria is called a
   A) phage.
   B) mage.
   C) rhinovirus.
   D) filovirus.
   E) coronavirus.

   Answer: A
   Topic: 10.1
   Skill: Factual Recall

4) When a T2 bacteriophage infects an *Escherichia coli* cell, which part of the phage enters the bacterial cytoplasm?
   A) the whole phage
   B) only the RNA
   C) only the DNA
   D) the protein "headpiece" and its enclosed nucleic acid
   E) the tail fibers

   Answer: C
   Topic: 10.1
   Skill: Factual Recall

5) The way that genetic material of a bacteriophage enters a bacterium is most like the way that
   A) a drug is injected with a hypodermic needle.
   B) a person swallows a pill.
   C) skin lotion is rubbed onto the hands.
   D) sugar dissolves in water.
   E) water soaks into a sponge.

Answer: A
Topic: 10.1
Skill: Conceptual Understanding

6) The monomers of DNA and RNA are
   A) amino acids.
   B) monosaccharides.
   C) nucleotides.
   D) fatty acids.
   E) nucleic acids.

Answer: C
Topic: 10.2
Skill: Factual Recall

7) Which of the following statements regarding DNA is *false*?
   A) DNA uses the sugar deoxyribose.
   B) DNA uses the nitrogenous base uracil.
   C) DNA is a nucleic acid.
   D) One DNA molecule can include four different nucleotides in its structure.
   E) DNA molecules have a sugar–phosphate backbone.

Answer: B
Topic: 10.2
Skill: Factual Recall

8) Which of the following statements regarding RNA is *false*?
   A) RNA uses the sugar dextrose.
   B) RNA uses the nitrogenous base uracil.
   C) RNA is a nucleic acid.
   D) One RNA molecule can include four different nucleotides in its structure.
   E) RNA molecules have a sugar–phosphate backbone.

Answer: A
Topic: 10.2
Skill: Factual Recall

9) Which of the following statements regarding the structure of DNA is *false*?
   A) The DNA molecule has a uniform diameter.
   B) In a DNA molecule, adenine bonds to thymine and guanine to cytosine.
   C) The DNA molecule is in the form of a double helix.
   D) Watson and Crick received a Nobel Prize for their description of the structure of DNA.
   E) The sequence of nucleotides along the length of a DNA strand is restricted by the base–pairing rules.

Answer: E
Topic: 10.3
Skill: Factual Recall

10) How would the shape of a DNA molecule change if adenine paired with guanine and cytosine paired with thymine?
   A) The DNA molecule would be longer.
   B) The DNA molecule would be shorter.
   C) The DNA molecule would be circular.
   D) The DNA molecule would have regions where no base–pairing would occur.
   E) The DNA molecule would have irregular widths along its length.

Answer: E
Topic: 10.3
Skill: Conceptual Understanding

11) The shape of a DNA molecule is most like
   A) a set of railroad tracks.
   B) a diamond ring.
   C) a twisted rope ladder.
   D) a gold necklace.
   E) the letter X.

Answer: C
Topic: 10.3
Skill: Conceptual Understanding

12) Which of the following statements regarding a DNA double helix is *always true*?
   A) The amount of adenine is equal to the amount of uracil, and the amount of guanine is equal to the amount of cytosine.
   B) The amount of adenine is equal to the amount of thymine, and the amount of guanine is equal to the amount of uracil.
   C) The amount of adenine is equal to the amount of guanine, and the amount of thymine is equal to the amount of cytosine.
   D) The amount of adenine is equal to the amount of cytosine, and the amount of guanine is equal to the amount of thymine.
   E) The amount of adenine is equal to the amount of thymine, and the amount of guanine is equal to the amount of cytosine.

Answer: E
Topic: 10.3
Skill: Factual Recall

13) DNA replication
    A) occurs through the addition of nucleotides to the end of the DNA molecule.
    B) results in the formation of four new DNA strands.
    C) produces two daughter DNA molecules that are complementary to each other.
    D) uses each strand of a DNA molecule as a template for the creation of a new strand.
    E) begins when two DNA molecules join together to exchange segments.

Answer: D
Topic: 10.4
Skill: Factual Recall

14) If one strand of DNA is CGGTAC, the corresponding strand would be
    A) GCCTAG.
    B) CGGTAC.
    C) GCCAUC.
    D) TAACGT.
    E) GCCATG.

Answer: E
Topic: 10.4
Skill: Application

15) The copying mechanism of DNA is most like
    A) using a photographic negative to make a positive image.
    B) mixing flour, sugar, and water to make bread dough.
    C) joining together links to make a chain.
    D) carving a figure out of wood.
    E) threading beads onto a string.

Answer: A
Topic: 10.4
Skill: Conceptual Understanding

16) When one DNA molecule is copied to make two DNA molecules, the new DNA contains
    A) none of the parent DNA.
    B) 25% of the parent DNA.
    C) 50% of the parent DNA.
    D) 75% of the parent DNA.
    E) 100% of the parent DNA

Answer: C
Topic: 10.4
Skill: Factual Recall

17) Multiple origins of replication on the DNA molecules of eukaryotic cells serve to
    A) remove errors in DNA replication.
    B) create multiple copies of the DNA molecule at the same time.
    C) shorten the time necessary for DNA replication.
    D) reduce the number of "bubbles" that occur in the DNA molecule during replication.
    E) assure the correct orientation of the two strands in the newly growing double helix.

Answer: C
Topic: 10.5
Skill: Factual Recall

18) Which of the following enzymes catalyzes the elongation of a new DNA strand?
   A) helicase
   B) primase
   C) ligase
   D) single-stranded binding protein
   E) DNA polymerase

Answer: E
Topic: 10.5
Skill: Factual Recall

19) Why does a DNA strand grow only in the 5' to 3' direction?
   A) because DNA polymerases can only add nucleotides to the 3' end of the growing molecule
   B) because DNA polymerases can only add nucleotides to the 5' end of the growing molecule
   C) because mRNA can only read a DNA molecule in the 5' to 3' direction
   D) because the DNA molecule only unwinds in the 5' to 3' direction
   E) because DNA polymerase requires the addition of a starter nucleotide at the 5' end

Answer: A
Topic: 10.5
Skill: Factual Recall

20) Which of the following options best depicts the flow of information when a gene directs the synthesis of a cellular component?
   A) RNA → DNA → RNA → protein
   B) DNA → RNA → protein
   C) protein → RNA → DNA
   D) DNA → amino acid → RNA → protein
   E) DNA → tRNA → mRNA → protein

Answer: B
Topic: 10.6
Skill: Factual Recall

21) The transfer of genetic information from DNA to RNA is called
   A) translation.
   B) transcription.
   C) initiation.
   D) elongation.
   E) promotion.

Answer: B
Topic: 10.6
Skill: Factual Recall

22) The "one gene–one polypeptide" theory states that
 A) the synthesis of each gene is catalyzed by one specific enzyme.
 B) the synthesis of each enzyme is catalyzed by one specific gene.
 C) the function of an individual gene is to dictate the production of a specific polypeptide.
 D) each polypeptide catalyzes a specific reaction.
 E) the function of each polypeptide is to regulate the synthesis of each corresponding gene.

Answer: C
Topic: 10.6
Skill: Conceptual Understanding

23) Experiments have demonstrated that the "words" of the genetic code (the units that specify amino acids) are
 A) single nucleotides.
 B) two–nucleotide sequences.
 C) three–nucleotide sequences.
 D) nucleotide sequences of various lengths.
 E) enzymes.

Answer: C
Topic: 10.7
Skill: Factual Recall

24) The directions for each amino acid in a polypeptide are indicated by a codon that consists of _____ nucleotide(s) in an RNA molecule.
 A) 5
 B) 4
 C) 3
 D) 2
 E) 1

Answer: C
Topic: 10.8
Skill: Factual Recall

25) We would expect that a 15–nucleotide sequence will direct the production of a polypeptide that consists of
 A) 2 amino acids.
 B) 3 amino acids.
 C) 4 amino acids.
 D) 5 amino acids.
 E) 6 amino acids.

Answer: C
Topic: 10.8
Skill: Application

26) A base substitution mutation in a gene does not always result in a different protein. Which of the following factors could account for this?
   A) the fact that the mutation affects only the sequence of the protein's amino acids, so the protein stays the same
   B) the double-ring structure of adenine and guanine
   C) a correcting mechanism that is part of the mRNA molecule
   D) the fact that such mutations are usually accompanied by a complementary deletion
   E) the fact that some amino acids are specified from more than one codon

Answer: E
Topic: 10.8
Skill: Conceptual Understanding

27) Which of the following enzymes catalyzes the linking together of RNA nucleotides to form RNA?
   A) RNA polymerase
   B) RNA ligase
   C) a ribozyme
   D) reverse transcriptase
   E) tRNA

Answer: A
Topic: 10.9
Skill: Factual Recall

28) Which of the following occurs when RNA polymerase attaches to the promoter DNA?
   A) elongation of the growing RNA molecule
   B) termination of the RNA molecule
   C) addition of nucleotides to the DNA template
   D) initiation of a new RNA molecule
   E) initiation of a new polypeptide chain

Answer: D
Topic: 10.9
Skill: Conceptual Understanding

29) _____ marks the end of a gene and causes transcription to stop.
   A) RNA polymerase
   B) RNA ligase
   C) A terminator
   D) Reverse transcriptase
   E) Methionine

Answer: C
Topic: 10.9
Skill: Factual Recall

30) Where do transcription and translation occur in prokaryotic cells?
   A) on the plasma membrane
   B) in the nucleus
   C) in the cytoplasm
   D) in chromatophores
   E) in the cell wall

Answer: C
Topic: 10.10
Skill: Factual Recall

31) Which of the following statements about eukaryotic RNA is *true*?
   A) Introns are added to the RNA.
   B) Exons are spliced together.
   C) A small cap of extra nucleotides is added to both ends of the RNA.
   D) A long tail of extra nucleotides is removed from the 5' end of the RNA.
   E) The modified RNA molecule is transported into the nucleus.

Answer: B
Topic: 10.10
Skill: Factual Recall

32) Which of the following takes place during translation?
   A) the conversion of genetic information from the language of nucleic acids to the language of proteins
   B) the conversion of genetic information from DNA nucleotides into RNA nucleotides
   C) the addition of nucleotides to a DNA template
   D) the conversion of genetic information from the language of proteins to the language of enzymes
   E) DNA replication

Answer: A
Topic: 10.11
Skill: Conceptual Understanding

33) Which of the following is a function of tRNA?
   A) joining to several types of amino acid
   B) recognizing the appropriate anticodons in mRNA
   C) transferring nucleotides to rRNA
   D) helping to translate codons into nucleic acids
   E) joining to only one specific type of amino acid

Answer: E
Topic: 10.11
Skill: Factual Recall

34) Which of the following is *not* needed in order for translation to occur?
   A) DNA template
   B) ribosomes
   C) tRNA
   D) various enzymes and protein "factors"
   E) sources of energy, including ATP

Answer: A
Topic: 10.11, 10.12
Skill: Conceptual Understanding

35) Which of the following statements about ribosomes is *false*?
  A) A ribosome consists of two subunits.
  B) Subunits of RNA are made of proteins and ribosomal RNA.
  C) The ribosomes of prokaryotes and eukaryotes are the same in structure and function.
  D) Each ribosome has two binding sites for tRNA.
  E) Ribosomes coordinate the functioning of mRNA and tRNA.

Answer: C
Topic: 10.12
Skill: Factual Recall

36) Which of the following statements is *false*?
  A) Translation consists of initiation, elongation, and termination.
  B) During polypeptide initiation, an mRNA, the first amino acid attached to its tRNA, and the two subunits of a ribosome are brought together.
  C) An mRNA molecule transcribed from DNA is shorter than the genetic message it carries.
  D) During the first step of initiation, an mRNA molecule binds to a small ribosomal subunit.
  E) During the second step of initiation, a large ribosomal subunit binds to a small ribosomal subunit.

Answer: C
Topic: 10.13
Skill: Factual Recall

37) Which of the following options most accurately lists the sequence of events in translation?
  A) codon recognition → translocation → peptide bond formation → termination
  B) peptide bond formation → codon recognition → translocation → termination
  C) codon recognition → peptide bond formation → translocation → termination
  D) codon recognition → peptide bond formation → termination → translocation
  E) peptide bond formation → translocation → codon recognition → termination

Answer: C
Topic: 10.14
Skill: Conceptual Understanding

38) Which of the following statements regarding the flow of genetic information is *false*?
  A) Polypeptides form proteins that determine the appearance and function of the cell and organism.
  B) Eukaryotic mRNA is processed in several ways before export out of the nucleus.
  C) The codons in a gene specify the amino acid sequence of a polypeptide.
  D) Transcription occurs in the cytoplasm of eukaryotic cells.
  E) Ribosomes function as factories that coordinate the functioning of mRNA and tRNA.

Answer: D
Topic: 10.15
Skill: Conceptual Understanding

39) Any change in the nucleotide sequence of DNA is called
   A) a mutation.
   B) an advantage.
   C) a codon.
   D) a translation.
   E) an anticodon.

Answer: A
Topic: 10.16
Skill: Factual Recall

40) Consider the following sentence: "The dog did not eat." Which of the following variations of this sentence is most like a base substitution mutation?
   A) The dog did not et.
   B) The dog dog did not eat.
   C) The did dog not eat.
   D) The doe did not eat.
   E) The dog did not.

Answer: D
Topic: 10.16
Skill: Application

41) Consider the following sentence: "The dog did not eat." Which of the following variations of this sentence is most like a reading frame mutation?
   A) The dog dog did not eat.
   B) The did dog not eat.
   C) The dod idn ote at.
   D) The did not eat.
   E) The dog did dog did not eat.

Answer: C
Topic: 10.16
Skill: Application

42) A physical or chemical agent that changes the nucleotide sequence of DNA is called a(n)
   A) reverse transcriptase.
   B) terminator.
   C) transposon.
   D) mutagen.
   E) anticodon.

Answer: D
Topic: 10.16
Skill: Factual Recall

43) A protein shell enclosing a viral genome is known as a(n)
   A) capsule.
   B) envelope.
   C) phage.
   D) capsid.
   E) prophage.

Answer: D
Topic: 10.17
Skill: Factual Recall

44) Which of the following features characterizes the lytic cycle of a viral infection?
    A) The cycle typically ends when the host bacterium divides.
    B) The cycle typically leads to the lysis of the host cell.
    C) The viral DNA is inserted into a bacterial chromosome.
    D) The virus reproduces outside of the host cell.
    E) The viral genes typically remain inactive once they are inside the host cell.

Answer: B
Topic: 10.17
Skill: Conceptual Understanding

45) Which of the following statements is *false*?
    A) Some prophage genes can cause the transformation of a nonpathogenic bacterium into a form that causes human disease.
    B) Sometimes an environmental signal can trigger a switchover from the lysogenic to the lytic cycle.
    C) The lysogenic cycle always occurs inside of host cells.
    D) The lysogenic cycle typically results in the rapid lysis of all infected cells.
    E) During a lysogenic cycle, viral DNA replication typically occurs without destroying the host cell.

Answer: D
Topic: 10.17
Skill: Conceptual Understanding

46) Viral DNA incorporated into host cell DNA is known as a(n)
    A) capsid.
    B) prophage.
    C) envelope.
    D) phage.
    E) genome.

Answer: B
Topic: 10.17
Skill: Factual Recall

47) The envelope of a flu virus
    A) helps the virus enter the cell.
    B) is coded by viral genes.
    C) helps the virus insert its DNA into the host cell genome.
    D) changes rapidly, thereby helping the virus evade an immune system response.
    E) accounts for viral resistance to antibiotics.

Answer: A
Topic: 10.18
Skill: Conceptual Understanding

48) Which of the following statements about herpesviruses is *false*?
   A) Herpesviruses reproduce inside the host cell's mitochondria.
   B) Herpesviruses acquire their envelopes from the host cell nuclear membrane.
   C) Herpesviruses are DNA viruses.
   D) Herpesviruses may remain latent for long periods of time while inside the host cell nucleus.
   E) Herpesviruses may cause cold sores or genital sores to appear during times of physical or emotional stress.

Answer: A
Topic: 10.18
Skill: Factual Recall

49) Which of the following statements about plant viruses is *false*?
   A) Once in a plant, a virus can spread from cell to cell through plasmodesmata.
   B) The genetic material in most plant viruses is RNA.
   C) Preventing infections and breeding resistant plants can control viral infection in plants.
   D) To infect a plant, a virus must first get past the plant's epidermis.
   E) There are many successful ways to rid infected plants of a virus.

Answer: E
Topic: 10.18
Skill: Factual Recall

50) Which of the following statements regarding viral diseases is *false*?
   A) RNA viruses tend to have an unusually high rate of mutation because their RNA genomes cannot be corrected by proofreading.
   B) New viral diseases often emerge when a virus infects a new host species.
   C) Very few new human diseases have originated in other animals because the genetic differences are too great.
   D) Some new viral diseases arise as a result of a mutation of existing viruses.
   E) AIDS was around for decades before becoming a widespread epidemic.

Answer: C
Topic: 10.19–Evolution Connection
Skill: Factual Recall

51) What will be the most likely cause of a new avian flu pandemic like the 1918–1919 flu pandemic that killed approximately 40 million people worldwide?
   A) sexual promiscuity
   B) intravenous drug use and abuse
   C) easy viral transmission from person to person
   D) blood transfusions with tainted blood
   E) increased international travel at affordable rates

Answer: C
Topic: 10.19–Evolution Connection
Skill: Application

52) What kind of virus is HIV?
    A) a herpesvirus
    B) a paramyxovirus
    C) a retrovirus
    D) a complex virus
    E) a provirus

Answer: C
Topic: 10.20
Skill: Factual Recall

53) Which of the following enzymes does HIV use to synthesize DNA on an RNA template?
    A) ligase
    B) RNA polymerase
    C) terminator enzyme
    D) reverse transcriptase
    E) DNA convertase

Answer: D
Topic: 10.20
Skill: Factual Recall

54) HIV does the greatest damage to
    A) the adrenal glands.
    B) pancreatic cells.
    C) nervous tissue.
    D) gametes.
    E) white blood cells.

Answer: E
Topic: 10.20
Skill: Factual Recall

55) How do viroids harm the plants that are infected with them?
    A) by increasing the plants' metabolic rate
    B) by altering the plants' growth
    C) by reducing the plants' seed production
    D) by preventing leaf production
    E) by destroying the root system

Answer: B
Topic: 10.21
Skill: Factual Recall

56) Which of the following statements about the treatment or prevention for a prion infection is *true*?
- A) Antibiotic therapies such as penicillin are very effective cures.
- B) High doses of anti–inflammatory drugs such as ibuprofen reduce the symptoms of prion infections.
- C) Corticosteroid therapy is the only drug therapy that can reverse the effects of a prion infection.
- D) Preventative vaccines have recently been shown to be effective in preventing prion infections.
- E) There is no known treatment or cure for prion infections.

Answer: E
Topic: 10.21
Skill: Factual Recall

57) In the 1920s, Frederick Griffith conducted an experiment in which he mixed the dead cells of a bacterial strain that can cause pneumonia with live cells of a bacterial strain that cannot. When he cultured the live cells, some of the daughter colonies proved able to cause pneumonia. Which of the following processes of bacterial DNA transfer does this experiment demonstrate?
- A) transduction
- B) conjugation
- C) transformation
- D) transposition
- E) crossing over

Answer: C
Topic: 10.22
Skill: Application

58) Transduction
- A) is the direct transfer of DNA from one bacterium to another.
- B) occurs when a bacterium acquires DNA from the surrounding environment.
- C) is the result of crossing over.
- D) occurs when a phage transfers bacterial DNA from one bacterium to another.
- E) requires DNA polymerase.

Answer: D
Topic: 10.22
Skill: Factual Recall

59) Conjugation
- A) is the direct transfer of DNA from one bacterium to another.
- B) occurs when a bacterium acquires DNA from the surrounding environment.
- C) is the result of crossing over.
- D) occurs when a phage transfers bacterial DNA from one bacterium to another.
- E) requires DNA polymerase.

Answer: A
Topic: 10.22
Skill: Factual Recall

60) Conjugation, transformation, and transduction are all ways that bacteria
    A) reduce their DNA content.
    B) increase the amount of RNA in the cytoplasm.
    C) change their ribosomes to eukaryotic ribosomes.
    D) increase their genetic diversity.
    E) alter their oxygen requirements.

Answer: D
Topic: 10.22
Skill: Conceptual Understanding

61) A friend accidentally sends an email to you that contains a computer virus from his computer. Without knowing it, you infect your computer with the virus when you open the email. This process of spreading the computer virus using emails is most like which of the following processes?
    A) binary fission
    B) conjugation
    C) transduction
    D) transformation
    E) mitosis

Answer: C
Topic: 10.22
Skill: Application

62) When a bacterial cell with a chromosome–borne F factor conjugates with another bacterium, how is the transmitted donor DNA incorporated into the recipient's genome?
    A) It is substituted for the equivalent portion of the recipient's chromosome by the process of crossing over.
    B) It circularizes and becomes one of the recipient cell's plasmids.
    C) The genes on the donor DNA of which the recipient does not have a copy are added to the recipient chromosome; the remainder of the donor DNA is degraded.
    D) The DNA of the recipient cell replicates, and the donor DNA is added to the end of the recipient DNA.
    E) The donor and recipient DNA are both chopped into segments by restriction enzymes, and a new, composite chromosome is assembled from the fragments.

Answer: A
Topic: 10.23
Skill: Factual Recall

63) In many bacteria, genes that confer resistance to antibiotics are carried on
    A) factors.
    B) R plasmids.
    C) dissimilation plasmids.
    D) transposons.
    E) exons.

Answer: B
Topic: 10.23
Skill: Factual Recall

64) Conjugation between a bacterium that lacks an F factor (F⁻) and a bacterium that has an F factor on its chromosome (F⁺) would typically produce which of the following results?

    A) The F⁻ bacterium ends up carrying one or more plasmids from the F⁺ bacterium; the F⁺ bacterium is unchanged.

    B) The F⁺ bacterium ends up with a recombinant chromosome that carries some genes from the F⁻ bacterium, and the F⁻ bacterium ends up with an unaltered chromosome.

    C) The F⁺ bacterium ends up with a recombinant chromosome that carries some genes from the F⁻ bacterium, and the F⁻ bacterium ends up with a chromosome that lacks those genes.

    D) The F⁻ bacterium ends up with a recombinant chromosome that carries some genes from the F⁺ bacterium, and the F⁺ bacterium ends up with an unaltered chromosome.

    E) The F⁻ bacterium ends up with a recombinant chromosome that carries some genes from the F⁺ bacterium, and the F⁺ bacterium ends up with a chromosome that lacks those genes.

Answer: D
Topic: 10.23
Skill: Application

65) A functional F factor that is an R plasmid must contain all of the following elements *except*

    A) genes for making sex pili.
    B) genes for making the enzymes needed for conjugation.
    C) a site for making the proteins needed for conjugation.
    D) a site where DNA replication can begin.
    E) genes for enzymes that confer resistance to antibiotics.

Answer: C
Topic: 10.23
Skill: Conceptual Understanding

66) Which of the following human activities has contributed to an increase in the number of bacteria having R plasmids?

    A) nitrogen fixation by genetically engineered plants
    B) widespread use of childhood vaccination in developing countries
    C) improper use of restriction enzymes in research and medical facilities
    D) increased carcinogen exposure from excessive fossil fuel burning
    E) heavy use of antibiotics in medicine and in agriculture

Answer: E
Topic: 10.23
Skill: Conceptual Understanding

Art Questions

1)

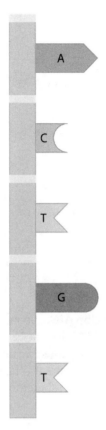

What nucleotide sequence would be found on the partner DNA strand of the strand shown?

    A) ACTGT
    B) UGAGA
    C) TGACA
    D) TGUGU
    E) TGTCA

Answer: C
Topic: 10.2, 10.3
Skill: Application

2)

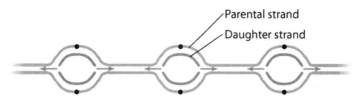

Parental strand
Daughter strand

How many origins of replication and how many replication forks are shown?
A) 3 origins and 3 replication forks
B) 3 origins and 6 replication forks
C) 6 origins and 3 replication forks
D) 6 origins and 6 replication forks
E) 6 origins and 12 replication forks
Answer: B
Topic: 10.5
Skill: Application

Scenario Questions

After reading the following paragraph, answer the question(s) below.

Exposure to the HIV virus doesn't necessarily mean that a person will develop AIDS. Some people have genetic resistance to infection by HIV. Dr. Stephen O'Brien from the U.S. National Cancer Institute has recently identified a mutant form of a gene, called CCR5, that can protect against HIV infection. The mutation probably originated in Europe among survivors of the bubonic plague. The mutated gene prevents the plague bacteria from attaching to cell membranes and, therefore, from entering and infecting body cells.

Although the HIV virus is very different from the bacteria that causes the plague, both diseases affect the exact same cells and use the same method of infection. The presence of the mutated gene in descendants of plague survivors helps prevent them from contracting AIDS. Pharmaceutical companies are using this information as the basis for a new approach to AIDS prevention. This would be very important in areas of the world where the mutation is scarce or absent, such as Africa.

1) The most likely method by which the mutated CCR5 gene prevents AIDS is by
A) covering the cell membrane.
B) rupturing the nuclear membrane.
C) attacking and destroying the HIV virus particles.
D) blocking transfer RNA from reaching the viral ribosomes.
E) coding for a protective protein in the cell membrane.
Answer: E
Topic: Opening Essay, 10.16, 10.19
Skill: Application

2) Which of the following shows the steps of a viral infection in the proper order?
   A) virus locates host cell → enters nucleus → alters host cell DNA → destroys cell
      membrane
   B) virus locates host cell → alters host cell DNA → host cell produces copies of virus
      → copies enter host cell nucleus → nucleus leaves cell
   C) virus kills host cell → enters nucleus → replaces all host DNA → releases copies of
      virus
   D) virus locates host cell → penetrates cell membrane → enters nucleus → alters host
      cell DNA → host cell produces copies of virus
   E) virus locates host cell → forms hydrogen bonds → changes DNA to RNA→ host
      cell produces copies of virus

Answer: D
Topic: Opening Essay, 10.16, 10.17
Skill: Factual Recall

Chapter 11   How Genes Are Controlled

Multiple-Choice Questions

1) Which of the following statements about the problems created by cloning is *false*?
   A) Cloned animals are less healthy than animals created by natural methods.
   B) Cloning does not increase genetic diversity in the cloned species.
   C) Cloning endangered species may de-emphasize the need to preserve critical natural habitats.
   D) Cloned animals live longer compared to naturally bred animals.
   E) Cloning leads to malfunctions in gene regulation.

   Answer: D
   Topic: Opening Essay
   Skill: Factual Recall

2) The fact that the nucleus from an adult somatic cell can be used to create all of the cell types in a new organism demonstrates that development depends upon
   A) the control of gene expression.
   B) the timing of mitosis and meiosis.
   C) the timing of meiosis and cell migrations.
   D) the deposition of materials in the extracellular matrix.
   E) the position of cells within an embryo.

   Answer: A
   Topic: Opening Essay
   Skill: Conceptual Understanding

3) The term "gene expression" refers to the
   A) fact that each individual of a species has a unique set of genes.
   B) fact that individuals of the same species have different phenotypes.
   C) process by which genetic information flows from genes to proteins.
   D) fact that certain genes are visible as dark stripes on a chromosome.
   E) flow of information from parent to offspring.

   Answer: C
   Topic: 11.1
   Skill: Conceptual Understanding

4) A gene operon consists of
   A) a transcribed gene only.
   B) a promoter only.
   C) a regulatory gene only.
   D) transcribed genes, an operator, and a promoter.
   E) transcribed genes, a promoter, and a regulatory gene.

   Answer: D
   Topic: 11.1
   Skill: Factual Recall

5) In a prokaryote, a group of genes with related functions, along with their associated control sequences, defines
   A) an allele.
   B) an operon.
   C) a locus.
   D) a transposon.
   E) a chromosome.

Answer: B
Topic: 11.1
Skill: Factual Recall

6) The *lac* operon in *E. coli*
   A) prevents lactose–utilizing enzymes from being expressed when lactose is absent from the environment.
   B) coordinates the production of tryptophan–utilizing enzymes when it is present.
   C) allows the bacterium to resist antibiotics in the penicillin family.
   D) regulates the rate of binary fission.
   E) uses activators to initiate the production of enzymes that break down lactose.

Answer: A
Topic: 11.1
Skill: Conceptual Understanding

7) Proteins that bind to DNA and turn on operons by making it easier for RNA polymerase to bind to a promoter are called
   A) regulators.
   B) inhibitors.
   C) operators.
   D) activators.
   E) repressors.

Answer: D
Topic: 11.1
Skill: Factual Recall

8) The *lac* operon of *E. coli* is _____ when the repressor is bound to lactose.
   A) active
   B) inactive
   C) elongated
   D) cloned
   E) unregulated

Answer: A
Topic: 11.1
Skill: Factual Recall

9) The expression of the tryptophan operon is controlled by
   A) a repressor that is active when it is alone.
   B) a repressor that is inactive when it binds to lactose.
   C) a repressor that is active when it binds to tryptophan.
   D) an activator that turns the operon on by binding to DNA.
   E) an activator that permanently deletes genes in the tryptophan operon.

Answer: C
Topic: 11.1
Skill: Conceptual Understanding

10) Which of the following is likely to occur in *E. coli* cells that are grown in skim milk?
   A) The *lac* operon is shut off and the cells will not produce lactose–utilizing enzymes.
   B) The *trp* repressor is activated and the cells will produce lactose–utilizing enzymes.
   C) The *trp* operon is turned on but the bacteria will not produce lactose–utilizing enzymes.
   D) The *trp* operon and the *lac* operon are both switched off.
   E) The *trp* operon and the *lac* operon are both switched on.

Answer: B
Topic: 11.1
Skill: Conceptual Understanding

11) A single cell, the zygote, can develop into an entirely new organism with many different specialized cells. Which of the following statements about this process is *false*?
   A) Additional genetic information for the formation of specialized cells is passed on to the developing embryo via the placenta.
   B) The descendant cells specialize by a process known as cellular differentiation.
   C) The zygote contains all of the genetic information required for the development of many different cell types.
   D) Only some of the genes in the zygote are expressed in all of its descendant cells.
   E) Differentiation of the zygote into a multicellular organism results from selective gene expression.

Answer: A
Topic: 11.2
Skill: Conceptual Understanding

12) The genes for the enzymes of glycolysis
   A) are active in all metabolizing cells, but the genes for specialized proteins are expressed only in particular cell types.
   B) are inactive in all metabolizing cells, but the genes for specialized proteins are expressed in all cell types.
   C) and the genes for all specialized proteins are expressed in all metabolizing cells.
   D) and the genes for specialized proteins are expressed in all nonembryonic cell types.
   E) and the genes for all specialized proteins are expressed in all embryonic cells.

Answer: A
Topic: 11.2
Skill: Conceptual Understanding

13) Which of the following statements regarding DNA packing is *false*?
   A) A nucleosome consists of DNA wound around a protein core of eight histone molecules.
   B) DNA packing tends to promote gene expression.
   C) Histones account for about half the mass of eukaryotic chromosomes.
   D) Highly compacted chromatin is generally not expressed at all.
   E) Prokaryotes have proteins analogous to histones.

Answer: B
Topic: 11.3
Skill: Factual Recall

14) The relationship between DNA and chromosomes is most like
   A) an egg yolk inside of an egg.
   B) a dozen eggs packaged within an egg carton.
   C) a spoon cradling some peas.
   D) thread wrapped around a spool.
   E) the candy shell surrounding the chocolate in a piece of M & M candy.

Answer: D
Topic: 11.3
Skill: Conceptual Understanding

15) In female mammals, the inactive X chromosome in each cell
   A) becomes a nucleotroph corpus.
   B) can be activated if mutations occur in the active X chromosome.
   C) is broken down, and its nucleotides are degraded and reused.
   D) is absorbed and used in energy production.
   E) becomes a Barr body.

Answer: E
Topic: 11.4
Skill: Conceptual Understanding

16) The tortoiseshell pattern on a cat
   A) usually occurs in males.
   B) is the result of a homozygous recessive condition.
   C) results from X chromosome inactivation.
   D) is a result of alleles on the Y chromosome.
   E) occurs in male cats 25% of the time and in female cats 50% of the time.

Answer: C
Topic: 11.4
Skill: Conceptual Understanding

17) Both prokaryotic and eukaryotic cells use _____ to turn certain genes on or off.
   A) DNA ligase
   B) RNA transcriptase
   C) intron segments
   D) regulatory proteins
   E) nucleosome packing

Answer: D
Topic: 11.5
Skill: Factual Recall

18) Enhancers are
   A) adjacent to the gene that they regulate.
   B) required to turn on gene expression when transcription factors are in short supply.
   C) the site on DNA to which activators bind.
   D) required to facilitate the binding of DNA polymerases.
   E) the products of transcription factors.

Answer: C
Topic: 11.5
Skill: Factual Recall

19) Silencers are sites in DNA that
   A) bind RNA promoters to promote the start of transcription.
   B) bind enhancers to promote the start of transcription.
   C) bind repressor proteins to inhibit the start of transcription.
   D) bind activators to inhibit the start of transcription.
   E) release mRNA.

Answer: C
Topic: 11.5
Skill: Factual Recall

20) RNA splicing involves the
   A) addition of a nucleotide "cap" to the molecule.
   B) addition of a nucleotide "tail" to the molecule.
   C) removal of introns from the molecule.
   D) removal of exons from the molecule.
   E) addition of introns to the molecule.

Answer: C
Topic: 11.6
Skill: Factual Recall

21) The coding regions of a gene (the portions that are expressed as polypeptide sequences) are called
   A) introns.
   B) exons.
   C) redundant coding sections.
   D) proto–oncogenes.
   E) nucleosomes.

Answer: B
Topic: 11.6
Skill: Factual Recall

22) Which of the following permits a single gene to code for more than one polypeptide?
   A) retention of different introns in the final version of the different mRNA strands
   B) alternative RNA splicing
   C) protein degradation
   D) genetic differentiation
   E) addition of different types of caps and tails to the final version of the mRNA strands

Answer: B
Topic: 11.6
Skill: Factual Recall

23) Small pieces of RNA that can regulate mRNA transcription are called
    A) microRNA.
    B) minuteRNA.
    C) miniRNA.
    D) monoRNA.
    E) minorRNA.

Answer: A
Topic: 11.7
Skill: Factual Recall

24) miRNA can be used by
    A) researchers to induce the production of more mRNA.
    B) researchers to stimulate the production of DNA.
    C) researchers to artificially turn on gene expression.
    D) viruses to stop the production of new proteins.
    E) cells to prevent infections from double–stranded RNA viruses.

Answer: E
Topic: 11.7
Skill: Factual Recall

25) Which of the following statements regarding RNA and proteins is *false*?
    A) Some genes are edited before they are translated.
    B) Some polypeptides are edited to make them functional.
    C) The length of time that mRNA remains functional in the cytoplasm is quite variable.
    D) In eukaryotes, the lifetime of a protein is closely regulated.
    E) In eukaryotes, one gene controls the production of just one functioning protein.

Answer: E
Topic: 11.6, 11.8
Skill: Factual Recall

26) All of the following mechanisms are used to regulate protein production *except*
    A) controlling the start of polypeptide synthesis.
    B) protein activation.
    C) protein breakdown.
    D) DNA editing.
    E) the breakdown of mRNA.

Answer: D
Topic: 11.8
Skill: Factual Recall

27) The textbook authors' analogy between the regulation of gene expression and the movement of water through pipes includes all of the following *except*
    A) the web of control that connects different genes.
    B) pretranscriptional events.
    C) post–transcriptional events.
    D) the editing of RNA.
    E) the multiple mechanisms by which gene expression is regulated.

Answer: A
Topic: 11.9
Skill: Factual Recall

28) Which of the following mechanisms of controlling gene expression occurs outside of the nucleus?
A) adding a cap and tail to RNA
B) transcription
C) DNA packing/unpacking
D) RNA splicing
E) translation

Answer: E
Topic: 11.9
Skill: Factual Recall

29) Which of the following statements about fruit fly development is *false*?
A) One of the earliest development events is the determination of the head and tail ends of the egg.
B) The location of the head and tail ends of the egg is primarily determined by the location of sperm entry during fertilization.
C) Cell signaling plays an important role in the development of fruit flies.
D) Homeotic genes regulate batteries of other genes that direct the anatomical identity of body parts.
E) Cascades of gene expression routinely direct fruit fly development.

Answer: B
Topic: 11.10
Skill: Factual Recall

30) A homeotic gene
A) turns on the genes necessary for synthesis of proteins.
B) serves as a master control gene that functions during embryonic development by controlling the developmental fate of groups of cells.
C) represses gene transcription and promotes mRNA translation.
D) produces a product that controls the transcription of other genes.
E) is found only in adult somatic cells.

Answer: B
Topic: 11.10
Skill: Conceptual Understanding

31) Which of the following statements about microarrays is *false*?
A) Microarrays enable scientists to determine the activity of thousands of genes at once.
B) Microarrays use tiny portions of double-stranded RNA fragments from a large number of genes.
C) Microarrays are used to determine which genes are active in different tissues or in tissues of different states of health.
D) Microarrays use fluorescently labeled cDNA molecules to identify particular genes expressed at a particular time.
E) Microarrays help scientists understand how genes interact, particularly during embryonic development.

Answer: B
Topic: 11.11
Skill: Factual Recall

32) Animal development is directed by
    A) cell receptors that detect transcription factors.
    B) the availability of certain "key" nutrients as cells divide.
    C) signal transduction pathways.
    D) cell–to–cell signaling.
    E) cell–to–cell signaling and signal transduction pathways.

Answer: E
Topic: 11.10, 11.12
Skill: Factual Recall

33) To initiate a signal transduction pathway, a signal binds to a receptor protein usually located in the
    A) cytosol.
    B) nucleus.
    C) plasma membrane.
    D) ER.
    E) cytoplasm.

Answer: C
Topic: 11.12
Skill: Factual Recall

34) Transcription factors attach to
    A) DNA.
    B) signal molecules.
    C) plasma membrane receptors.
    D) proteins.
    E) mRNA.

Answer: A
Topic: 11.12
Skill: Factual Recall

35) A signal outside a cell triggers changes in the transcription and translation inside the cell through the process of
    A) post–translational editing.
    B) signal transduction pathways.
    C) protein activation.
    D) protein breakdown.
    E) X chromosome inactivation.

Answer: B
Topic: 11.12
Skill: Conceptual Understanding

36) The basis of cellular differentiation is
    A) the operon.
    B) cellular specialization.
    C) selective gene expression.
    D) cloning.
    E) mutation.

Answer: C
Topic: 11.12, 11.14
Skill: Conceptual Understanding

37) Yeast are able to communicate with each other
   A) by close cell–to–cell contact.
   B) with signal transduction pathways.
   C) only if they can touch each other and have merged cell walls.
   D) with pseudopodia.
   E) only when a yeast cell has died and released its internal organelles into the external environment.

Answer: B
Topic: 11.13–Evolution Connection
Skill: Conceptual Understanding

38) Signal transduction pathways
   A) are found strictly in multicellular organisms for cell–to–cell communication.
   B) first appeared in animals when primates began to walk upright.
   C) are limited for use in sexual identification.
   D) originally evolved in vertebrates.
   E) are mechanisms of communication that evolved in the ancient prokaryotes.

Answer: E
Topic: 11.13–Evolution Connection
Skill: Conceptual Understanding

39) Most differentiated cells retain
   A) only a tiny fraction of their original set of genes.
   B) only a tiny fraction of their original set of genes, but can regenerate lost genes as needed.
   C) a complete set of their genes, but lose the ability to express most of those genes.
   D) a complete set of their genes, and retain the ability to express those genes under certain circumstances.
   E) the ability to dedifferentiate, but then cannot return to their original differentiated state.

Answer: D
Topic: 11.14
Skill: Conceptual Understanding

40) Why can some plants be cloned from a single cell?
   A) Plant cells do not differentiate even when mature, so any cell can grow into an entire plant.
   B) Plant cells can dedifferentiate and give rise to all of the specialized cells required to produce an entire plant.
   C) Plant cells are able to retrieve genes lost to the environment during development.
   D) Plant cells can produce genes to replace those lost during development.
   E) Plant cells are capable of self-renewal by utilizing cellular components from adjacent cells .

Answer: B
Topic: 11.14
Skill: Conceptual Understanding

41) Which of the following processes occurs when a salamander regenerates a lost limb?
   A) Oncogenes that cause accelerated cell division are turned on.
   B) Certain cells in the limb dedifferentiate, divide, and then redifferentiate to form a new limb.
   C) A new salamander develops from the lost limb.
   D) The homeotic genes of the regenerating cells turn off.
   E) The cell cycle is arrested and apoptosis begins.

Answer: B
Topic: 11.14
Skill: Conceptual Understanding

42) The cloning of Dolly the sheep
   A) demonstrated that the nuclei from differentiated mammalian cells can retain their full genetic potential.
   B) demonstrated that differentiated cells contain only a fraction of their full genetic potential.
   C) demonstrated, for the first time, that eggs are haploid and body cells are diploid.
   D) revealed that cloned mammals most resemble the egg donor.
   E) revealed that cloned mammals most resemble the sperm donor.

Answer: A
Topic: 11.15
Skill: Factual Recall

43) Cloning to produce embryonic stem cells is called
   A) regenerative cloning.
   B) transplantational cloning.
   C) reproductive cloning.
   D) therapeutic cloning.
   E) dedifferentiation.

Answer: D
Topic: 11.15
Skill: Factual Recall

44) Which of the following mammals has not yet been cloned and brought through the complete gestation cycle?
   A) cow
   B) human
   C) pig
   D) dog
   E) cat

Answer: B
Topic: 11.16
Skill: Conceptual Understanding

45) Which of the following possible uses of reproductive cloning is still considered by most to be an unresolved ethical issue?
    A) the production of genetically identical animals for experimentation
    B) the production of potentially valuable drugs
    C) the production of organs in pigs for transplant into humans
    D) the improvement of the quality of farm animals
    E) the production of genetically identical humans for therapeutic purposes.

Answer: E
Topic: 11.16
Skill: Conceptual Understanding

46) Which of the following statements regarding stem cells is *false*?
    A) Embryonic stem cells can be induced to differentiate.
    B) Embryonic stem cells can give rise to all the different specialized cells in the body.
    C) Adult, but not embryonic, stem cells can be grown in laboratory culture.
    D) Adult stem cells are present in adult tissues.
    E) Adult stem cells are partway along the road to differentiation.

Answer: C
Topic: 11.17
Skill: Factual Recall

47) Adult stem cells have limited therapeutic potential
    A) because they are fully differentiated.
    B) because they lack a complete set of genes.
    C) due to their excessive numbers in tissues.
    D) because scientists have no reliable method of identification.
    E) because their developmental potential is limited to certain tissues.

Answer: E
Topic: 11.17
Skill: Factual Recall

48) A gene that can cause cancer when present in a single copy in a cell is called a(n)
    A) oncogene.
    B) enhancer gene.
    C) silencer gene.
    D) carcinogen.
    E) proto-oncogene.

Answer: A
Topic: 11.18
Skill: Factual Recall

49) Which of the following statements about proto-oncogenes is *false*?
    A) Proto-oncogenes are normal genes with the potential to become oncogenes.
    B) Many proto-oncogenes code for growth factors.
    C) A mutation must occur in a cell's DNA for a proto-oncogene to become an oncogene.
    D) A mutation in a tumor-suppressor gene can stop cell division immediately.
    E) One of the earliest clues to understanding cancer was the discovery of a virus that causes cancer in chickens.

Answer: D
Topic: 11.18
Skill: Factual Recall

50) Which of the following is *not* a factor that contributes to normal cells becoming cancerous?
    A) the conversion of a proto-oncogene to an oncogene
    B) damage to a tumor-suppressor gene
    C) the acquisition of an oncogene from a virus
    D) one or more of the cell's genes being removed by a virus
    E) excessive replication of proto-oncogenes

Answer: D
Topic: 11.18
Skill: Conceptual Understanding

51) Cancer of the colon is caused by
    A) a single gene mutation.
    B) several somatic cell mutations.
    C) exposure of colon cells to a mutagen.
    D) lack of vitamin K.
    E) the proto-oncogene, *lac*.

Answer: B
Topic: 11.19
Skill: Factual Recall

52) The development of colon cancer occurs slowly and is more prominent in the elderly than the young. This is most likely because
    A) cancer cells don't have mitochondria, so they grow slowly.
    B) four or more somatic mutations must occur to give rise to the cancer, which takes time.
    C) cancer cells suppress the growth of each other in a tissue.
    D) cancer cells have to wait until new blood vessels grow into the area, which takes much time.
    E) most cancer mutations interfere with mitosis, so cell division occurs more slowly.

Answer: B
Topic: 11.19
Skill: Conceptual Understanding

53) Mutations in the proto-oncogenes *ras* and *p53*
    A) increase protein synthesis by the cell.
    B) are rarely associated with cancers.
    C) can improve the chance of avoiding cancer as one ages.
    D) can enhance further mutations, which can develop into cancer.
    E) disrupt normal regulation of the cell cycle.

Answer: E
Topic: 11.20
Skill: Factual Recall

54) Mutations in the *p53* gene can lead to cancer by
    A) causing the production of excessive amounts of relay proteins.
    B) turning off a gene for a protein that inhibits cell division.
    C) increasing the production of glycogen, which nourishes the cell cycle.
    D) promoting the expression of mRNA that can interact with DNA, resulting in new
       mutations.
    E) increasing the production of growth hormones, which trigger faster cell cycles.

Answer: B
Topic: 11.20
Skill: Conceptual Understanding

55) The carcinogen known to cause the most cases of cancer is
    A) plutonium.
    B) ultraviolet light.
    C) alcohol.
    D) salt.
    E) tobacco.

Answer: E
Topic: 11.21
Skill: Factual Recall

56) Which of the following statements regarding cancer risk factors is *false*?
    A) Factors that alter DNA and make cells cancerous are called carcinogens.
    B) Mutagens are usually not carcinogens.
    C) X-rays and ultraviolet radiation are two of the most potent carcinogens.
    D) Eating 20-30 grams of plant fiber daily and reducing the intake of animal fat can
       reduce your risk of developing colon cancer.
    E) Broccoli and cauliflower are thought to be especially rich in substances that help
       prevent cancer.

Answer: B
Topic: 11.21
Skill: Factual Recall

Art Questions

1)

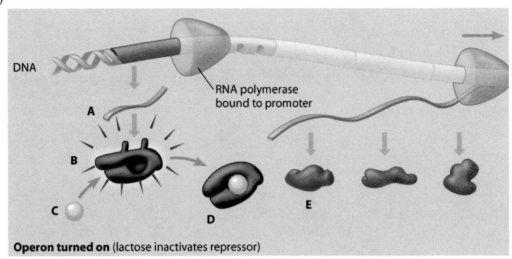

DNA

RNA polymerase
bound to promoter

A

B

C

D

E

Operon turned on (lactose inactivates repressor)

In this drawing of the *lac* operon, which molecule is an inactive repressor?

   A) molecule A
   B) molecule B
   C) molecule C
   D) molecule D
   E) molecule E

Answer: D
Topic: 11.1
Skill: Application

2)

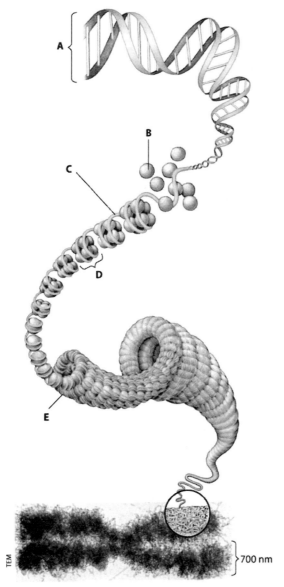

Metaphase chromosome

Which structure in this figure shows one complete nucleosome?

  A) structure A
  B) structure B
  C) structure C
  D) structure D
  E) structure E

Answer: D
Topic: 11.3
Skill: Factual Recall

Scenario Questions

After reading the following paragraph, answer the question(s) below.

All apples in the United States, regardless of variety or where they're purchased, are produced by cloning. For more than 2,000 years, apple growers around the world have used a type of cloning called grafting to produce larger, better-tasting apples. Why has cloning become the primary method of apple growing? Apples grown from seeds usually don't produce apples with the same taste and appearance as that of the parent tree because there's a high degree of genetic variability among the seeds. Making identical genetic copies of the preferred fruit is the only way to get reliable apple quality.

In grafting, the shoots and branches of the desired fruit, called a scion, are attached onto the trunk and root system of a previously existing tree, called the rootstock. Both components of the graft are needed. The rootstock controls gene expression in scion, triggering production of apples that match the cloned scion.

Grafting research can be used to produce some interesting tree combinations that are beneficial for intensive agriculture. For example, if you graft the root of a small tree variety, such as the crab apple, onto the shoot from a larger apple tree, such as the Gala, you can produce Gala apples on a much smaller tree. Other scientists are trying to create disease-resistant varieties that would need less pesticides. This is beneficial for the environment and also lowers the price of apples in the grocery store.

1) Why don't the grafted hybrids produce apples with a blend of traits from the scion and the rootstock?
   A) The rootstock suppresses activation of the scion genes, which alters fruit production.
   B) The rootstock is unable to perform photosynthesis and so can't produce fruit.
   C) Transplanted nuclei from scion cells regulate gene expression in the rootstock.
   D) The rootstock regulates gene expression in the scion, but contributes no genetic information for fruit production.
   E) The *lac* operon in the scion is the only regulator of gene expression in the hybrid.

Answer: D
Topic: 11.9, 11.14
Skill: Conceptual Understanding

2) Half the trees in an orchard were derived from rootstock "A" and half from rootstock "B," but all the trees had the same scion. If the trees grafted onto rootstock "A" were infected by a parasite that causes blossom rot, the trees grafted onto rootstock B
   A) would be less likely to become infected because they're grafted onto different rootstocks.
   B) would be more likely to become infected, since the pathogen would spread through the soil to the roots of other trees.
   C) would be very likely to become infected, because the remaining scions are genetically identical to those that are already infected.
   D) Only half of the remaining trees are likely to become infected because they're in a different location in the orchard.
   E) There's no way to determine the likelihood of infection, since genetic variability gives all the trees different characteristics.

Answer: C
Topic: 11.9, 11.14
Skill: Conceptual Understanding

Chapter 12 DNA Technology and Genomics

Multiple-Choice Questions

1) When DNA fingerprinting was first used,
   A) genetic evidence was collected using only DNA from blood.
   B) blood samples from the crime scene were used to match the blood of a person who confessed.
   C) the two semen samples did not match the person who initially confessed.
   D) genetic testing revealed that the two murdered girls were killed by two different people.
   E) the DNA evidence was not convincing enough to convict the suspect.

Answer: C
Topic: Opening Essay
Skill: Factual Recall

2) Biotechnology
   A) is a modern scientific discipline that has existed for only a few decades.
   B) is strictly concerned with the manipulation of DNA.
   C) has only been used successfully in the area of forensic science.
   D) has been around since the dawn of civilization.
   E) is generally considered more harmful than valuable to society.

Answer: D
Topic: 12.1
Skill: Factual Recall

3) When DNA from two sources is combined into one single piece of DNA, it is known as
   A) cloned DNA.
   B) recombinant DNA.
   C) a vector.
   D) a plasmid.
   E) a DNA library.

Answer: B
Topic: 12.1
Skill: Factual Recall

4) The production of multiple identical copies of gene-sized pieces of DNA defines
   A) gene cloning.
   B) plasmid transformation.
   C) clonal selection.
   D) tissue culturing.
   E) plasmolysis.

Answer: A
Topic: 12.1
Skill: Factual Recall

5) In the process of human gene cloning using recombinant plasmids, the bacterial plasmid
   A) functions as a vector.
   B) is the source of the gene to be cloned.
   C) is cultured inside the human cell, which contains the gene to be cloned.
   D) is used to insert the human gene into the bacterial chromosome.
   E) comes from the same organism as the gene of interest.

Answer: A
Topic: 12.1
Skill: Factual Recall

6) DNA ligase binds
   A) exons together.
   B) polymerase to the promotor.
   C) nucleotides together.
   D) introns together.
   E) an intron to an exon.

Answer: C
Topic: 12.1
Skill: Factual Recall

7) When plasmids are used to produce a desired protein,
   A) the plasmids are inserted into the bacterial chromosome.
   B) the plasmids multiply and produce the protein outside of the bacterium.
   C) the bacterial chromosome is genetically engineered and the plasmid is used to help the bacterium replicate.
   D) the desired gene is inserted into the plasmid and the plasmid is returned to the bacterium by transformation.
   E) the bacterial genome and plasmid are inserted into the genome of the cell containing the desired gene (perhaps the cell of a plant or animal).

Answer: D
Topic: 12.1
Skill: Factual Recall

8) _____ are a major source of restriction enzymes.
   A) Chief cells
   B) DNA technologies
   C) Parietal cells
   D) Archaea
   E) Bacteria

Answer: E
Topic: 12.2
Skill: Factual Recall

9) Restriction enzymes
    A) edit proteins.
    B) cut DNA at specific sites.
    C) stop transcription.
    D) bind together strands of DNA.
    E) bind RNA fragments together.

Answer: B
Topic: 12.2
Skill: Factual Recall

10) Restriction enzymes specifically recognize and cut short sequences of DNA called
    A) promoter sequences.
    B) short terminal repeats.
    C) sticky ends.
    D) DNA fragments.
    E) restriction sites.

Answer: E
Topic: 12.2
Skill: Factual Recall

11) "Sticky ends" are
    A) produced by the action of DNA ligase.
    B) produced by PCR.
    C) always long sequences of a single nucleotide.
    D) used by mRNA to attach to ribosomes.
    E) DNA fragments with single-stranded ends.

Answer: E
Topic: 12.2
Skill: Factual Recall

12) The feature of "sticky ends" that makes them especially useful in DNA recombination is their ability to
    A) bind to DNA and thereby activate transcription.
    B) bind to ribosomes and thereby activate translation.
    C) form hydrogen-bonded base pairs with complementary single-stranded stretches of DNA.
    D) allow plasmids to attach to the main bacterial chromosome.
    E) insert a segment of RNA into a bacterial chromosome.

Answer: C
Topic: 12.2
Skill: Conceptual Understanding

13) DNA fragments that have matching sticky ends are joined by covalent bonds formed by the action of
   A) DNA ligase.
   B) DNA polymerase.
   C) DNA helicase.
   D) covalentase.
   E) a restriction enzyme.

Answer: A
Topic: 12.2
Skill: Factual Recall

14) The _____ approach to gene cloning employs a mixture of fragments from the entire genome of an organism.
   A) HIV
   B) shotgun
   C) Ti
   D) AK–47
   E) V–protein

Answer: B
Topic: 12.2
Skill: Factual Recall

15) A collection of DNA fragments obtained from the genome of one organism, inserted by recombinant DNA techniques into the genome of a host organism (one fragment per host genome), and maintained there is called a
   A) DNA collection.
   B) genomic library.
   C) DNA file.
   D) gene bank.
   E) vector battery.

Answer: B
Topic: 12.3
Skill: Factual Recall

16) Genomic libraries can be constructed using either bacterial plasmids or what other vector?
   A) ribosomes
   B) tRNA
   C) human chromosomes
   D) phages
   E) endospore

Answer: D
Topic: 12.3
Skill: Factual Recall

17) Retroviruses such as HIV use _____ to convert information stored in their RNA to information stored in DNA.
   A) DNA ligase
   B) reverse transcriptase
   C) a restriction enzyme
   D) a terminator enzyme
   E) RNA polymerase

Answer: B
Topic: 12.4
Skill: Conceptual Understanding

18) A cDNA library differs from a genomic library in that
   A) the cDNA was constructed from introns only.
   B) genomic libraries are only stored in bacterial cells.
   C) the cDNA library contains more genes.
   D) cDNA libraries are more stable.
   E) cDNA libraries only contain information from active genes.

Answer: E
Topic: 12.4
Skill: Factual Recall

19) An advantage of using reverse transcriptase to prepare a gene for cloning is that
   A) reverse transcriptase is more efficient than RNA polymerase.
   B) the resulting DNA strand will lack exons.
   C) reverse transcriptase is more efficient than DNA polymerase.
   D) the resulting DNA strand will lack introns.
   E) RNA is the genetic material of bacteria.

Answer: D
Topic: 12.4
Skill: Factual Recall

20) A nucleic acid probe is
   A) a virus that transfers DNA to a recipient cell.
   B) a piece of radioactively labeled DNA that is used to locate a specific gene.
   C) an enzyme that locates a specific restriction site on RNA.
   D) a promoter site that is associated with a specific set of genes.
   E) a plasmid that recognizes a specific DNA sequence.

Answer: B
Topic: 12.5
Skill: Factual Recall

21) Which of the following statements about nucleic acid probes is *false*?
   A) A nucleic acid probe is a double-stranded section of DNA.
   B) A nucleic acid probe can be used to find a specific gene.
   C) A nucleic acid probe can be made of DNA or RNA.
   D) A nucleic acid probe bonds hydrogen to a complimentary sequence in the gene of interest.
   E) A nucleic acid probe is usually labeled with a radioactive isotope or fluorescent tag to help identify its location.

Answer: A
Topic: 12.5
Skill: Factual Recall

22) The type of recombinant bacteria most often used to mass-produce genes is
   A) *Pseudomonas aeruginosa.*
   B) *Agrobacterium tumefaciens.*
   C) *Escherichia coli.*
   D) *Rhizobium.*
   E) *Saccharomyces cerevisiae.*

Answer: C
Topic: 12.6
Skill: Factual Recall

23) The only recombinant cells that can correctly attach sugars to proteins to form glycoprotein products are
   A) yeast cells.
   B) *E. coli* cells.
   C) mammalian cells.
   D) algal cells.
   E) elm tree cells.

Answer: C
Topic: 12.6
Skill: Factual Recall

24) The advantage of being able to clone the gene for human insulin is that
   A) human insulin is more variable than other sources of insulin, so cloning provides a greater chance of obtaining a form that can be used by the diabetic's muscles.
   B) there are too few cows, pigs, and horses to provide an adequate supply of their insulin.
   C) human insulin is less likely to provoke an allergic reaction than cow, pig, or horse insulin.
   D) cow, pig, or horse insulin cannot keep a diabetic alive for more than three months.
   E) using human insulin increases the probability that, in the future, the person suffering from diabetes can be weaned from a dependence on insulin.

Answer: C
Topic: 12.7
Skill: Conceptual Understanding

25) A vaccine works by
    A) inhibiting bacterial replication.
    B) stimulating the immune system.
    C) inhibiting viral replication.
    D) preventing the translation of mRNA.
    E) stimulating the secretion of insulin.

Answer: B
Topic: 12.7
Skill: Factual Recall

26) Which of the following statements about DNA technology is *false*?
    A) DNA technology is now used to mass–produce human insulin.
    B) DNA technology is now used to mass–produce human growth hormone.
    C) DNA technology is now used to create cells that can identify and kill cancer cells.
    D) DNA technology is now used to produce vaccines that are harmless mutants of a
       pathogen.
    E) DNA technology is now used to produce vaccines that use the smallpox virus but
       replace some of the genes that produce immunity to smallpox with genes that
       produce immunity to other diseases.

Answer: C
Topic: 12.7
Skill: Factual Recall

27) Golden rice is golden in color because it is rich in
    A) vitamin A.
    B) vitamin C.
    C) beta–carotene.
    D) chromium picolinate.
    E) protein.

Answer: C
Topic: 12.8
Skill: Factual Recall

28) A transgenic animal is
    A) an animal that is the first of its kind to bear a particular allele.
    B) an animal in which a genetic defect has been corrected using recombinant DNA
       therapy.
    C) an animal containing a gene from a third "parent," which may even be another
       species.
    D) an animal containing genes from both its parents.
    E) an animal containing genes from three or more species.

Answer: C
Topic: 12.8
Skill: Factual Recall

29) Which of the following statements regarding genetically modified organisms is *false*?
   A) Transgenic animals have been engineered to be pharmaceutical factories.
   B) Golden rice is a transgenic plant that has been engineered to produce grains containing beta–carotene.
   C) The majority of American soybean and cotton crops are genetically modified.
   D) Genetic modification of plants increases the amount of tillage and use of chemical insecticides.
   E) GM plants have received genes that make the plants more resistant to pests and herbicides.

Answer: D
Topic: 12.8
Skill: Conceptual Understanding

30) Which of the following has *not* been a significant issue in the creation of genetically modified (GM) organisms?
   A) the fact that some plants carrying genes from other species might represent a threat to the environment
   B) the fact that GM organisms cannot be modified to prevent them from reproducing once they pass beyond the experimental stage
   C) the fact that rogue microbes might transfer dangerous genes into other organisms
   D) the fact that transgenic plants might pass their new genes to close relatives
   E) the fact that allergens may be transferred in the process of producing GM organisms

Answer: B
Topic: 12.9
Skill: Conceptual Understanding

31) In order for gene therapy to be permanent,
   A) the defective gene must first be removed from all somatic cells.
   B) the normal gene must be added to the germ line cells.
   C) the defective gene must undergo restriction enzyme analysis first.
   D) the normal gene must first be treated with UV radiation to ensure noninfectivity.
   E) the normal gene must be transferred to somatic cells that can continuously multiply.

Answer: E
Topic: 12.10
Skill: Factual Recall

32) Gene therapy can currently be considered
   A) far off in the future.
   B) impossible.
   C) promising.
   D) established and reliable.
   E) cheap and easy.

Answer: C
Topic: 12.10
Skill: Conceptual Understanding

33) Genetically modifying _____ cells may directly affect future generations.
   A) intestinal
   B) basal
   C) somatic
   D) germ
   E) T

Answer: D
Topic: 12.10
Skill: Conceptual Understanding

34) What is the preferred name of the technique used to determine if DNA comes from a particular individual?
   A) DNA fingerprinting
   B) DNA scrutiny
   C) DNA profiling
   D) DNA outline
   E) DNA synopsis

Answer: C
Topic: 12.11
Skill: Factual Recall

35) If you commit a crime, you need to make sure that you do not leave even the smallest speck of blood, hair, or other organic matter from your body. If you do, the DNA in this material can be amplified by _____, subjected to genetic analysis, and used to identify you as the perpetrator of the crime.
   A) ATP
   B) PCR
   C) blotting
   D) RFLP
   E) reverse transcriptase

Answer: B
Topic: 12.12
Skill: Application

36) The polymerase chain reaction relies upon unusual, heat–resistant _____ that were isolated from bacteria living in hot springs.
   A) DNA polymerase molecules
   B) phages
   C) mRNA
   D) restriction enzymes
   E) plasmids

Answer: A
Topic: 12.12
Skill: Factual Recall

37) Gel electrophoresis sorts DNA molecules on the basis of their
   A) nucleotide sequence.
   B) solubility in water.
   C) ability to bind to mRNA.
   D) solubility in the gel.
   E) size.

Answer: E
Topic: 12.13
Skill: Factual Recall

38) During the process of electrophoresis, the _____ functions like a thick filter, separating the samples according to their size.
   A) sample well
   B) sample mixture
   C) positively charged electrode
   D) negatively charged electrode
   E) gel

Answer: E
Topic: 12.13
Skill: Application

39) Which of the following statements regarding repetitive DNA is *false*?
   A) Repetitive DNA is usually found between the exons.
   B) Repetitive DNA can be short or long sequences of DNA.
   C) Repetitive DNA is identical in all humans.
   D) Repetitive DNA is usually repeated many times in the genome.
   E) Repetitive DNA can show great variation among individuals.

Answer: C
Topic: 12.14
Skill: Factual Recall

40) What is the standard tool used for DNA profiling by forensic scientists?
   A) STR analysis
   B) PCR
   C) Gel electrophoresis
   D) RFLP
   E) DNA microarrays

Answer: A
Topic: 12.14
Skill: Factual Recall

41) What is the smallest number of cells needed to perform a successful DNA profile?
   A) 10
   B) 20
   C) 200
   D) 1,000
   E) 1,200

Answer: B
Topic: 12.15
Skill: Factual Recall

42) Which of the following pieces of evidence would be considered the best for establishing biological relatedness?
   A) birth certificates
   B) pictures from family reunions
   C) testimony from relatives
   D) a very close match in the DNA profile
   E) legal documents

Answer: D
Topic: 12.15
Skill: Factual Recall

43) The genetic variation of one nucleotide in at least 1% of the population is known as
   A) single nucleotide polymorphism.
   B) short tandem repeats.
   C) recombinant DNA.
   D) variable DNA.
   E) complementary DNA.

Answer: A
Topic: 12.16
Skill: Factual Recall

44) Which of the following statements about genome sequencing is *false*?
   A) The genomes of about 500 species have been completely or almost completely sequenced.
   B) The first multicellular organism to have its genome sequenced was a nematode.
   C) The first eukaryotic organism to have its genome sequenced was yeast.
   D) Most of the genomes that have been sequenced to date are eukaryotes.
   E) The genome of a mouse has been sequenced.

Answer: D
Topic: 12.17
Skill: Factual Recall

45) Which of the following statements about genomics is *false*?
   A) The first complete genome to be sequenced was a prokaryote.
   B) Whole sets of genes and their interactions are studied in the field of genomics.
   C) Genes from different species that have analogous sequences suggest similar function.
   D) DNA technology limits genomic studies to prokaryotes.
   E) When comparing the genomes of different species, genes that are more similar in sequence suggest the species are more closely related.

Answer: D
Topic: 12.17
Skill: Conceptual Understanding

46) Approximately what percentage of human DNA is noncoding?
   A) 37%
   B) 49%
   C) 79%
   D) 98.5%
   E) 99.9%

Answer: D
Topic: 12.18
Skill: Factual Recall

47) The type of repetitive DNA composed of sequences of large repeated units is often associated with
   A) sequences of shorter repeated units.
   B) diseases of the nervous system.
   C) transposable elements.
   D) sex–linked genes.
   E) transcription factors.

Answer: C
Topic: 12.18
Skill: Factual Recall

48) Segments of eukaryotic DNA that can move or be copied from one site to another in the genome are called
   A) exons.
   B) plasmids.
   C) transposable elements.
   D) introns.
   E) vectors.

Answer: C
Topic: 12.18
Skill: Factual Recall

49) Which of the following statements regarding DNA is *false*?
   A) Long stretches of repetitive DNA are prominent at centromeres and ends of chromosomes.
   B) Scientists think that the typical human gene probably specifies just one polypeptide.
   C) Current estimates are that there are 20,000 genes in the human genome.
   D) Much of the DNA between genes consists of repetitive DNA.
   E) Telomeres seem to have a structural function.

Answer: B
Topic: 12.18
Skill: Factual Recall

50) Why is the whole-genome shotgun method currently the tool of choice for analyzing genomes?
    A) It is extremely accurate.
    B) Multiple genomes can be analyzed simultaneously.
    C) It is fast and inexpensive.
    D) It is very labor-intense.
    E) It has no limitations.

Answer: C
Topic: 12.19
Skill: Factual Recall

51) Which of the following statements regarding proteomics is *correct*?
    A) Proteomics is the study of protein interaction within a cell.
    B) Proteomics involves the complete analysis of the prokaryotes.
    C) Proteomics is a straightforward task that is technically simple.
    D) Proteomics is the systematic study of the full set of proteins encoded by a genome.
    E) Proteomics and genomics allow scientists to study life in an ever-increasing reductive approach.

Answer: D
Topic: 12.20
Skill: Factual Recall

52) The number of proteins in humans
    A) has been determined by comparing the number of genes.
    B) is approximately equal to the number of genes.
    C) cannot be determined because the human genome is too complex.
    D) is less than half the number of genes.
    E) is much greater than the number of genes.

Answer: E
Topic: 12.20
Skill: Factual Recall

53) Genome sequence analysis supports the theory that there are three fundamental domains of life: Bacteria, Archaea, and
    A) Animalia.
    B) Plants.
    C) Protista.
    D) Eukarya.
    E) Monera.

Answer: D
Topic: 12.21-Evolution Connection
Skill: Factual Recall

54) Approximately what percentage of the human genome is identical to that of a chimpanzee?
   A) 50.0%
   B) 62.3%
   C) 88.5%
   D) 92.0%
   E) 98.8%

Answer: E
Topic: 12.21–Evolution Connection
Skill: Factual Recall

Art Questions

1)

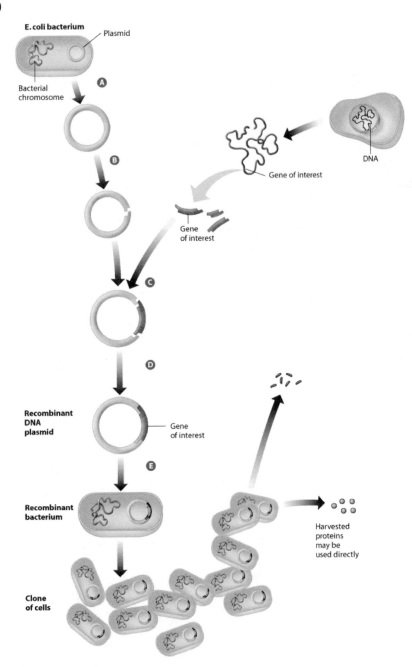

Which step in this process requires use of restriction enzymes?
   A) step A
   B) step B
   C) step C
   D) step D
   E) step E

Answer: B
Topic: 12.1
Skill: Application

2)

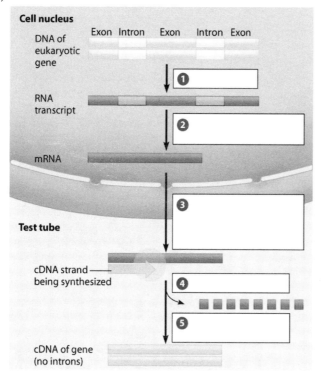

Which step in the creation of cDNA involves the use of reverse transcriptase?
   A) step 1
   B) step 2
   C) step 3
   D) step 4
   E) step 5

Answer: C
Topic: 12.4
Skill: Application

Scenario Questions

After reading the following paragraph, answer the question(s) below.

Four decades after the end of the Vietnam War, the remains of an Air Force pilot were discovered and returned to the United States. A search of Air Force records identified three families to which the remains might possibly belong. Each family had a surviving twin of a missing service member. The following STR profiles were obtained from the remains of the pilot and the surviving twins from the three families.

	Air Force Pilot	Family 1	Family 2	Family 3
1		—		
2	—	—		—
3	—			—
4		—		
5	—	—	—	—
6			—	
7	—	—	—	—
8			—	
9		—		
10	—			—
11			—	
12		—		
13	—		—	—

1) In order to match the pilot's remains to the correct family using DNA profiling,
  A) the majority of the STR bands must match.
  B) each of the 13 STR bands must match.
  C) the bands for site 13 must match.
  D) bands 5 and 7 must match.
  E) 50% of the STR bands must match.

Answer: B
Topic: 12.11–12.15
Skill: Conceptual Understanding

2) Based on analysis of the STR sites shown, does the missing pilot belong to any of these three families?
    A) No, none of the families match.
    B) Yes, family 1 matches.
    C) Yes, family 2 matches.
    D) Yes, family 3 matches.
    E) The information provided is not sufficient to determine whether or not there is a match.

Answer: D
Topic: 12.11–12.15
Skill: Application

Chapter 13 How Populations Evolve

Multiple-Choice Questions

1) Blue-footed boobies have webbed feet and are comically clumsy when they walk on land. Evolutionary scientists view these feet as
   A) an example of a trait that is poorly adapted.
   B) the outcome of a tradeoff: webbed feet perform poorly on land, but are very helpful in diving for food.
   C) an example of a trait that has not evolved.
   D) a curiosity that has little to teach us regarding evolution.
   E) one of the unsolvable mysteries of nature.

Answer: B
Topic: Opening Essay
Skill: Application

2) The core theme of biology is
   A) taxonomy.
   B) genetics.
   C) ecology.
   D) evolution.
   E) metabolism.

Answer: D
Topic: Opening Essay
Skill: Factual Recall

3) Aristotle believed that
   A) species evolve through natural selection and other mechanisms.
   B) an individual's use of a body part causes it to further evolve.
   C) species are fixed (permanent) and perfect.
   D) the best evidence for change within species is seen in fossils.
   E) no two individual organisms are alike and all types of organisms are equally valuable.

Answer: C
Topic: 13.1
Skill: Factual Recall

4) Darwin found that some of the species on the Galápagos islands resembled species of the South American mainland
   A) less than they resembled animals on ecologically similar but distant islands.
   B) more than they resembled animals on ecologically similar but distant islands.
   C) less than they resembled animals in Europe.
   D) less than they resembled animals from Australia.
   E) very closely; in most cases, the species from the mainland and the islands were identical.

Answer: B
Topic: 13.1
Skill: Conceptual Understanding

5) Which of the following statements would Darwin have disagreed with?
    A) Species change over time.
    B) Living species have arisen from earlier life forms.
    C) Modern species arose through a process known as "descent with modification."
    D) Descent with modification occurs through inheritance of acquired characteristics.
    E) Descent with modification occurs by natural selection.
    Answer: D
    Topic: Opening Essay, 13.1, 13.2
    Skill: Conceptual Understanding

6) Lyell's book *Principles of Geology*, which Darwin read on board the H.M.S. *Beagle*, argued in favor of which of the following concepts?
    A) Earth's surface is shaped mainly by occasional catastrophic events.
    B) Earthquakes were less important than sedimentary processes in creating the landscape of South America.
    C) Meteorite impacts may have been a major cause of periodic mass extinctions.
    D) Earth's surface is shaped by natural forces that act gradually and are still acting.
    E) The processes that shape Earth today are very different from those that were at work in the past.
    Answer: D
    Topic: 13.1
    Skill: Factual Recall

7) Who developed a theory of evolution almost identical to Darwin's?
    A) Lyell
    B) Wallace
    C) Aristotle
    D) Lamarck
    E) Mendel
    Answer: B
    Topic: 13.1
    Skill: Factual Recall

8) During the 1950s, a scientist named Lysenko tried to solve the food shortages in the Soviet Union by breeding wheat that could grow in Siberia. He theorized that if individual wheat plants were exposed to cold, they would develop additional cold tolerance and pass it to their offspring. Based on the ideas of artificial and natural selection, do you think this project worked as planned?
   A) Yes, the wheat probably evolved better cold tolerance over time through inheritance of acquired characteristics.
   B) No, because Lysenko took his wheat seeds straight to Siberia instead of exposing them incrementally to cold.
   C) No, because there was no process of selection based on inherited traits. Lysenko assumed that exposure could induce a plant to develop additional cold tolerance and that this tolerance would be passed to the plant's offspring.
   D) No, because Lysenko used wheat varieties that had lost their cold tolerance as a result of disuse.
   E) Yes, because this is generally the method used by plant breeders to develop new crops.

Answer: C
Topic: 13.2
Skill: Application

9) Broccoli, cabbages, and brussels sprouts all descend from the same wild mustard and can still interbreed. These varieties were produced by
   A) speciation.
   B) artificial selection.
   C) natural selection.
   D) genetic drift.
   E) inheritance of acquired characteristics.

Answer: B
Topic: 13.2
Skill: Factual Recall

10) Which of the following best expresses the concept of natural selection?
   A) differential reproductive success based on inherited characteristics
   B) inheritance of acquired characteristics
   C) change in response to need
   D) a process of constant improvement, leading eventually to perfection
   E) survival of the fittest

Answer: A
Topic: 13.2
Skill: Conceptual Understanding

11) Which of the following assumptions or observations contradicts Darwin's idea of natural selection?
   A) Whether an organism survives and reproduces is almost entirely a matter of random chance.
   B) Heritable traits that promote successful reproduction should gradually become more common in a population.
   C) Populations produce more offspring than their environment can support.
   D) Organisms compete for limited resources.
   E) Organisms vary in heritable ways.

Answer: A
Topic: 13.2
Skill: Conceptual Understanding

12) Which of the following thinkers argued that organisms tend to produce many more offspring than the environment can support, leading to a struggle for existence, an argument that later influenced Charles Darwin's ideas of natural selection?
   A) Aristotle
   B) Charles Lyell
   C) Thomas Malthus
   D) Jean–Baptiste Lamarck
   E) Gregor Mendel

Answer: C
Topic: 13.2
Skill: Factual Recall

13) A dog breeder wishes to develop a breed that does not bark. She starts with a diverse mixture of dogs. Generation after generation, she allows only the quietest dogs to breed. After 30 years of work she has a new breed of dog with interesting traits, but on average, the dogs still bark at about the same rate as other dog breeds. Which of the following would be a logical explanation for her failure?
   A) There is no variation for the trait (barking).
   B) The tendency to bark is not a heritable trait.
   C) The selection was artificial, not natural, so it did not produce evolutionary change.
   D) There was no selection (differential reproductive success) related to barking behavior.
   E) She did not breed enough of the frequently barking dogs to obtain the desired result.

Answer: B
Topic: 13.2
Skill: Application

14) Which of the following statements regarding natural selection is *false*?
   A) Natural selection is more of an editing process than a creative mechanism.
   B) Natural selection depends on the local environment at the current time.
   C) Natural selection starts with the creation of new alleles that are directed toward improving an organism's fitness.
   D) Natural selection and evolutionary change can occur in a short period of time (a few generations).
   E) Natural selection can be observed working in organisms alive today.

Answer: C
Topic: 13.3
Skill: Conceptual Understanding

15) Which of the following would prevent an organism from becoming part of the fossil record when it dies?
   A) It is fully decomposed by bacteria and fungi.
   B) It is buried in fine sediments at the bottom of a lake.
   C) It gets trapped in sap.
   D) It falls into an acid bog.
   E) It is frozen in ice.

Answer: A
Topic: 13.4
Skill: Conceptual Understanding

16) Which of the following statements regarding the currently available fossil record is *false*?
   A) The currently available fossil record shows that the earliest fossils of life are about 3.5 billion years old.
   B) The currently available fossil record shows that younger strata were laid down on top of older strata.
   C) The currently available fossil record shows that single–celled eukaryotes appeared before multicellular eukaryotes.
   D) The currently available fossil record documents gradual evolutionary changes that link one group of organisms to another.
   E) The currently available fossil record shows that the first life forms were eukaryotes.

Answer: E
Topic: 13.4
Skill: Factual Recall

17) Which of the following disciplines has found evidence for evolution based on the native distributions (locations) of living species?
   A) molecular biology
   B) comparative anatomy
   C) biogeography
   D) paleontology
   E) embryology

Answer: C
Topic: 13.5
Skill: Factual Recall

18) Humans share several features with salamanders. Certain genes and proteins are nearly identical between the two species; both species have four limbs with a similar skeletal structure; the species' early embryos are very similar; and where the salamander has a functional tail, humans have a vestigial tailbone. In evolutionary terms, these are examples of
  A) biogeographic similarity.
  B) homology.
  C) independently acquired characteristics.
  D) adaptation by natural selection.
  E) coincidental similarity.

Answer: B
Topic: 13.5
Skill: Application

19) Which of the following represents a pair of homologous structures?
  A) the wing of a bat and the scales of a fish
  B) the wing of a bat and the flipper of a whale
  C) the antennae of an insect and the eyes of a bird
  D) the feathers of a bird and the wing membrane of a bat
  E) the wing of a bat and the wing of a butterfly

Answer: B
Topic: 13.5
Skill: Application

20) Deep branch points near the base, or trunk, of an evolutionary tree represent _____, while branch points near the tips of the branches represent _____.
  A) relatively recent common ancestors . . . relatively ancient common ancestors
  B) relatively ancient common ancestors . . . relatively recent common ancestors
  C) organisms that share homologous structures . . . organisms that do not share any homologous structures
  D) organisms with relatively simple traits . . . organisms with very complex traits
  E) complex organisms . . . simpler organisms

Answer: B
Topic: 13.6
Skill: Conceptual Understanding

21) Darwin was the first person to draw an evolutionary tree, a diagram that represents
  A) records of breeding in domesticated animals.
  B) records of lineages in humans (also known as a family tree).
  C) final, factually established evolutionary relationships among different groups of organisms.
  D) evidence–based hypotheses regarding our understanding of patterns of evolutionary descent.
  E) groupings of organisms based on overall similarity.

Answer: D
Topic: 13.6
Skill: Factual Recall

22) A population is
    A) a group of individuals of the same species living in the same place at the same time.
    B) all individuals of a species, regardless of location or time period in which they live.
    C) a group of individuals of different species living in the same place at the same time.
    D) a group of individuals of a species plus all of the other species with which they interact.
    E) a group of species that share a common characteristic.

Answer: A
Topic: 13.7
Skill: Factual Recall

23) Microevolution, or evolution at its smallest scale, occurs when
    A) an individual's traits change in response to environmental factors.
    B) a geographic area is altered by erosion, volcanic eruptions, or other geological forces.
    C) a community of organisms changes due to the extinction of several dominant species.
    D) a new species arises from an existing species.
    E) a population's allele frequencies change over a span of generations.

Answer: E
Topic: 13.7
Skill: Factual Recall

24) The ultimate source of all new alleles is
    A) mutation in parent cells (asexual organisms) or in cells that produce gametes (sexual organisms).
    B) any form of mutation, regardless of the cell type.
    C) chromosomal duplication.
    D) genetic drift.
    E) natural selection.

Answer: A
Topic: 13.8
Skill: Factual Recall

25) In the Hardy–Weinberg equation, the frequency of homozygous dominant individuals in a population is equal to
    A) q or p.
    B) p^2.
    C) $2pq$.
    D) q^2.
    E) $2p$.

Answer: B
Topic: 13.9
Skill: Conceptual Understanding

26) Which of the following terms represents the frequency of heterozygotes in a population that is in Hardy–Weinberg equilibrium?
   A) p
   B) q
   C) $2pq$
   D) q^2
   E) p^2

Answer: C
Topic: 13.9
Skill: Conceptual Understanding

27) Which of the following conditions would tend to make the Hardy–Weinberg equation more accurate for predicting the genotype frequencies of future generations in a population of a sexually reproducing species?
   A) a small population size
   B) little gene flow with surrounding populations
   C) a tendency on the part of females to mate with the healthiest males
   D) frequent interbreeding with individuals from a second population with different values of p and q
   E) mutations that alter the gene pool

Answer: B
Topic: 13.9
Skill: Factual Recall

28) Imagine that you are studying a very large population of moths that is isolated from gene flow. A single gene controls wing color. Half of the moths have white–spotted wings (genotype **WW** or **Ww**) and half of the moths have plain brown wings (**ww**). There are no new mutations, individuals mate randomly, and there is no natural selection on wing color. How will p, the frequency of the dominant allele, change over time?
   A) p will increase; the dominant allele will eventually take over and become most common in the population.
   B) p will neither increase nor decrease; it will remain more or less constant under the conditions described.
   C) p will decrease because of genetic drift.
   D) p will increase initially, then decrease until the W allele vanishes from the population.
   E) p will fluctuate rapidly and randomly because of genetic drift.

Answer: B
Topic: 13.9
Skill: Application

29) The recessive allele of a gene causes cystic fibrosis. For this gene among Caucasians, $p = 0.98$. If a Caucasian population is in Hardy–Weinberg equilibrium with respect to this gene, what proportion of babies is born homozygous recessive, and therefore suffers cystic fibrosis?

    A) $0.02^2 = 0.0004$

    B) 0.02

    C) $0.98^2 = 0.9604$

    D) $2(0.02 \times 0.98) = 0.0392$

    E) 0.98

Answer: A
Topic: 13.10
Skill: Application

30) Genetic drift resulting from a disaster that drastically reduces population size is called

    A) natural selection.

    B) gene flow.

    C) the bottleneck effect.

    D) nonrandom mating.

    E) the founder effect.

Answer: C
Topic: 13.11
Skill: Factual Recall

31) In populations of the greater prairie chicken in Illinois, genetic diversity was

    A) lost through mutation and restored by natural selection.

    B) lost through genetic drift and restored by natural selection.

    C) lost through gene flow and restored by mutation.

    D) lost through genetic drift and restored by gene flow.

    E) lost through directional selection and restored by balancing selection.

Answer: D
Topic: 13.11
Skill: Conceptual Understanding

32) A population of 1,000 birds exists on a small Pacific island. Some of the birds are yellow, a characteristic determined by a recessive allele. The others are green, a characteristic determined by a dominant allele. A hurricane on the island kills most of the birds from this population. Only ten remain, and those birds all have yellow feathers. Which of the following statements is *true*?

    A) Assuming that no new birds come to the island and no mutations occur, future generations of this population will contain both green and yellow birds.

    B) The hurricane has caused a population bottleneck and a loss of genetic diversity.

    C) This situation illustrates the principle of adaptive radiation.

    D) This situation illustrates the effect of a mutation event.

    E) The ten remaining birds will mate only with each other, and this will contribute to gene flow in the population.

Answer: B
Topic: 13.11
Skill: Application

33) Thirty people are selected for a long-term mission to colonize a planet many light years away from Earth. The mission is successful and the population rapidly grows to several hundred individuals. However, certain genetic diseases are unusually common in this group, and their gene pool is quite different from that of the Earth population they have left behind. Which of the following phenomena has left its mark on this population?
    A) founder effect
    B) bottleneck effect
    C) gene flow
    D) high rates of mutation
    E) natural selection

Answer: A
Topic: 13.11
Skill: Application

34) Genetic differences between populations tend to be reduced by
    A) gene flow.
    B) mutation.
    C) the founder effect.
    D) the bottleneck effect.
    E) natural selection.

Answer: A
Topic: 13.11
Skill: Factual Recall

35) Which sentence best describes the true nature of natural selection?
    A) Survival of the fittest.
    B) Only the strongest survive.
    C) The strong eliminate the weak in the race for survival.
    D) Organisms change by random chance.
    E) Heritable traits that promote reproduction become more frequent in a population from one generation to the next.

Answer: E
Topic: 13.12
Skill: Conceptual Understanding

36) Which of the following will tend to produce adaptive changes in populations?
    A) genetic drift
    B) gene flow
    C) mutation
    D) natural selection
    E) the founder effect

Answer: D
Topic: 13.12
Skill: Conceptual Understanding

37) An elk herd is observed over many generations. Most of the full-grown bull elk have antlers of nearly the same size, although a few have antlers that are significantly larger or smaller than this average size. The average antler size remains constant over the generations. Which of the following effects probably accounts for this situation?
   A) directional selection
   B) stabilizing selection
   C) a bottleneck effect that resulted in low genetic diversity
   D) a founder effect
   E) a high rate of gene flow

Answer: B
Topic: 13.13
Skill: Application

38) After a copper smelter begins operation, local populations of plants downwind of the plant begin to adapt to the resulting air pollution. Scientists document, for example, that the acid tolerance of several plant species has increased significantly in the polluted area. This is an example of a response to
   A) stabilizing selection.
   B) disruptive selection.
   C) directional selection.
   D) genetic drift.
   E) heterozygote advantage.

Answer: C
Topic: 13.13
Skill: Application

39) A rabbit population consists of animals that are either very dark on top or very light on top. The color pattern is not related to sex. No rabbit shows intermediate coloration (medium darkness). This pattern might result from
   A) disruptive selection.
   B) directional selection.
   C) stabilizing selection.
   D) sexual selection.
   E) random mating.

Answer: A
Topic: 13.13
Skill: Application

40) Large antlers in male elk, which are used for battles between males, are a good example of a trait favored by
   A) intersexual selection.
   B) intrasexual selection.
   C) disruptive selection.
   D) directional selection.
   E) stabilizing selection.

Answer: B
Topic: 13.14
Skill: Application

41) Mate-attracting features such as the bright plumage of a male peacock result from
    A) intersexual selection.
    B) intrasexual selection.
    C) disruptive selection.
    D) directional selection.
    E) stabilizing selection.

Answer: A
Topic: 13.14
Skill: Application

42) A woman struggling with a bacterial illness is prescribed a month's supply of a potent antibiotic. She takes the antibiotic for about two weeks and feels much better. Should she save the remaining two-week supply, or should she continue taking the drug?
    A) She should save the drug for later, because if she keeps taking it the bacteria will evolve resistance.
    B) She should save the drug for use the next time the illness strikes.
    C) She should save the drug because antibiotics are in short supply and she may need it to defend herself against a bioterrorism incident.
    D) She should continue taking the drug because otherwise the bacteria will evolve by genetic drift.
    E) She should continue taking the drug until her immune system can completely eliminate the infection. Otherwise the remaining bacteria in her system may recover, and they will probably be resistant.

Answer: E
Topic: 13.15-Evolution Connection
Skill: Application

43) If you had to choose, where would you rather get infected with a serious bacterial disease?
    A) In a hospital, where most of the bacteria are probably already weakened by antibiotics in the environment.
    B) In a livestock barn where the animals have been treated with antibiotics.
    C) In a big city where antibiotics are routinely prescribed by doctors.
    D) In a remote, sparsely populated area where the bacteria have not been exposed to antibiotic drugs.
    E) It doesn't make any difference—a serious bacterial illness is going to have a similar impact on your health regardless of where you pick it up.

Answer: D
Topic: 13.15-Evolution Connection
Skill: Application

44) Which of the following would *most quickly* be eliminated by natural selection?
    A) a harmful allele in an asexual, haploid population
    B) a harmful recessive allele in a sexual, diploid population
    C) a harmful recessive allele in a sexual, polyploid population
    D) any harmful allele, regardless of the system of inheritance in a population
    E) neutral variation, because it is not needed

Answer: A
Topic: 13.16
Skill: Conceptual Understanding

45) The sickle-cell allele produces a serious blood disease in homozygotes. Why doesn't natural selection eliminate this allele from all human populations?
   A) Natural selection is a positive force, so it does not eliminate alleles.
   B) In populations where endemic malaria is present, heterozygotes have an important advantage: They are resistant to malaria and therefore are more likely to survive and produce offspring that carry the allele.
   C) Genetic drift tends to keep the allele present in human populations.
   D) Mutations keep bringing the allele back into circulation.
   E) Natural selection occurs very slowly, but elimination of the sickle-cell allele is expected to occur soon.

Answer: B
Topic: 13.16
Skill: Application

46) Frequency-dependent selection, as seen in the case of the scale-eating fish in Lake Tanganyika, tends to
   A) eliminate rare alleles and favor whichever allele is initially most frequent.
   B) maintain two phenotypes in a dynamic equilibrium in a population.
   C) produce random changes in allele frequencies.
   D) lead to heterozygote advantage.
   E) stimulate new mutations.

Answer: B
Topic: 13.16
Skill: Factual Recall

47) Tay-Sachs is inherited as an autosomal recessive allele. Homozygous individuals die within the first few years of life. However, there is some evidence that heterozygous individuals are more resistant to tuberculosis. Which of the following statements about Tay-Sachs is *true*?
   A) The allele for Tay-Sachs is selected against.
   B) This situation is an example of heterozygote advantage if tuberculosis is present in a population.
   C) This situation is an example of directional selection.
   D) This situation is an example of disruptive selection.
   E) Heterozygotes will be more fit than either homozygote regardless of environmental conditions.

Answer: B
Topic: 13.16
Skill: Application

48) In a particular environment, there are no fitness differences among individuals with dark hair and individuals with light hair. The term that best describes this situation is
   A) random mating.
   B) random selection.
   C) natural selection.
   D) differential reproductive success.
   E) neutral variation.

Answer: E
Topic: 13.16
Skill: Conceptual Understanding

49) A lot of your DNA is inherited "junk": It doesn't code for any protein and has no known function in gene regulation. How do nucleotide sequences of "junk DNA" evolve?
   A) They evolve through natural selection.
   B) They evolve through genetic drift and other chance processes.
   C) They evolve to be more useful by taking on new functions.
   D) "Junk DNA" does not evolve. Changes in junk DNA sequences would not serve any purpose for an organism.
   E) They evolve by gradually being eliminated from the gene pool.

Answer: B
Topic: 13.16
Skill: Conceptual Understanding

50) Mothers and teachers have often said they need another pair of eyes on the backs of their heads. And another pair of hands would come in handy in many situations. You can imagine that these traits would have been advantageous to our early hunter-gatherer ancestors as well. According to sound evolutionary reasoning, what is the most likely explanation for why humans do not have these traits?
   A) Because they actually would not be beneficial to the fitness of individuals who possessed them. Natural selection always produces the most beneficial traits for a particular organism in a particular environment.
   B) Because every time they have arisen before, the individual mutants bearing these traits have been killed by chance events. Chance and natural selection interact.
   C) Because these variations have probably never appeared in a healthy human. As tetrapods we are pretty much stuck with a four-limbed, two-eyed body plan; natural selection can only edit existing variations.
   D) Because humans are a relatively young species. If we stick around and adapt for long enough, it is inevitable that the required adaptations will arise.
   E) Because it is physically impossible to have a six-limbed organism with more than one set of eyes. Natural selection cannot break physical laws.

Answer: C
Topic: 13.17
Skill: Application

Art Questions

1)

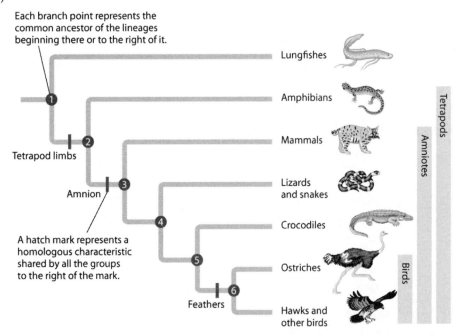

Each branch point represents the common ancestor of the lineages beginning there or to the right of it.

A hatch mark represents a homologous characteristic shared by all the groups to the right of the mark.

According to this figure, which pair of organisms shares the most recent common ancestor?

A) lungfish and amphibian
B) amphibian and mammal
C) amphibian and lizard
D) mammal and crocodile
E) lizard and ostrich

Answer: E
Topic: 13.6
Skill: Application

2)

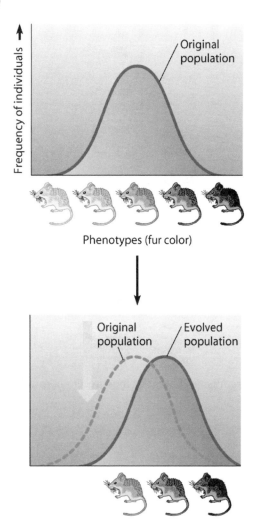

Which statement best describes the mode of selection depicted in the figure?
- A) stabilizing selection, changing the average color of the population over time
- B) stabilizing selection, leading to darker and darker populations over time
- C) directional selection, favoring the average individual
- D) directional selection, changing the average color of the population over time
- E) disruptive selection, favoring the average individual

Answer: D
Topic: 13.13
Skill: Conceptual Understanding

Scenario Questions

After reading the following paragraph, answer the question(s) below.

Desert pupfish live in springs of the American Southwest. Today there are about 30 species of pupfish, but they all evolved from a common Pleistocene ancestor. The southwestern United States was once much wetter than it is now, and the Pleistocene pupfish flourished over a wide geographic area. Over thousands of years, however, the Sierra Nevada Mountain range was pushed upward by geological forces, blocking rainfall from the Pacific Ocean. As the large lakes dried up, small groups of pupfish remained in springs and pools fed by groundwater seepage. Now, although many of these small springs still have pupfish, each population has evolved to become very different from pupfish in other springs.

1) Which of the following statements represents the most probable explanation for the differences between pupfish populations?
   A) The types of genes in the population increased.
   B) The frequency of genotypes reached equilibrium.
   C) New genes entered the population through migration.
   D) The isolated populations had a restricted gene pool.
   E) Each new species contains all the original genotypes of the larger populations.

   Answer: D
   Topic: 13.1, 13.7, 13.11
   Skill: Conceptual Understanding

2) The variation in gene pools between the 30 pupfish populations occurred through an evolutionary mechanism called
   A) the bottleneck effect.
   B) directional selection.
   C) random mating.
   D) the Hardy–Weinberg equilibrium.
   E) interaction of alleles between populations.

   Answer: A
   Topic: 13.11
   Skill: Factual Recall

Chapter 14 The Origin of Species

Multiple-Choice Questions

1) What is the significance of color in the diversification of cichlids in Lake Victoria?
    A) Female choice for specific male color patterns could reproductively isolate subpopulations of cichlids.
    B) Bright color patterns scare potential predators, allowing more species to thrive in the lake.
    C) Bright color patterns allow biologists to recognize differences among species they would otherwise fail to notice.
    D) Bright color patterns in female cichlids are an exception to the rule that males are usually showier.
    E) Bright colors appear only in species that live in murky, polluted water.

    Answer: A
    Topic: Opening Essay
    Skill: Conceptual Understanding

2) Speciation, or the formation of new species, is
    A) a form of microevolution.
    B) completed when the new species is able to interbreed with at least one additional species.
    C) the bridge between microevolution and macroevolution.
    D) a process that requires at least 1 million years, as seen in the Lake Victoria cichlids.
    E) an event that has occurred only a few times in the history of the planet.

    Answer: C
    Topic: Opening Essay
    Skill: Factual Recall

3) Which of the following would a biologist describe as microevolution?
    A) the formation of new species
    B) the extinction of species
    C) dramatic biological changes, such as the origin of flight, within a taxon
    D) the generation of biodiversity
    E) a change in allele frequencies within the gene pool of a population

    Answer: E
    Topic: 14.1
    Skill: Conceptual Understanding

4) A biological species is defined as a group of organisms that
    A) are physically similar.
    B) are genetically similar.
    C) share a recent common ancestor.
    D) live together in a location and carry out identical ecological roles.
    E) have the potential to interbreed in nature and produce fertile offspring.

    Answer: E
    Topic: 14.2
    Skill: Factual Recall

5) The biological species concept is
   A) applicable to all forms of life, past and present.
   B) applicable to all present life forms, but not to fossil organisms whose reproductive behavior cannot be observed.
   C) easy to apply to all present sexually reproducing organisms, but harder to apply to asexual organisms and fossils.
   D) difficult to put into practice even for present sexual organisms, and useless for asexual organisms and fossils.
   E) based on DNA, so it applies to all forms of life from which a DNA sample can be collected.

Answer: D
Topic: 14.2
Skill: Conceptual Understanding

6) Which of the following statements regarding the definition of species is *false*?
   A) Taxonomy is the branch of biology concerned with naming and classifying the diverse forms of life.
   B) The ecological species concept identifies species in terms of their ecological niches.
   C) The phylogenetic species concept defines a species as a set of organisms with a unique genetic history.
   D) The morphological species concept relies upon comparing the DNA sequences of organisms.
   E) A biological species is a group of sexual organisms that can take its own evolutionary path.

Answer: D
Topic: 14.2
Skill: Conceptual Understanding

7) Which provides the *most* general and correct description of the idea of a reproductive barrier?
   A) any feature (of geography, behavior, or morphology) that keeps one species from mating with another
   B) a biological difference between two species that prevents them from successfully interbreeding
   C) a geographic barrier that separates two species and prevents gene flow between them
   D) a difference in reproductive biology between two species that makes hybrid individuals less fertile
   E) a difference in behavior that keeps two species from interbreeding

Answer: B
Topic: 14.3
Skill: Conceptual Understanding

8) Two populations of organisms belong to the same biological species when they
   A) can't mate with each other, because mating occurs at different times.
   B) mate with each other, but produce offspring that are not vigorous (suffer reduced viability).
   C) use different types of behaviors or physical features to attract mates.
   D) have anatomical features that make it difficult for organisms from the different populations to mate.
   E) encounter each other, mate, and produce viable, fertile offspring under natural conditions.

Answer: E
Topic: 14.3
Skill: Conceptual Understanding

9) Which of the following types of reproductive barriers separates a pair of species that could interbreed except that one mates at dusk and the other at dawn?
   A) temporal isolation
   B) habitat isolation
   C) behavioral isolation
   D) mechanical isolation
   E) gametic isolation

Answer: A
Topic: 14.3
Skill: Application

10) Which of the following types of reproductive barriers separates a pair of insect species that could interbreed except that one mates on goldenrod flowers and the other on autumn daisies that both blossom at the same time?
   A) temporal isolation
   B) habitat isolation
   C) behavioral isolation
   D) mechanical isolation
   E) gametic isolation

Answer: B
Topic: 14.3
Skill: Application

11) Which of the following types of reproductive barriers separates a pair of moth species that could interbreed except that the females' mating pheromones are not attractive to the males of the other species?
   A) temporal isolation
   B) habitat isolation
   C) behavioral isolation
   D) mechanical isolation
   E) gametic isolation

Answer: C
Topic: 14.3
Skill: Application

12) Which of the following types of reproductive barriers separates two flowering plant species that could interbreed except that one has a deep flower tube and is pollinated by bumblebees, whereas the other has a short, narrow flower tube and is pollinated by honeybees?
    A) temporal isolation
    B) habitat isolation
    C) behavioral isolation
    D) mechanical isolation
    E) gametic isolation

Answer: D
Topic: 14.3
Skill: Application

13) Which of the following types of reproductive barriers separates two species of sea cucumbers, whose sperm and eggs often bump into each other but do not cross–fertilize because of incompatible proteins on their surfaces?
    A) temporal isolation
    B) habitat isolation
    C) behavioral isolation
    D) mechanical isolation
    E) gametic isolation

Answer: E
Topic: 14.3
Skill: Application

14) Two species that occasionally mate and produce zygotes, but which have incompatible genes that prevent the resulting embryo from developing, are separated by
    A) mechanical isolation.
    B) gametic isolation.
    C) reduced hybrid fertility.
    D) reduced hybrid viability.
    E) hybrid breakdown.

Answer: D
Topic: 14.3
Skill: Application

15) Two species that sometimes mate and produce vigorous but sterile offspring are separated by
    A) mechanical isolation.
    B) gametic isolation.
    C) reduced hybrid fertility.
    D) reduced hybrid viability.
    E) hybrid breakdown.

Answer: C
Topic: 14.3
Skill: Application

16) Two species interbreed occasionally and produce vigorous, fertile hybrids. When the hybrids breed with each other or with either parent species, however, the offspring are feeble or sterile. These species are separated by
   A) mechanical isolation.
   B) gametic isolation.
   C) reduced hybrid fertility.
   D) reduced hybrid viability.
   E) hybrid breakdown.

Answer: E
Topic: 14.3
Skill: Application

17) Frequently, a group of related species will each have a unique courtship ritual that must be performed correctly for both partners to be willing to mate. Such a ritual constitutes a _____, _____ reproductive barrier.
   A) mechanical . . . postzygotic
   B) behavioral . . . prezygotic
   C) mechanical . . . prezygotic
   D) temporal . . . prezygotic
   E) gametic . . . postzygotic

Answer: B
Topic: 14.3
Skill: Application

18) The Monterey pine and the Bishop's pine inhabit some of the same areas of central California. The Monterey pine releases pollen in February, while the Bishop's pine does so in April. This is an example of _____ isolation.
   A) behavioral
   B) postzygotic
   C) temporal
   D) habitat
   E) mechanical

Answer: C
Topic: 14.3
Skill: Application

19) The geographic isolation of a population from other members of the species and the subsequent evolution of reproductive barriers between it and the parent species describes _____ speciation.
   A) punctuated
   B) phylogenetic
   C) sympatric
   D) allopatric
   E) biogeographic

Answer: D
Topic: 14.4
Skill: Factual Recall

20) The likelihood of allopatric speciation increases when a splinter population is _____ and _____ the broader range of the species.
   A) small . . . isolated from
   B) large . . . nearby
   C) large . . . isolated from
   D) small . . . nearby
   E) large . . . continuous with

Answer: A
Topic: 14.4
Skill: Conceptual Understanding

21) Uplift and formation of a mountain range divides a freshwater snail species into two isolated populations. Erosion eventually lowers the mountain range and brings the two populations together again, but when they mate, the resulting hybrids all produce sterile young. This scenario is an example of
   A) sympatric speciation.
   B) allopatric speciation.
   C) incomplete speciation.
   D) diversifying speciation.
   E) punctuated equilibrium.

Answer: B
Topic: 14.4
Skill: Application

22) In which of the following situations would speciation occur *most* rapidly? (Assume the conditions described persist as long as necessary and that the species have similar generation times.)
   A) A population of juniper shrubs is split in two by the Grand Canyon. Every few years, strong winds carry the shrub's pollen across the canyon.
   B) A Japanese mollusk species whose larvae are often carried from port to port in ship bilge water now flourishes in San Francisco Bay, a busy commercial port.
   C) Bighorn sheep occupy mountains from Canada through Death Valley in Southern California, interbreeding all the way. The populations at the two ends of the range live in very different environments.
   D) Seven monkeys escape from an amusement park and zoo in South Florida. To everyone's surprise, they establish a small but viable population, coexisting successfully with humans in a partly suburban environment very different from their native African habitat.
   E) The growth of the Isthmus of Panama separates an abundant fish species into two very large, completely isolated populations.

Answer: D
Topic: 14.4
Skill: Application

23) Speciation without geographic isolation is called _____ speciation.
  A) sympatric
  B) allopatric
  C) incomplete
  D) diversifying
  E) punctuated

Answer: A
Topic: 14.5
Skill: Factual Recall

24) Organisms that possess more than two complete sets of chromosomes are said to be
  A) haploid.
  B) polyploid.
  C) diploid.
  D) hybrids.
  E) allopatric.

Answer: B
Topic: 14.5
Skill: Factual Recall

25) Most polyploid species arise from
  A) a single diploid parent plant.
  B) a single triploid parent plant.
  C) a single tetraploid parent plant.
  D) the hybridization of two parent species and subsequent chromosome duplications.
  E) the hybridization of a diploid and a tetraploid parent species.

Answer: D
Topic: 14.5
Skill: Conceptual Understanding

26) When a tetraploid flower pollinates a diploid flower of the parental species, the resulting offspring will be
  A) pentaploid and fertile.
  B) pentaploid and sterile.
  C) diploid and fertile.
  D) triploid and fertile.
  E) triploid and sterile.

Answer: E
Topic: 14.5
Skill: Conceptual Understanding

27) Sympatric speciation commonly occurs through _____ in plants, but is more likely to occur through _____ in animals.
  A) polyploidy . . . habitat differentiation and sexual selection
  B) habitat differentiation and sexual selection . . . polyploidy
  C) asexual reproduction . . . chromosome duplications
  D) polyploidy . . . geographic barriers
  E) self-pollination . . . polyploidy and other genetic mechanisms

Answer: A
Topic: 14.5
Skill: Factual Recall

28) Ancestral diploid wheat species had $2n = 14$ chromosomes. What happened when two of these species hybridized?
    A) They produced a viable, fertile hybrid species with 14 chromosomes.
    B) They produced a hybrid species that could not complete mitosis so it did not develop properly.
    C) They produced a hybrid species with 14 chromosomes that was sterile, because the chromosomes from the two different parent species did not pair up properly in meiosis.
    D) They produced a hybrid species with 28 chromosomes.
    E) They produced a hybrid species with $2n = 7$ chromosomes through the process of chromosomal reduction.

Answer: C
Topic: 14.6–Evolution Connection
Skill: Conceptual Understanding

29) Which of the following statements about plant speciation and hybridization is *false*?
    A) Plant biologists estimate that 80% of all living plant species are descended from ancestors that formed by polyploid speciation.
    B) Most polyploid plants form by hybridization.
    C) Bread wheat is the ancestral diploid wheat plant.
    D) Modern plant geneticists use chemicals to induce meiotic and mitotic errors to try to create new hybrid plants with special qualities.
    E) Bread wheat grown widely today is the result of several hybridization events.

Answer: C
Topic: 14.6–Evolution Connection
Skill: Factual Recall

30) Diane Dodd's experiments using fruit flies demonstrated that
    A) the evolution of reproductive barriers occurs much too slowly to produce measurable effects in the laboratory.
    B) new species can form in a single generation by the production of new reproductive structures.
    C) reproductive barriers can evolve rapidly as long as there is plenty of gene flow between the two populations.
    D) formation of a reproductive barrier between two populations is more likely if they experience and adapt to different environmental conditions.
    E) reproductive barriers usually are absolute—either two populations are fully willing and able to interbreed, or they are strictly separated by a fully effective reproductive barrier.

Answer: D
Topic: 14.7
Skill: Conceptual Understanding

31) Two bird species overlap in a hybrid zone. They are isolated by a slight difference in the male songs and by the females' tendency to select males with the "correct" song. Hybrid offspring tend to have reduced fertility compared to either of the parent species. What effect should natural selection have in this situation?
- A) Natural selection will favor males with less distinctive calls and/or females that are less "choosy."
- B) Natural selection will favor males with more distinctive calls and/or females that are more "choosy." As a result, the reproductive barrier between the two species will be reinforced.
- C) Natural selection does not play a role in macroevolution, so it is not relevant to this problem.
- D) Natural selection will lead to the hybrid species taking over and eliminating the weaker parent species.
- E) Natural selection will lead to the stronger of the two species taking over and eliminating the other species.

Answer: B
Topic: 14.8
Skill: Application

32) In a hybrid zone, _____ can occur if the reproductive barrier between two species is weak, as seen among cichlids in the murky waters of modern Lake Victoria.
- A) reinforcement
- B) fusion
- C) allopatric speciation
- D) sympatric speciation
- E) reproductive isolation

Answer: B
Topic: 14.8
Skill: Factual Recall

33) In their 30-year studies of Darwin's finches, the Grants have discovered that while the ground finch and cactus finch occasionally form hybrids, these hybrids
- A) usually die before hatching.
- B) are unable to feed themselves and die soon after leaving the nest.
- C) can only survive during wet years when there are plenty of soft, small seeds.
- D) reproduce with the parent species, showing that ground finches and cactus finches are all one species.
- E) are unable to produce a song and are therefore unable to find a mate.

Answer: C
Topic: 14.9
Skill: Factual Recall

34) Which of the following statements about the Galápagos finches is *false*?
   A) There are 14 species of Galápagos finches.
   B) The Galápagos finch species differ in their feeding habitats.
   C) Each island in the Galápagos chain has one and only one isolated, unique species of Darwin's finch.
   D) Most speciation events of the Galápagos finches occurred when some finches made it to another island, evolved in isolation, and accumulated enough changes to become a new species.
   E) The evolution of the Galápagos finches is an excellent example of adaptive radiation.

Answer: C
Topic: 14.10
Skill: Factual Recall

35) The emergence of many diverse species from a common ancestor that finds itself in a new environment is called
   A) adaptive radiation.
   B) gradualism.
   C) disruptive selection.
   D) allopatric speciation.
   E) hybridization.

Answer: A
Topic: 14.10
Skill: Factual Recall

36) Which of the following would tend to promote adaptive radiation?
   A) An area has a high number of species that exploit most of the available ecological opportunities.
   B) An organism has a very stable set of features and capabilities over long spans of evolutionary time.
   C) An organism colonizes an isolated area that is habitable but relatively devoid of life.
   D) An organism colonizes an area that already has a high level of existing species diversity.
   E) A single species goes extinct, but it has several competitors that quickly expand to assume its ecological roles.

Answer: C
Topic: 14.10
Skill: Conceptual Understanding

37) The _____ suggests that speciation occurs in brief spurts.
   A) adaptive model of the origin of species
   B) book of Genesis
   C) idea of descent with modification as proposed by Darwin
   D) gradualism model of the origin of species
   E) punctuated equilibrium model

Answer: E
Topic: 14.11
Skill: Factual Recall

38) The emergence of a new plant species over a brief period of time, followed by a long period of little change, is consistent with which of the following theories?
    A) the gradualism model
    B) allopatric speciation
    C) punctuated equilibrium
    D) phylogenetic divergence
    E) adaptive radiation

Answer: C
Topic: 14.11
Skill: Application

39) One of the key contributions of the punctuated equilibrium model is that it helps explain
    A) why transitional fossils are more common than Darwin would have predicted.
    B) why transitional fossils tend to be rare and certain common fossil species remain unchanged for long time spans.
    C) how new species arise from hybridization events.
    D) why genetic drift is not a significant force in evolution.
    E) why large, widespread populations tend to be the ones that evolve most rapidly and unpredictably.

Answer: B
Topic: 14.11
Skill: Conceptual Understanding

40) Which of the following descriptions *best* represents the gradualism model of speciation?
    A) Speciation occurs regularly as a result of the accumulation of many small changes.
    B) An isolated population differentiates quickly from its parent stock as it adapts to its local environment.
    C) Speciation occurs under unusual circumstances and therefore transitional fossils are hard to find.
    D) Species undergo little change over long periods interrupted only by short periods of rapid change.
    E) New species appear suddenly and unpredictably.

Answer: A
Topic: 14.11
Skill: Conceptual Understanding

41) One of the finest available sequences of fossils shows how horses have changed slowly and by subtle steps from small shrub–browsing ancestors to the large, grass–grazing modern horse. A large number of fossil species have been named, and it is often difficult to decide on the identity of a fossil horse because transitional forms are common. This record of evolution best fits the idea of
    A) the gradualism model.
    B) punctuated equilibrium.
    C) adaptive radiation.
    D) inheritance of acquired characteristics.
    E) hybrid breakdown.

Answer: A
Topic: 14.11
Skill: Application

42) The fossil record shows that for many plant and animal groups, the time between speciation events
    A) is 4,000 years or less.
    B) is usually about 50,000 years.
    C) varies greatly, but is usually greater than 500,000 years and averages 6.5 million years.
    D) is always greater than 40 million years.
    E) is equivalent to the length of a single generation of a species.

Answer: C
Topic: 14.11
Skill: Factual Recall

Art Questions

1)

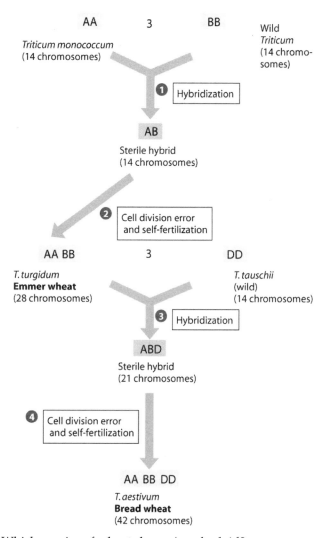

Which species of wheat shown is polyploid?
- A) *T. monococcum*
- B) wild *Triticum*
- C) the AB sterile hybrid
- D) *T. turgidun*
- E) *T. tauschiii*

Answer: D
Topic: 14.5, 14.6
Skill: Application

2)

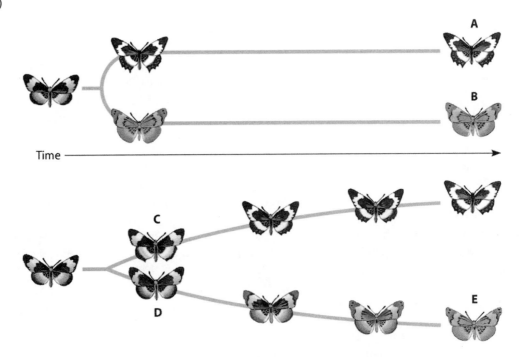

Which butterfly has changed gradually but significantly from its ancestor through microevolutionary events that were not part of a speciation event?

A) butterfly A
B) butterfly B
C) butterfly C
D) butterfly D
E) butterfly E

Answer: E
Topic: 14.11
Skill: Application

Scenario Questions

After reading the following paragraph, answer the question(s) below.

In 2004, scientists announced the discovery of the fossil remains of some extremely short early humans on the Indonesian island of Flores. The new species has been named *Homo floresiensis*. It evolved from *Homo erectus*, another early human species. How did a population of *H. erectus* become isolated on this remote island? Early humans constructed boats and rafts, so perhaps they were blown far off course by strong winds during a storm.

H. erectus averaged almost 6 feet in height, but the remains show that adults of *H. floresiensis* were only about 3 feet tall. It's hypothesized that limited resources on this hot and humid island (only 31 square miles) exerted selection pressure and succeeding generations began to shrink in size. Small bodies require less food, use less energy, and are easier to cool than larger individuals. Evolution of small size in similar circumstances has been observed in many other species, but never before in humans. This find demonstrates that evolutionary forces operate on humans in the same way as on all other organisms.

1) The evolution of *Homo floresiensis* is an example of
  A) sympatric speciation.
  B) allopatric speciation.
  C) adaptive radiation.
  D) hybridization.
  E) punctuated equilibrium.

Answer: B
Topic: 14.4, 14.7
Skill: Conceptual Understanding

2) If *H. floresiensis* were reunited with *H. erectus* at a much later date, but the two populations could no longer interbreed, it would be correct to conclude that *H. floresiensis*
  A) had experienced genetic drift.
  B) is no longer fertile as a species.
  C) had been isolated for more than 50,000 years.
  D) has become less fit than *H. erectus*.
  E) had evolved reproductive barriers.

Answer: E
Topic: 14.8
Skill: Application

Chapter 15 Tracing Evolutionary History

Multiple-Choice Questions

1) Which of the following statements correctly describes the relationship between pterosaurs and birds?
   A) Birds descend from pterosaurs and inherited their flight ability from them.
   B) Birds descend from feathered dinosaurs. Pterosaurs are a distinct group that went extinct about the time that birds arose.
   C) Birds, bats, and pterosaurs are all descendants of a common winged ancestor.
   D) Birds have membranous wings, which distinguishes them from pterosaurs, which were feathered.
   E) The evolutionary relationship between birds and pterosaurs remains uncertain because no fossils exist that help to determine the relationship.

   Answer: B
   Topic: Opening Essay
   Skill: Conceptual Understanding

2) The "big bang" that produced the universe is thought to have occurred
   A) 50 trillion years ago.
   B) 40 billion years ago.
   C) 10 to 20 billion years ago.
   D) 4.6 billion years ago.
   E) 4 million years ago.

   Answer: C
   Topic: 15.1
   Skill: Factual Recall

3) When the Earth first solidified, what were conditions like?
   A) The atmosphere was similar to today's atmosphere, but there was more volcanic activity.
   B) The atmosphere was rich in gases released in volcanic eruptions, but otherwise physical conditions were similar to those seen on Earth today.
   C) The atmosphere was rich in gases released in volcanic eruptions, and volcanic activity was intense, but very little ultraviolet light reached Earth's surface because of the thick atmosphere.
   D) The atmosphere was rich in gases released in volcanic eruptions; volcanic activity, lightning, and ultraviolet radiation were all much more intense than on today's Earth.
   E) It was just like Earth today, except there was no life.

   Answer: D
   Topic: 15.1
   Skill: Factual Recall

4) The earliest discovered fossils are of _____ dating back to _____ years ago.
   A) single–celled eukaryotes . . . 4.5 billion
   B) prokaryotes . . . 3.5 billion
   C) algae . . . 1 billion
   D) fish . . . 600 million
   E) dinosaurs . . . 180 million

Answer: B
Topic: 15.1
Skill: Factual Recall

5) The findings of Pasteur and others have established that
   A) living organisms regularly self–assemble (arise spontaneously) from nonliving matter.
   B) living organisms do not arise from nonliving matter today, nor did they arise from nonlife in the past.
   C) advanced organisms cannot arise from nonliving matter, but simple microbial life often does arise from nonlife today.
   D) even advanced organisms such as insects can arise spontaneously from nonliving matter if conditions are right.
   E) life does not arise from nonliving matter today, but in the conditions of early Earth, such an event could have occurred.

Answer: E
Topic: 15.1
Skill: Conceptual Understanding

6) Miller was the first to show that
   A) amino acids and other organic molecules could have been generated on a lifeless Earth.
   B) the earliest forms of life were photosynthetic.
   C) eukaryotic life evolved from early prokaryotes.
   D) the primitive atmosphere contained ammonia and methane.
   E) the earliest forms of life had an RNA genome.

Answer: A
Topic: 15.2
Skill: Factual Recall

7) Which highly reactive gas was probably absent from the Earth's primitive atmosphere?
   A) methane
   B) nitrogen
   C) carbon dioxide
   D) O_2 (oxygen gas)
   E) water vapor

Answer: D
Topic: 15.2
Skill: Factual Recall

8) What was the probable role of oxygen gas in the early stages of life's appearance on Earth?
   A) Cellular respiration, which depends on oxygen availability, provided abundant energy to the first life forms.
   B) Oxygen promoted the formation of complex organic molecules through physical processes.
   C) Oxygen gas tends to disrupt organic molecules, so its absence promoted the formation and stability of complex organic molecules on the early Earth.
   D) Abundant atmospheric oxygen would have created an ozone layer, which blocked out ultraviolet light and thereby protected the earliest life forms.
   E) The lack of oxygen forced organisms to develop cellular respiration.

Answer: C
Topic: 15.2
Skill: Conceptual Understanding

9) Experiments and chemical principles suggest that _____ powered the synthesis of complex organic compounds on prebiotic Earth.
   A) mild heat from the sun
   B) lightning or intense ultraviolet radiation
   C) water currents
   D) the built-in tendency of atoms to join into complex molecules
   E) oxygen

Answer: B
Topic: 15.2
Skill: Factual Recall

10) Miller-Urey-type experiments have shown that
    A) simple cells could be produced in the laboratory using a "soup" of small organic molecules.
    B) complex organic molecules can be produced by physical processes from inorganic components.
    C) living cells could survive in primitive Earth's atmosphere.
    D) microspheres could be formed from amino acids.
    E) given the conditions of early Earth, the formation of life would still require additional materials from meteorites and asteroids.

Answer: B
Topic: 15.2
Skill: Conceptual Understanding

11) Which of the following environments is thought to have promoted the dehydration synthesis of polypeptides and other macromolecules from smaller organic monomers on a prebiotic Earth?
    A) quiet saltwater bodies
    B) freshwater swamps and marshes
    C) deep-sea hydrothermal vents
    D) hot sand, clay, or rock along the seashore
    E) sediments at the bottom of the world's oceans

Answer: D
Topic: 15.3
Skill: Conceptual Understanding

12) _____ are membranes containing concentrated organic molecules and have some lifelike properties, but are not alive.
    A) Prokaryotes
    B) Polypeptides
    C) Protobionts
    D) Ribozymes
    E) Pseudocells

Answer: C
Topic: 15.3
Skill: Factual Recall

13) A current leading hypothesis about the first system of inheritance in the earliest life forms involves
    A) self–replicating DNA molecules (the "DNA world" hypothesis).
    B) self–replicating RNA molecules aided by ribozymes.
    C) proteins that served as templates for RNA molecules, leading to the formation of DNA.
    D) self–replicating polypeptides aided by ribosomes.
    E) lipids that directed the synthesis of simple proteins.

Answer: B
Topic: 15.3
Skill: Factual Recall

14) Some RNA molecules can function like enzymes. These particular enzymatic RNA molecules are called
    A) enzoRNA.
    B) proteins.
    C) eRNA.
    D) ribozymes.
    E) renzymes.

Answer: D
Topic: 15.3
Skill: Factual Recall

15) Which of the following options lists major events in the history of life on Earth in the proper order, from earliest to most recent?
    A) first prokaryotes; photosynthesis; colonization of land by plants and fungi; first eukaryotes
    B) first eukaryotes; photosynthesis; colonization of land by plants and fungi; first prokaryotes
    C) first prokaryotes; first eukaryotes; photosynthesis; colonization of land by plants and fungi
    D) first prokaryotes; photosynthesis; first eukaryotes; colonization of land by plants and fungi
    E) photosynthesis; first prokaryotes; first eukaryotes; colonization of land by plants and fungi

Answer: D
Topic: 15.4
Skill: Conceptual Understanding

16) Plants and fungi first became established on land during the
    A) Archaean.
    B) early Proterozoic.
    C) late Proterozoic.
    D) Paleozoic.
    E) Cenozoic.

Answer: D
Topic: 15.4
Skill: Factual Recall

17) If all of Earth's history were compressed into an hour, humans would first appear less than
    A) 1 second ago.
    B) 10 seconds ago.
    C) 1 minute ago.
    D) 10 minutes ago.
    E) 50 minutes ago.

Answer: A
Topic: 15.4
Skill: Application

18) The technique called radiometric dating is based on
    A) the steady, clocklike decay of certain radioactive isotopes over time.
    B) the assumption that radioactive isotopes accumulate in fossils at a constant rate.
    C) the formation of radioactive molecules in rocks after they are laid down.
    D) the conversion of carbon–12 to carbon–14 after an organism dies.
    E) the use of fossils of known age to determine how fast carbon–14 decays.

Answer: A
Topic: 15.5
Skill: Factual Recall

19) The $^{14}C:^{12}C$ ratio can be used to date fossils that are up to approximately how old?
    A) 100 million years
    B) 7 million years
    C) 75,000 years
    D) 7,500 years
    E) 750 years

Answer: C
Topic: 15.5
Skill: Factual Recall

20) You find the frozen remains of a woolly mammoth in an Alaskan glacier. You analyze a bit of the tusk and find that its ^{14}C:^{12}C ratio is about one-fourth (25%) of the baseline level typically found in living organisms. Given that the half-life of ^{14}C is 5,730 years, when did the mammoth die?
   A) 5,730 years ago
   B) almost 12,000 years ago
   C) at least 25,000 years ago
   D) approximately 75,000 years ago
   E) over one million years ago

Answer: B
Topic: 15.5
Skill: Application

21) If an isotope has a half-life of 4 million years, and a fossil is 16 million years old, how much of the original isotope will be found in the fossil?
   A) all of the original amount
   B) half the original amount
   C) one-quarter of the original amount
   D) one-eighth of the original amount
   E) one-sixteenth of the original amount

Answer: E
Topic: 15.5
Skill: Application

22) Potassium-40 can be used to date _____ that are _____ old.
   A) fossils . . . thousands of years
   B) volcanic rocks and associated fossils . . . hundreds of millions of years
   C) potassium-rich fossils . . . millions of years
   D) sedimentary rocks . . . hundreds of years
   E) carbon-containing materials . . . up to 75,000 years

Answer: B
Topic: 15.5
Skill: Factual Recall

23) The Mesozoic era is often called the age of reptiles. Which of the following also occurred during this era?
   A) the origin of animals in the oceans
   B) the first plants appeared on land
   C) the first animals (tetrapods and insects) appeared on land
   D) the first mammals and flowering plants appeared on land
   E) the first primates appeared

Answer: D
Topic: 15.6
Skill: Factual Recall

24) The earliest known land plants date to the
A) Precambrian.
 B) Ordovician (early Paleozoic era).
 C) Carboniferous (late Paleozoic era).
 D) Jurassic (Mesozoic era).
 E) Oligocene (Cenozoic era).

Answer: B
Topic: 15.6
Skill: Factual Recall

25) Which of the following options correctly lists the varieties of life in the order that they appear in the geologic record, from earliest to most recent?
A) amphibians; reptiles; land arthropods; plants and fungi on land; flowering plants
 B) plants and fungi on land; flowering plants; amphibians; land arthropods; reptiles
 C) land arthropods; plants and fungi on land; flowering plants; reptiles; amphibians
 D) plants and fungi on land; land arthropods; amphibians; reptiles; flowering plants
 E) plants and fungi on land; land arthropods; reptiles; amphibians; flowering plants

Answer: D
Topic: 15.6
Skill: Factual Recall

26) The earliest known flowering plants date to the
A) Precambrian.
 B) Paleozoic.
 C) Triassic (early Mesozoic era).
 D) Cretaceous (late Mesozoic era).
 E) Cenozoic.

Answer: D
Topic: 15.6
Skill: Factual Recall

27) Geologists have evidence that over the past 1.5 billion years,
A) Earth's continents have remained essentially in their current shape and positions.
 B) Earth's continents have joined into a single continent and split back apart again once.
 C) Earth's land masses have joined into a single continent and split back apart again on three occasions.
 D) Earth's land masses have moved about extensively but have remained separate.
 E) Earth's land masses have been entirely submerged in water on three occasions.

Answer: C
Topic: 15.7
Skill: Factual Recall

28) Earth's continents and seafloors together form a thin outer layer of the planet called the
    A) mantle.
    B) crust.
    C) strata.
    D) biosphere.
    E) Pangean supercontinent.

Answer: B
Topic: 15.7
Skill: Factual Recall

29) How is the merging of continents to form Pangaea believed to have altered Earth's
    environments at the end of the Paleozoic era?
    A) It eliminated all multicellular eukaryotes, allowing evolution to start anew.
    B) It reduced the extent of coastal and shallow–sea environments, leading to the
       extinction of many marine species.
    C) It made the climate warmer and moister for terrestrial organisms in the center of the
       new land mass.
    D) It reduced competition among terrestrial organisms by producing new barriers to
       dispersal.
    E) It prompted an immediate increase in Earth's biodiversity.

Answer: B
Topic: 15.7
Skill: Conceptual Understanding

30) It is estimated that the modern continents began to take shape
    A) 3.5 billion years ago.
    B) 1.3 million years ago.
    C) 650 million years ago.
    D) 65 million years ago.
    E) 6,000 years ago.

Answer: D
Topic: 15.7
Skill: Factual Recall

31) When the continent of Pangaea first split apart, it formed
    A) a northern landmass called Laurasia and a southern landmass called Gondwana.
    B) thousands of small islands that later joined to form the modern continents.
    C) a western landmass corresponding to North and South America and an eastern
       landmass corresponding to the other modern continents.
    D) a western landmass corresponding to North and South America, an eastern
       landmass corresponding to Eurasia, and a southern landmass corresponding to
       Africa, Australia, India, and Antarctica.
    E) an array of landmasses similar to the current ones in a single separation along
       multiple existing fractures.

Answer: A
Topic: 15.7
Skill: Factual Recall

32) The Himalayas are an example of a mountain range formed as a result of
  A) the collision of two continental plates.
  B) the lateral sliding of one continental plate alongside another.
  C) the separation of two continental plates.
  D) the buildup of sediments and conversion to rock.
  E) volcanic eruptions.

Answer: A
Topic: 15.7
Skill: Factual Recall

33) Which of the following lines of evidence suggests that lungfishes evolved while Pangaea was intact?
  A) Modern lungfishes on different continents show similar patterns of behavior.
  B) Lungfishes are found today in Africa, Australia, and South America.
  C) Fossil lungfishes have been found on every continent except Antarctica.
  D) Lungfishes are restricted to Australia and neighboring islands.
  E) Lungfishes are present on North America but not South America.

Answer: C
Topic: 15.7
Skill: Conceptual Understanding

34) Geological evidence indicates that two land masses became separated by a deep ocean channel 45 million years ago and have been moving apart ever since. You are studying a group of organisms that is widespread as a native part of the biota on both of the land masses. What can you conclude about the group's evolutionary history?
  A) The group's ancestors *were definitely present* on the original land mass before it broke up.
  B) The group's ancestors *cannot have been present* on the original land mass before it broke up.
  C) It depends on the dispersal abilities of the organism. If the organism cannot move across the open ocean, it is very likely that the group's ancestors were present on the original land mass before it broke up.
  D) Nothing. Continental drift is a geological theory and cannot shed light on biological evolution.
  E) The group's ancestors *must* have independently colonized each of the land masses from a third location within the past 45 million years.

Answer: C
Topic: 15.7
Skill: Application

35) Over the past 500 million years, _____ mass extinctions have occurred in which at least _____ of the species on Earth became extinct.
  A) two . . . 25%
  B) two . . . 50%
  C) five . . . 25%
  D) five . . . 50%
  E) twelve . . . 96%

Answer: D
Topic: 15.9
Skill: Factual Recall

36) During the _____, over 96% of marine species and many terrestrial species became extinct, possibly because intense volcanic activity warmed Earth's climate.
    A) Precambrian
    B) Permian
    C) Cretaceous
    D) Mesozoic
    E) Cenozoic

Answer: B
Topic: 15.9
Skill: Factual Recall

37) One of the strongest lines of evidence of a meteor or comet impact in the late Cretaceous is
    A) the extinction of the dinosaurs.
    B) the increase in the diversity of mammals.
    C) a thin layer of potassium–40 in late Cretaceous fossil strata.
    D) a thin layer of iridium–enriched clay in late Cretaceous fossil strata.
    E) the warming of Earth's climate in the late Cretaceous.

Answer: D
Topic: 15.9
Skill: Factual Recall

38) Scientists evaluating the Cretaceous mass extinctions have concluded that
    A) many factors, including climate change, volcanic activity, and an extraterrestrial impact, may have played a role.
    B) only an extraterrestrial impact could have caused such a big extinction event.
    C) climate change could not have been involved in producing the extinctions.
    D) there is no evidence of increased volcanic activity during the late Cretaceous.
    E) ecological factors such as disease and competition probably caused the dinosaurs to go extinct.

Answer: A
Topic: 15.9
Skill: Conceptual Understanding

39) Mass extinctions
    A) remove many species, but they are replaced within a million years or less by an even greater diversity of life.
    B) mainly serve to "weed out" poorly adapted organisms and make room for new, more advanced species.
    C) permanently and irreversibly reduce the total number of species on Earth.
    D) remove well–adapted species and groups from the Earth, so that it may take tens of millions of years for species diversity to recover.
    E) are caused by human activity and did not occur prior to the expansion of the Earth's human population.

Answer: D
Topic: 15.9
Skill: Conceptual Understanding

40) Over the past 400 years, humans have documented the extinction of more than _____ species. This modern rate of species extinction is estimated to be _____ the normal extinction rate seen in the fossil record.
   A) 100 . . . about the same as
   B) 400 . . . about double
   C) 1,000 species . . . about ten times greater than
   D) 1,000 . . . over 100 times greater than
   E) 10,000 . . . t least 1 million times greater than

Answer: D
Topic: 15.9
Skill: Factual Recall

41) Scientists believe that a major factor promoting the adaptive radiation of mammals was probably
   A) their development of fur.
   B) the mass extinction of most dinosaurs, an event that opened up new ecological opportunities.
   C) internal fertilization.
   D) their tetrapodal body plan, which gave mammals new capabilities.
   E) the origin and diversification of flowering plants.

Answer: B
Topic: 15.10–Evolution Connection
Skill: Factual Recall

42) How can the success of one group of organisms promote the adaptive radiation of a second group?
   A) by providing new food resources, habitats, etc. for the second group
   B) by competing with the second group, promoting its adaptive radiation
   C) by preying on the second group, which hastens its adaptation
   D) by developing new adaptations, which are then "copied" by the second group through directed mutation
   E) by filling most of the available niches, which forces the second group to evolve greater diversity

Answer: A
Topic: 15.10–Evolution Connection
Skill: Conceptual Understanding

43) According to "evo–devo" thinking, an organism's body form can be substantially changed
   A) only through multiple mutations that produce a large number of new proteins.
   B) through mutations that change sexually selected traits.
   C) only when changes in the environment directly alter the major protein–coding genes in the organism's genome.
   D) through better nutrition.
   E) through mutations or changes in the expression of one or a few "master control" genes that regulate development.

Answer: E
Topic: 15.11
Skill: Conceptual Understanding

44) In the axolotl, development is altered. Adult axolotls retain features (external gills and aquatic life) that were juvenile in its ancestors, a phenomenon known as
    A) "evo–devo."
    B) paedomorphosis.
    C) delinquent evolution.
    D) evolutionary novelty.
    E) homology.
Answer: B
Topic: 15.11
Skill: Factual Recall

45) Studies of skull structure suggest that the main genetic differences between humans and chimpanzees are
    A) due not so much to the genes themselves, but rather in how genes are expressed during development.
    B) due to the fact that humans have a greater total number of genes, which makes humans more complex.
    C) related to the unique nature of the sexual life cycle in humans, since humans are diploid and chimpanzees are not.
    D) differences in the proteins our genes can produce.
    E) limited to a few key brain proteins, which account for the extraordinary intelligence of *Homo sapiens*.
Answer: A
Topic: 15.11
Skill: Conceptual Understanding

46) The example of the stickleback indicates that morphology can be altered
    A) only by changing the sequences of protein–coding genes.
    B) by changing where and when a gene is expressed, but only if the gene itself is also altered.
    C) by altering the expression of a developmental gene in some parts of the body but not others.
    D) by environmental factors (in this case, pollution).
    E) by the elimination of a gene (*Pitx1*) from a population, which leads to loss of the trait (body armor and spines).
Answer: C
Topic: 15.11
Skill: Conceptual Understanding

47) Anti–evolutionary thinkers sometimes argue that natural selection could not produce a complex structure like the vertebrate eye. They claim that all of the parts of the eye must have arisen at once, asking why natural selection would favor the development of *part* of an eye that is not yet capable of forming a focused image. Which of the following statements is consistent with a survey of eye structure in the molluscs?

    A) The argument has a great deal of merit. Only full–blown image–forming eyes are present in modern organisms.

    B) There are many intermediate stages of eye complexity that fulfill different adaptive functions.

    C) The vertebrate eye must have arisen by a very dramatic single mutation within an eyeless ancestor.

    D) The vertebrate eye is the ancestral form, and other types of organisms have degenerate eyes that have lost most of their original structure and function.

    E) The vertebrate eye is completely distinct from the eyes found in molluscs and other invertebrates.

Answer: B
Topic: 15.12
Skill: Conceptual Understanding

48) The concept of _____ suggests that feathers originally evolved _____.

    A) adaptation . . . for flight

    B) adaptation . . . for some other function and only later became adapted for flight

    C) exaptation . . . in anticipation of future use in the development of flight

    D) exaptation . . . for some other function and only later became adapted for flight

    E) exaptation . . . because the ancestors to birds needed to evolve flight to deal with a changing environment

Answer: D
Topic: 15.12
Skill: Conceptual Understanding

49) Over a span of several thousand years, a number of species show adaptations to climate change: drier, warmer conditions select for succulent vegetation and deep taproots in plants, burrowing in mammals and amphibians, and other similar adaptive changes. What will happen if the climate shifts in the opposite direction and becomes progressively wetter and cooler?

    A) Ongoing processes of adaptation will continue because of evolutionary inertia.

    B) The current trend toward hardiness in dry conditions is consistent with evolution's overall goal of making organisms better–prepared to deal with stress, so it will continue.

    C) Different adaptive trends will probably be favored in the new climatic environment.

    D) Current adaptive trends will continue but organisms will now also have to add on adaptations to deal with cool, wet conditions.

    E) Adaptation will cease because cool, wet conditions are generally favorable for life.

Answer: C
Topic: 15.13
Skill: Application

50) The model of species selection is analogous to natural selection. In this analogy, _____ are like individuals within a population, and _____ is analogous to reproduction.
   A) major groups of organisms . . . extinction
   B) species . . . speciation
   C) populations . . . the founding of new populations
   D) genes . . . gene duplication
   E) families . . . interbreeding

Answer: B
Topic: 15.13
Skill: Factual Recall

51) Structures that evolved from the same structure in a common ancestor are
   A) homologous.
   B) heterologous.
   C) analogous.
   D) homoplasies.
   E) convergent adaptations.

Answer: A
Topic: 15.14
Skill: Factual Recall

52) The process through which species not closely related may come to resemble one another if they live in a similar environment is known as
   A) coevolution.
   B) homology.
   C) similar evolution.
   D) convergent evolution.
   E) paedomorphosis.

Answer: D
Topic: 15.14
Skill: Factual Recall

53) Cave-dwelling catfish and cave-dwelling salamanders share striking similarities: both organisms lack pigmentation and their eyes are reduced or absent. The most recent common ancestor to these organisms had normal pigmentation and fully developed eyes. The similarities between cave catfish and cave salamanders are an example of
   A) convergent homology.
   B) analogy (convergent evolution).
   C) homology.
   D) exaptation.
   E) coincidental similarity.

Answer: B
Topic: 15.14
Skill: Application

54) The similarities in function of hummingbird wings and the wings of a butterfly reflect
    A) homology but not analogy.
    B) homology through convergent evolution.
    C) analogy and homology.
    D) analogy but not homology.
    E) analogy, homology, and convergent evolution.

Answer: D
Topic: 15.4
Skill: Application

55) You notice that a structure is similar between two organisms. The outward appearance of the structure is not very similar, but the feature is quite complex and there are many striking similarities in the fine details of how it is put together. Which of the following is most probable?
    A) The organisms both inherited the structure from a common ancestor that had a similarly arranged structure.
    B) The organisms each independently evolved the structure.
    C) The organisms independently evolved the structure, and the similarities are explained by the similar environments in which they evolved.
    D) The organisms probably are not related by ancestry.
    E) There is more going on than meets the eye. The details must be similar for some adaptive reason; this is probably the only structural design that can function effectively.

Answer: A
Topic: 15.14
Skill: Application

56) Ever since Darwin, systematics has tried to
    A) organize species into groups based on logical categories.
    B) classify species in groups that reflect evolutionary relationships.
    C) classify species in groups that predict their characteristics.
    D) prove the existence of evolution using laboratory experiments.
    E) keep classification and naming as a practical science, separate from controversies involving evolution.

Answer: B
Topic: 15.15
Skill: Conceptual Understanding

57) Which of the following options lists taxonomic categories in the correct order from most specific to most general?
    A) genus, family, class, order, phylum
    B) genus, phylum, family, order, class
    C) genus, family, order, class, phylum
    D) family, genus, order, phylum, class
    E) family, genus, class, order, phylum

Answer: C
Topic: 15.15
Skill: Factual Recall

58) _____ and _____ mean the same thing.
   A) Clade . . . parsimony
   B) Parsimony . . . analogy
   C) Clade . . . monophyletic taxon
   D) Derived . . . ancestral
   E) Derived . . . outgroup

Answer: C
Topic: 15.16
Skill: Conceptual Understanding

59) In mammals, the presence of four limbs is _____ and hair is _____.
   A) an optional feature . . . a required feature
   B) a shared derived character . . . a shared ancestral character that places mammals in the tetrapod clade
   C) a shared ancestral character . . . a shared derived character unique to mammals
   D) a homologous feature . . . an analogous feature
   E) monophyletic . . . parsimonious

Answer: C
Topic: 15.16
Skill: Factual Recall

60) A systematist includes a lizard in a phylogenetic analysis of relationships among bird families. In this analysis, the lizard would be treated as
   A) the ingroup.
   B) the outgroup.
   C) a derived group.
   D) an analogous group.
   E) an independent origin of avian traits.

Answer: B
Topic: 15.16
Skill: Application

61) In accordance with the principle of parsimony, scientists prefer
   A) simpler phylogenetic trees that minimize the number of evolutionary changes.
   B) complex phylogenetic trees in which adaptations repeatedly arise, disappear, and reappear.
   C) phylogenetic trees with many small clades to those with a few major clades.
   D) phylogenetic trees to nonphylogenetic classifications.
   E) the Linnaean system of nomenclature to the use of common names.

Answer: A
Topic: 15.16
Skill: Conceptual Understanding

62) A mother comes home to find cookie crumbs on the kitchen counter and children who are not interested in eating any dinner. She asks if they ate cookies and they deny doing so. Instead, the children explain that a pack of dogs broke into the home and ate the cookies. Then the dogs left. Now the kids don't feel like eating. The mother doubts the story, using the principle of
  A) parsimony.
  B) phylogenetic analysis.
  C) inheritance of acquired characteristics.
  D) natural selection.
  E) outgroup comparison.

Answer: A
Topic: 15.16
Skill: Application

63) How can a phylogenetic tree be used to make predictions?
  A) Current trends of evolution will continue into the future. Complex models can be used to accurately predict future branching patterns and the nature of future adaptations.
  B) Features shared between two groups are likely to have been present in their common ancestor.
  C) Features found in one clade are likely to be found in other clades inhabiting different environments.
  D) Complex predictions based on phylogenetic trees can be compared to simpler predictions based on parsimony.
  E) An existing organism's characteristics can be confidently assumed to fit the patterns in the tree. This procedure eliminates the need to collect data about organisms through direct observation or sampling.

Answer: B
Topic: 15.16
Skill: Conceptual Understanding

64) The existence of nest-building in crocodiles and birds led to a prediction that this behavior was also present in _____.
  A) fossil lizards
  B) Komodo dragons
  C) fossil dinosaurs
  D) invertebrates
  E) alligators

Answer: C
Topic: 15.16
Skill: Conceptual Understanding

65) _____ makes it possible to trace phylogenies among microbial groups for which there is no fossil record.
   A) Parsimony
   B) Cladistic analysis of derived morphological traits
   C) Comparison to vertebrate outgroups
   D) Horizontal gene transfer
   E) Molecular systematics

Answer: E
Topic: 15.17
Skill: Factual Recall

66) Molecular data can be used to assess relationships among the major groups of living organisms whose common ancestors lived millions or billions of years ago. Similar techniques can be used to assess relationships among populations within a species. How can molecular techniques be useful for such varied comparisons?
   A) Scientists are generally skeptical about using molecular data to infer phylogeny, regardless of the degree of relatedness among the species involved.
   B) You have to look at a lot more genes if you want to compare closely related species.
   C) The same data can be used for any comparison with equal efficiency.
   D) Faster–evolving gene sequences provide better data for comparisons among close relatives, whereas very slowly evolving sequences work best for distantly related taxa.
   E) The relationships between very different groups such as bacteria and whales are assessed using mtDNA sequences, whereas rRNA sequences are used for very closely related groups.

Answer: D
Topic: 15.17
Skill: Conceptual Understanding

67) Which of the following statements regarding genetics is *false*?
   A) Genes shown to have a reliable average rate of change can be used as a molecular clock.
   B) In keeping with our greater complexity, the human genome has about 100 times more genes than that of yeast.
   C) Gene duplication helps to explain how mammals can detect and discriminate among such a wide range of odors.
   D) About 99% of the genes of humans and mice are related by descent from a common ancestor.
   E) The more recently two species have branched from a common ancestor, the more similar we expect their DNA sequences to be.

Answer: B
Topic: 15.17
Skill: Factual Recall

68) How do scientists calibrate a molecular clock for a group of organisms with known nucleotide sequences?
   A) They measure differences in morphology. Body shape evolves at a constant rate, so scientists convert body shape change to mutation rates and then use the clock on groups whose body measurements are uncertain.
   B) They measure protein differences. Evolutionary rates in proteins are well-known and can be used to check results obtained using nucleotide sequences.
   C) They use radioactive isotopes to measure the age of DNA material directly.
   D) They graph the number of nucleotide differences against the dates of evolutionary branch points known from the fossil record.
   E) They analyze fossilized DNA of known age and compare its nucleotide sequences to modern DNA sequences.

Answer: D
Topic: 15.18
Skill: Conceptual Understanding

69) Divergence time estimates based on molecular clocks are
   A) best interpreted with caution, since they depend on assumptions that are difficult to test.
   B) likely to be correct plus or minus a few decades.
   C) probably worthless since we cannot directly observe divergence times unless we invent a time machine.
   D) more reliable than divergence dates that are based on analysis of the fossil record.
   E) only reliable if the same evolution rate is used for all genes, taxa, and time periods.

Answer: A
Topic: 15.18
Skill: Conceptual Understanding

70) A(n) _____ has been used to estimate that HIV-1 M first spread to humans in the 1930s.
   A) parsimony analysis
   B) cladistic method
   C) epidemiological study
   D) outgroup comparison
   E) molecular clock

Answer: E
Topic: 15.18
Skill: Factual Recall

71) You compare homologous nucleotide sequences between several pairs of species with known divergence times. A pair of species that diverged 1 million years ago has two nucleotide differences, a pair that diverged 2 million years ago has four nucleotide differences, and a pair that diverged 3 million years ago has six nucleotide differences. You have sequence data for another pair of species where the divergence time is unknown. There are five nucleotide differences between them. Based on your clock, when did their line of ancestry diverge?
   A) 4 million years ago
   B) 3.5 million years ago
   C) 3 million years ago
   D) 2.5 million years ago
   E) 2 million years ago

Answer: D
Topic: 15.18
Skill: Application

72) In the three-domain system, the eukaryotes are represented
   A) only within the domain Eukarya.
   B) only within the domain Archaea.
   C) by the domains Bacteria and Archaea.
   D) by the kingdom Protista.
   E) in all three domains.

Answer: A
Topic: 15.19
Skill: Factual Recall

73) The three-domain system
   A) no longer recognizes eukaryotes as a monophyletic group.
   B) subdivides the eukaryotes into two different domains.
   C) subdivides the prokaryotes into two different domains.
   D) separates plants, animals, and fungi into domains.
   E) is based upon the presence or absence of cell walls.

Answer: C
Topic: 15.19
Skill: Factual Recall

74) The branching "tree of life" analogy
   A) accurately reflects evolution. Once a split occurs, species on different branches evolve absolutely independently.
   B) has been discredited because it does not help us understand evolutionary relationships among organisms.
   C) does not describe ecological interactions between species, so it should be replaced by the web of life.
   D) fails to account for horizontal gene transfer, in which species on different branches exchange genes.
   E) cannot be true because each domain began with an independent origin of life from nonliving matter.

Answer: D
Topic: 15.19
Skill: Conceptual Understanding

Art Questions

1)

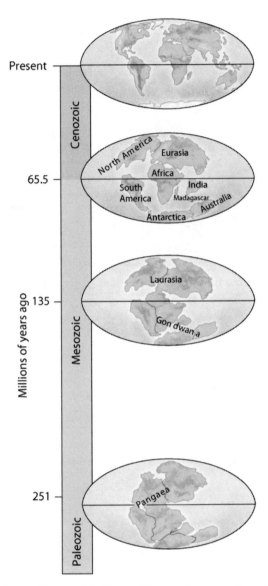

According to this figure, if a species were found only in Laurasia 135 million years ago, on which modern continents would its descendants most likely be found today?

    A) North America only
    B) Europe and Asia only
    C) North America, Europe, and Asia
    D) Africa and South America
    E) Africa, South America, Antarctica and Australia

Answer: C
Topic: 15.7
Skill: Application

2)

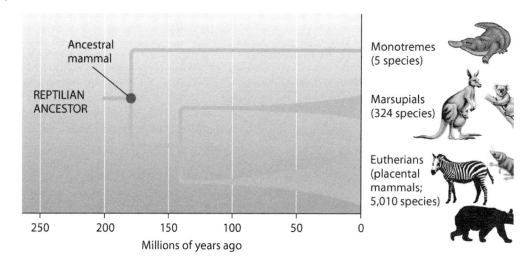

Adapted from Hickman, Roberts, and Larson. 1997, *Zoology*, 10/e, Wm. C. Brown, fig. 31.1.

According to this figure, during what time frame was there an adaptive radiation of eutherians?
    A) about 200 million years ago
    B) about 170 million years ago
    C) about 140 million years ago
    D) from 140 to 100 million years ago
    E) from 100 million years ago to the present

Answer: E
Topic: 15.10
Skill: Application

Scenario Questions

After reading the following paragraph, answer the question(s) below.

The first fossil of *Archaeopteryx*, which lived about 150 million years ago, was found in the Solnhofen Quarry in Germany. *Archaeopteryx* has an interesting collection of characteristics that led to the hypothesis that it represented an evolutionary transition between birds and small bipedal dinosaurs. The fossil reveals the imprint of feathers, which connect *Archaeopteryx* to birds, although they don't present direct evidence of flight.

Unlike birds, however, the fossil record reveals that *Archaeopteryx* had teeth, functional claws on the wings that may have been used for climbing trees or holding prey, and a long, bony tail. Birds have a fused collarbone, and this was found in *Archaeopteryx* also. However, there were differences in the structure of the sternum. In birds, the sternum is keeled (raised and slightly concave). The keel of the sternum serves as an attachment site for the flight muscles. *Archaeopteryx* had a flat sternum, similar to that found in reptiles.

1) The feathers of *Archaeopteryx* may have been used for flight. However, it's likely that their original function was for
    A) insulation.
    B) protection from predators.
    C) swimming.
    D) nest building.
    E) protection from parasites.

Answer: A
Topic: 15.12
Skill: Factual Recall

2) If you were constructing a phylogenetic tree for the evolution of birds, which characteristics found in *Archaeopteryx* might provide evidence that birds and dinosaurs had a common ancestor?
    A) feathers, wings, wishbone
    B) claws, feathers, hollow bones
    C) teeth, feathers, keeled sternum
    D) teeth, flat sternum, claws
    E) keeled sternum, claws, long forelimbs

Answer: D
Topic: 15.12; 15.16
Skill: Factual Recall

Chapter 16 The Origin and Evolution of Microbial Life: Prokaryotes and Protists

Multiple-Choice Questions

1) A stromatolite is
   A) a distinctive layered structure formed by heterotrophic bacteria.
   B) a distinctive layered structure formed by photosynthetic prokaryotes.
   C) an early protozoan.
   D) a fossil layer containing plants.
   E) a living algal mat formed by plasmodial slime molds.

   Answer: B
   Topic: Opening Essay
   Skill: Conceptual Understanding

2) Which of the following organisms first introduced oxygen into Earth's atmosphere?
   A) cyanobacteria
   B) methanogens
   C) early protozoans
   D) plants
   E) green algae

   Answer: A
   Topic: Opening Essay
   Skill: Factual Recall

3) Individual prokaryote cells are about _____ eukaryote cells; collectively, all prokaryote cells on Earth _____.
   A) the same size as . . . weigh about one-tenth the total mass of eukaryote cells
   B) ten times bigger than . . . weigh about ten times as much as the total mass of eukaryote cells
   C) one-tenth as big as . . . weigh about one-tenth the total mass of eukaryote cells
   D) one-tenth as big as . . . weigh about as much as the total mass of eukaryote cells
   E) one-tenth as big as . . . weigh about ten times as much as the total mass of eukaryote cells

   Answer: E
   Topic: 16.1
   Skill: Factual Recall

4) Eukaryotes are _____ prokaryotes.
   A) more ancient than
   B) more important in chemical cycling than
   C) dependent upon
   D) more widespread than
   E) more numerous than

   Answer: C
   Topic: 16.1
   Skill: Conceptual Understanding

5) Prokaryotes are classified into
    A) domain Monera and domain Archaea.
    B) kingdom Bacteria and kingdom Archaea.
    C) domain Bacteria and domain Archaea.
    D) kingdom Protista and kingdom Monera.
    E) domain Bacteria and domain Monera.

Answer: C
Topic: 16.2
Skill: Factual Recall

6) Evidence for the relatively close relationship of archaea to eukaryotes includes
    A) the absence of ribosomes in both of these groups.
    B) the absence of introns from genes in both groups.
    C) the fact that both contain circular DNA without histones.
    D) the presence of peptidoglycan in the cell walls of both groups.
    E) the fact that their growth is not inhibited by certain antibiotics that inhibit bacterial growth.

Answer: E
Topic: 16.2
Skill: Factual Recall

7) Unlike archaean and eukaryote cell walls, bacterial cell walls contain a unique substance called
    A) cellulose.
    B) peptidoglycan.
    C) phospholipid.
    D) glycogen.
    E) proteinoid.

Answer: B
Topic: 16.2
Skill: Factual Recall

8) Pairs of rod–shaped bacteria are called
    A) cocci.
    B) bacilli.
    C) diplobacilli.
    D) spirochetes.
    E) vibrios.

Answer: C
Topic: 16.3
Skill: Factual Recall

9) Curved bacterial cells that are shaped like commas are called
    A) cocci.
    B) bacilli.
    C) diplobacilli.
    D) spirochetes.
    E) vibrios.

Answer: E
Topic: 16.3
Skill: Factual Recall

10) Prokaryotic cell walls function
    A) as a site for phagocytosis.
    B) to promote flexibility and formation of pseudopodia.
    C) to prevent the cell from bursting in a hypotonic environment.
    D) to propel cells (locomotion).
    E) as a site of metabolic reactions (photosynthesis and cellular respiration).

Answer: C
Topic: 16.4
Skill: Factual Recall

11) An unknown bacterial species is recovered from a sick patient's digestive tract. It has a membrane outside the cell wall that contains toxic lipids. This observation indicates
    A) that the infection should be relatively easy to control with common antibiotics, because the pathogen is a gram–positive species.
    B) that the infection should be relatively easy to control with common antibiotics, because the pathogen is a gram–negative species.
    C) that the infection may be quite threatening and difficult to control, because the pathogen is a gram–positive species.
    D) that the infection may be quite threatening and difficult to control, because the pathogen is a gram–negative species.
    E) that the infective agent forms endospores.

Answer: D
Topic: 16.4
Skill: Application

12) Which of the following options correctly pairs a structure with its function in prokaryote cells?
    A) pili = help prokaryotes stick to each other and to surfaces
    B) capsule = rigid protective structure enclosing cell
    C) flagella = feeding appendages
    D) endospore = food digestion vacuole
    E) cell wall = food absorption membrane

Answer: A
Topic: 16.4
Skill: Factual Recall

13) You culture the dried soup from a 4,000–year–old cooking pot found in an Egyptian tomb and obtain a distinctive species of prokaryote. You immerse a test tube of these bacteria in boiling water for several hours, but the colony grows back. This species is probably
    A) halophilic.
    B) a methanogen.
    C) endospore-forming.
    D) a spirochete.
    E) a cyanobacteria.

Answer: C
Topic: 16.4
Skill: Application

14) Prokaryotes
    A) have membrane–enclosed organelles that are important in cell respiration and photosynthesis.
    B) sometimes have folded internal membranes that are important in cell respiration and photosynthesis.
    C) have ribosomes but never have any kind of internal membranes within their cells.
    D) do not have ribosomes or any kind of internal cell membranes.
    E) have a genome that is bigger than is typical for eukaryotes, especially if plastids are included in the gene count.

Answer: B
Topic: 16.4
Skill: Factual Recall

15) Prokaryote genomes often include a central ring of DNA plus small accessory rings of DNA that carry genes involved in "contingency" functions. These secondary rings of DNA are called
    A) flagella.
    B) pili.
    C) endospores.
    D) ribosomes.
    E) plasmids.

Answer: E
Topic: 16.4
Skill: Factual Recall

16) Chemoautotrophic bacteria obtain their carbon from _____ and their energy from
_____ .
    A) CO_2 . . . sunlight
    B) CO_2 . . . reactions involving inorganic chemicals
    C) methane . . . sunlight
    D) organic molecules . . . enzymes
    E) organic molecules . . . sunlight

Answer: B
Topic: 16.5
Skill: Factual Recall

17) The largest group of prokaryotes is the _____, which obtain both energy and carbon from _____.
    A) autotrophs . . . inorganic molecules
    B) chemoautotrophs . . . decaying organic material
    C) chemoheterotrophs . . . organic molecules
    D) photoautotrophs . . . light
    E) parasites . . . a living host

Answer: C
Topic: 16.5
Skill: Factual Recall

18) A bacterium living in an underground septic tank thrives by absorbing organic compounds from decomposing wastes. What is it?
A) a chemoautotroph
B) a chemoheterotroph
C) a photoautotroph
D) a photoheterotroph
E) a hemotroph

Answer: B
Topic: 16.5
Skill: Application

19) A slimy layer of bacteria coating a surface is also known as a _____.
A) prokaryocommune
B) bioaggregate
C) tissue
D) biofilm
E) plague

Answer: D
Topic: 16.5
Skill: Factual Recall

20) Intestinal gas is evidence of active _____ in one's digestive tract.
A) thermophiles
B) digestive enzymes
C) methanogens
D) yeast cultures
E) halophiles

Answer: C
Topic: 16.6
Skill: Factual Recall

21) Which of the following is a member of the domain Archaea?
A) proteobacteria
B) gram–positive bacteria
C) methanogens
D) spirochetes
E) chlamydias

Answer: C
Topic: 16.6
Skill: Factual Recall

22) Which of the following organisms are common soil decomposers and grow in a filamentous mass of branched cell chains that superficially resembles a fungus?
A) actinomycetes
B) basidiomycetes
C) yeasts
D) halobacteria
E) cocci

Answer: A
Topic: 16.7
Skill: Factual Recall

23) Cyanobacteria
   A) are photosynthetic archaea.
   B) are eukaryotes and are the earliest type of algae.
   C) are chemoautotrophs.
   D) are of the same nutritional type as the earliest forms of life.
   E) are the only prokaryotes with plantlike oxygen-generating photosynthesis.

Answer: E
Topic: 16.7
Skill: Factual Recall

24) _____ are toxic proteins secreted by pathogenic bacteria, whereas _____ are components of the outer membrane of gram-negative pathogens.
   A) Endotoxins . . . phosphotoxins
   B) Endotoxins . . . botulinum toxins
   C) Toxozymes . . . endotoxins
   D) Exotoxins . . . enterotoxins
   E) Exotoxins . . . endotoxins

Answer: E
Topic: 16.8
Skill: Factual Recall

25) Which of the following causes food poisoning and typhoid fever?
   A) *E. coli*
   B) *Staphylococcus aureus*
   C) *Bacillus anthracis*
   D) *Clostridium botulinum*
   E) *Salmonella*

Answer: E
Topic: 16.8
Skill: Factual Recall

26) A patient comes to the doctor with a large red rash, shaped like a bull's-eye with a clear patch in the center. Originally there was a tick bite in the middle of the rash. The patient lives in a suburban area of the United States where deer are common. Which of the following diseases will the physician immediately suspect?
   A) syphilis
   B) anthrax
   C) smallpox
   D) Lyme disease
   E) malaria

Answer: D
Topic: 16.8
Skill: Application

27) The three diseases that represent high–priority threats as biological weapons today are
   A) smallpox, influenza, and typhus.
   B) syphilis, *Chlamydia*, and HIV.
   C) anthrax, plague, and botulinum toxin.
   D) anthrax, smallpox, and *Thiobacillus.*
   E) syphilis, plague, and typhus.

Answer: C
Topic: 16.9
Skill: Factual Recall

28) Which of the following statements best describes the status of biological weapons research and use today?
   A) Biological weapons are routinely used in all military conflicts by both legitimate governments and terrorist organizations.
   B) Since 1975 the United States has not operated a publicly acknowledged offensive bioweapons program. However, the United States has continued defensive research and development, and terrorist organizations have developed and used biological weapons.
   C) Since September 11, 2001, the United States has publicly acknowledged and accelerated its offensive bioweapons research and development programs as a means of deterring terrorists from using biological weapons against the U.S. population.
   D) Terrorist groups and deranged individuals have refrained from using biological weapons because they fear that they will be killed by their own weapons.
   E) The Soviet Union and the United States remain locked in a bioweapons arms race; most experts agree that the Soviet Union is lagging behind at this point, but U.S. research and bioweapons production continue to accelerate.

Answer: B
Topic: 16.9
Skill: Conceptual Understanding

29) The use of prokaryotes and other organisms to clean up pollution is called _____.
   A) biofilm uptake
   B) decomposition
   C) nitrogen fixation
   D) bioremediation
   E) biocomposting

Answer: D
Topic: 16.10
Skill: Factual Recall

30) The trickling filter at a sewage treatment plant works by
  A) passing wastewater through fine sand, mechanically removing fine pollution particles.
  B) forcing wastewater through a membrane filtration system, producing drinkable water.
  C) passing wastewater through a thick bed of rocks that contain chemicals that sterilize the water and neutralize chemical pollutants or bind with them to produce a harmless precipitate.
  D) passing wastewater through a thick bed of rocks. Biofilms of bacteria and fungi on the rocks absorb and decompose organic material dissolved in the wastewater.
  E) adding fertilizer to wastewater and passing it through a culture medium rich in oil–eating prokaryotes.

Answer: D
Topic: 16.10
Skill: Conceptual Understanding

31) _____ are heterotrophic protists; _____ are photoautotrophic protists.
  A) Protozoans . . . protoplants
  B) Protozoans . . . algae
  C) Protozoans . . . plants
  D) Fungi . . . algae
  E) Fungi . . . plants

Answer: B
Topic: 16.11
Skill: Factual Recall

32) The term for a close association between organisms of two or more species is
  A) symbiosis.
  B) interdependence.
  C) associative living.
  D) colonialism.
  E) mutualism.

Answer: A
Topic: 16.11
Skill: Factual Recall

33) Which of the following options lists the events of protist evolution in the correct order, according to current science?
  A) Mitochondria evolved through primary endosymbiosis; chloroplasts then evolved through secondary endosymbiosis.
  B) Chloroplasts and then mitochondria evolved through primary endosymbiosis; later, protozoans were incorporated into several other groups of protists through secondary endosymbiosis.
  C) Mitochondria and then chloroplasts evolved through primary endosymbiosis; later, protozoans were incorporated into several other groups of protists through secondary endosymbiosis.
  D) Chloroplasts and then mitochondria evolved through primary endosymbiosis; later, algae were incorporated into several other groups of protists through secondary endosymbiosis.
  E) Mitochondria and then chloroplasts evolved through primary endosymbiosis; later, algae were incorporated into several other groups of protists through secondary endosymbiosis.

Answer: E
Topic: 16.12
Skill: Conceptual Understanding

34) Euglenazoans, dinoflagellates, apicomplexans, and stramenopiles all are protists groups in which some—but not all—species are photoautotrophic. According to current thinking, the organelles that enable photosynthesis in these groups are
  A) chloroplasts that formed when their ancestors engulfed cyanobacteria.
  B) chloroplasts derived from land plants through horizontal gene transfer.
  C) remnants of plants that their ancestors tried to eat.
  D) remnants of green or red algae that their ancestors tried to eat.
  E) complex infoldings of the plasma membrane like those that enable photosynthesis in cyanobacteria.

Answer: D
Topic: 16.12
Skill: Conceptual Understanding

35) Protists include
  A) a single clade of eukaryotes that are distantly related to animals.
  B) two clades of eukaryotes: one that is related to animals, and another that is related to fungi and plants.
  C) a diverse mix of eukaryotes that formed through multiple origins of the eukaryotic cell.
  D) two clades of eukaryotes: algae and protozoans.
  E) multiple clades of eukaryotes: some that are closely related to plants, and others that are closely related to animals and fungi.

Answer: E
Topic: 16.13
Skill: Conceptual Understanding

36) Diplomonads
    A) have mitochondria with no DNA or electron transport chains.
    B) are photoautotrophic.
    C) require high concentrations of oxygen gas.
    D) group.
    E) include the malaria parasite.

Answer: A
Topic: 16.14
Skill: Factual Recall

37) While on a camping trip, you drink untreated stream water. After a few days you develop severe diarrhea. Microscopic examination of a fecal sample from you is most likely to reveal
    A) *Plasmodium,* an apicomplexan.
    B) *Trypanosoma,* a euglenazoan.
    C) *Paramecium,* an apicomplexan parasite.
    D) *Giardia,* a parasitic diplomonad.
    E) *Amoeba,* a cause of severe dysentery.

Answer: D
Topic: 16.14
Skill: Application

38) Which of the following causes African sleeping sickness?
    A) *Plasmodium,* an apicomplexan
    B) *Trypanosoma,* a euglenazoan
    C) *Paramecium,* an apicomplexan parasite
    D) *Giardia,* a parasitic diplomonad
    E) *Amoeba,* a cause of severe dysentery

Answer: B
Topic: 16.15
Skill: Factual Recall

39) Alveolates are characterized by
    A) membrane–enclosed sacs under the plasma membrane.
    B) membrane–enclosed nuclei, each with more than one nucleolus.
    C) mitochondria that do not have an outer mitochondrial membrane.
    D) flagella that lack microtubules.
    E) abundant ribosomes that pack the cytoplasm.

Answer: A
Topic: 16.16
Skill: Factual Recall

40) Dinoflagellates are best described as
   A) protozoans that use cilia to move and feed.
   B) protozoans that live in the guts of termites.
   C) marine and freshwater algae that can produce harmful red tides.
   D) parasitic protozoans that must spend part of their life cycles in vertebrate hosts.
   E) large, multicellular algae that resemble plants but do not have true leaves, stems, or roots.

Answer: C
Topic: 16.16
Skill: Factual Recall

41) *Plasmodium,* the organism that causes malaria, is a(n)
   A) amoeba.
   B) stramenopile.
   C) ciliate.
   D) apicomplexan.
   E) dinoflagellate.

Answer: D
Topic: 16.16
Skill: Factual Recall

42) _____ are stramenopiles that commonly are found decomposing dead animals in freshwater habitats.
   A) Diatoms
   B) Brown algae
   C) Water molds
   D) Cellular slime molds
   E) Plasmodial slime molds

Answer: C
Topic: 16.17
Skill: Factual Recall

43) Which of the following groups include organisms that are a key source of food in all aquatic environments and whose fossilized forms are used as a filter and as a grinding and polishing agent?
   A) diatoms
   B) brown algae
   C) ameobozoans
   D) dinoflagellates
   E) apicomplexans

Answer: A
Topic: 16.17
Skill: Factual Recall

44) Kelp and many other seaweeds are stramenopiles known as
    A) water molds.
    B) brown algae.
    C) green algae.
    D) euglenozoans.
    E) diatoms.

Answer: B
Topic: 16.17
Skill: Factual Recall

45) Which of the following cellular structures is characteristic of amoebas?
    A) pseudopodia
    B) microvilli
    C) cilia
    D) flagella
    E) stereocilia

Answer: A
Topic: 16.18
Skill: Factual Recall

46) Plasmodial slime molds
    A) are photoautotrophic.
    B) are marine decomposers.
    C) contain many nuclei in one mass of cytoplasm.
    D) reproduce only by asexual division.
    E) are primitive fungi.

Answer: C
Topic: 16.18
Skill: Factual Recall

47) You collect a protist from a rotting log and grow it in a petri dish containing *E. coli*, which it engulfs. For a while the protists multiply as single cells. Then the *E. coli* run short, and the protists aggregate to form a clump, which rises up to become a stalked structure with a globular head. What kind of protist have you got?
    A) an actinomycete
    B) a plasmodial slime mold
    C) a cellular slime mold
    D) a free–living amoeba
    E) a water mold

Answer: C
Topic: 16.18
Skill: Application

48) Which three groups of protists all produce hard mineralized skeletal structures or cell walls that contribute to marine sediments and form fossils?
    A) green algae, brown algae, and diatoms
    B) diatoms, forams, and radiolarians
    C) dinoflagellates, diatoms, and green algae
    D) diplomonads, radiolarians, and apicomplexans
    E) amoebas, trypanosomes, and apicomplexans

Answer: B
Topic: 16.17, 16.19
Skill: Factual Recall

49) There is a good chance you will eat carrageenan today and that you will eat nori at some point in your life, if you haven't already. In either case, you will be eating a product of
    A) cyanobacteria.
    B) brown algae.
    C) red algae.
    D) green algae.
    E) diatoms.

Answer: C
Topic: 16.20
Skill: Factual Recall

50) Seaweeds
    A) are marine plants.
    B) are all members of the brown algae.
    C) lack true stems, roots, and leaves.
    D) are generally toxic to humans.
    E) reproduce strictly through asexual mechanisms.

Answer: C
Topic: 16.17, 16.20
Skill: Factual Recall

51) In what way does the green alga *Ulva* resemble land plants?
    A) It produces diploid gametes.
    B) It has a complex life cycle with diploid body cells and haploid gametes.
    C) It has a complex life cycle with alternation between multicellular diploid and haploid generations.
    D) It has a multicellular haploid stage that alternates with a unicellular diploid stage.
    E) It has true stems, roots, and leaves and is good to eat, hence its common name, "sea lettuce."

Answer: C
Topic: 16.20
Skill: Factual Recall

52) According to current scientific thinking, true multicellular organisms
    A) are all descended from a single colonial protist ancestor.
    B) descend from several different kinds of unicellular protists, which became
        multicellular through specialization and cooperation among cells within a colony.
    C) cannot be traced to any existing or fossil intermediate stages; thus, there is no
        current scientific theory for the process that generated multicellular organisms from
        unicellular ancestors.
    D) formed through the fusion of several separate species of unicellular protists, who
        carried out different complementary functions within the evolving organism.
    E) include only animals.

Answer: B
Topic: 16.21
Skill: Conceptual Understanding

53) The first multicellular eukaryotes appeared about _____ years ago, and the first
    multicellular life on land appeared about _____ years ago.
    A) 3.5 billion . . . 1.2 billion
    B) 1.5 billion . . . 1.2 billion
    C) 1.2 billion . . . 500 million
    D) 600 million . . . 200 million
    E) 120 million . . . 50 million

Answer: C
Topic: 16.21
Skill: Factual Recall

Art Questions

1)

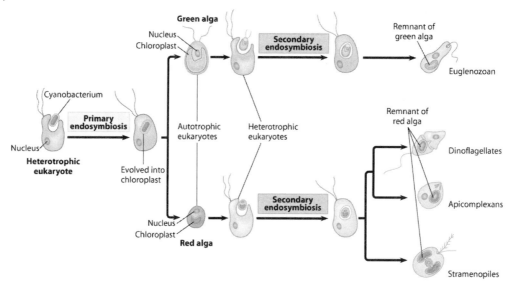

According to the figure, which type of protist resulted from a single endosymbiosis event in its ancestry?

A) red algae
B) dinoflagellates
C) apicomplexans
D) stramenophiles
E) euglenozoa

Answer: A
Topic: 16.12
Skill: Application

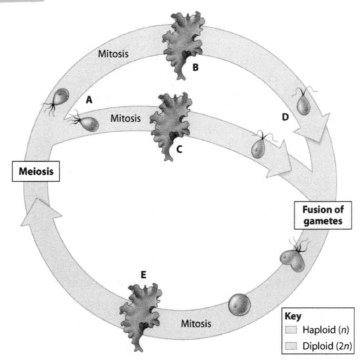

Which stage of the life cycle shown is the sporophyte?
    A) stage A
    B) stage B
    C) stage C
    D) stage D
    E) stage E

Answer: A
Topic: 16.20
Skill: Factual Recall

Scenario Questions

After reading the following paragraph, answer the question(s) below.

In the 1930s, the Navajo Nation treated sheep and cattle for ticks and other parasites by using concrete "dip tanks." Animals were herded through one end of the tank and out the other. Each day, the tanks were filled with 200,000 gallons of insecticide and any remaining chemicals were emptied onto the ground. The pesticide solution seeped into the ground, ditches, and pits around the tanks. This was a common practice in the United States during that period.

The EPA Emergency Response Team (ERT) was called to the Navajo Nation during the 1990s to investigate the problem. They concluded that bioremediation procedures were the best for this site. Certain types of bacteria are able to feed on and digest toxic organic substances, such as pesticides, and use them as fuel for cell respiration. The ERT distributed the pesticide–eating microorganisms through the contaminated soil to remove the chemical residues. Once the contaminants are degraded, these microorganism populations die off because they've used all of their food supply.

1) The degraded pesticides are converted to _____ by bacterial respiration.
   A) sugars and oxygen
   B) inactive chemical residues
   C) arsenic and other heavy metals
   D) carbon dioxide and water
   E) nitrates and phosphates

   Answer: D
   Topic: 16.6, 16.10
   Skill: Conceptual Understanding

2) Based on the above scenario, the pesticide–eating bacteria probably evolved from species that
   A) fed on pesticides present on the early planet Earth.
   B) were previously adapted to feed on oil spills.
   C) fed on the tissues and blood of cattle and sheep.
   D) were previously adapted to colonize anaerobic environments.
   E) fed on molecules with a chemical structure similar to pesticides.

   Answer: E
   Topic: 16.6, 16.10
   Skill: Conceptual Understanding

Chapter 17 Plants, Fungi, and the Colonization of Land

Multiple-Choice Questions

1) The intimate, mutually beneficial association formed between a fungus and the root of a plant is called a(n)
   A) ingrowth.
   B) mycorrhiza.
   C) parasitic infection.
   D) hypha.
   E) mycelium.

   Answer: B
   Topic: Opening Essay
   Skill: Factual Recall

2) To reduce the need for fertilizers, some citrus growers
   A) add mycorrhizal fungi to the soil.
   B) eliminate harmful soil fungi.
   C) use fungicides.
   D) add mycorrhizal bacteria.
   E) eliminate harmful soil bacteria.

   Answer: A
   Topic: Opening Essay
   Skill: Factual Recall

3) The ancestors of land plants were probably _____ that lived in _____.
   A) green algae similar to charophytes . . . the open ocean
   B) green algae similar to charophytes . . . coral reef habitats
   C) green algae similar to charophytes . . . coastal marshes or lake fringes
   D) cyanobacteria . . . coastal marshes or lake fringes
   E) cyanobacteria . . . moist soil crust communities

   Answer: C
   Topic: 17.1
   Skill: Factual Recall

4) The land plants are a clade whose members all possess the following derived characters: alternation of haploid and diploid generations; walled spores produced in sporangia; multicellular, dependent embryos; and
   A) the ability to carry out photosynthesis.
   B) production of air- or animal-dispersed pollen grains.
   C) cell walls reinforced by lignin.
   D) male and female gametangia to protect gametes.
   E) xylem tissue to facilitate transport.

   Answer: D
   Topic: 17.1
   Skill: Conceptual Understanding

5) Gas exchange in most land plants occurs through structures called
   A) stomata.
   B) spiracles.
   C) phloem.
   D) gas pores.
   E) cuticles.

Answer: A
Topic: 17.1
Skill: Factual Recall

6) The _____, a zone of rapid cell division that produces growth, is found at primary root and stem tips.
   A) sporangium
   B) cuticle
   C) apical meristem
   D) lignin
   E) gametangium

Answer: C
Topic: 17.1
Skill: Conceptual Understanding

7) In plants, the vascular tissue made of dead cells that transport water and minerals from the roots is called
   A) xylem.
   B) phloem.
   C) stomata.
   D) transport tissue.
   E) meristem.

Answer: A
Topic: 17.1
Skill: Factual Recall

8) In plants, the vascular tissue that consists of living cells that distribute sugars throughout the plant is called
   A) xylem.
   B) phloem.
   C) stomata.
   D) transport tissue.
   E) meristem.

Answer: B
Topic: 17.1
Skill: Factual Recall

9) In all plants, the zygote and earliest stages of the developing embryo are
   A) enclosed within a seed.
   B) a free–living, independent phase of the sexual life cycle.
   C) enclosed within a pollen grain.
   D) attached to and nourished by the parent plant.
   E) able to disperse in a tough–walled spore.

Answer: D
Topic: 17.1
Skill: Factual Recall

10) Mosses belong to the group of plants known as the
   A) angiosperms.
   B) gymnosperms.
   C) bryophytes.
   D) vascular plants.
   E) lichens.

Answer: C
Topic: 17.2
Skill: Factual Recall

11) Which of the following statements regarding ferns is *true*?
   A) Ferns do not have lignified cell walls.
   B) Ferns have well–developed vascular tissue, roots, and stems.
   C) Ferns produce seeds.
   D) Ferns produce pollen.
   E) Ferns reproduce effectively in dry conditions.

Answer: B
Topic: 17.2
Skill: Factual Recall

12) The majority of plant species today are
   A) angiosperms.
   B) bryophytes.
   C) gymnosperms.
   D) lycophytes.
   E) seedless vascular plants.

Answer: A
Topic: 17.2
Skill: Conceptual Understanding

13) Which of the following characteristics tends to limit bryophytes and seedless vascular plants to habitats that are relatively moist?
   A) absence of cuticle
   B) presence of flagellated sperm
   C) presence of free–living, independent zygotes and early embryos
   D) presence of lignified vascular tissues
   E) presence of seeds and pollen

Answer: B
Topic: 17.2
Skill: Conceptual Understanding

14) Which of the following options correctly represents the most likely sequence of the evolution of plants, from earliest to most recent?
   A) bryophytes, seedless vascular plants, gymnosperms, angiosperms
   B) seedless vascular plants, bryophytes, angiosperms, gymnosperms
   C) bryophytes, seedless vascular plants, angiosperms, gymnosperms
   D) bryophytes, gymnosperms, seedless vascular plants, angiosperms
   E) seedless vascular plants, angiosperms, bryophytes, gymnosperms

Answer: A
Topic: 17.2
Skill: Factual Recall

15) The type of life cycle seen in plants is called
   A) haplodiploidy.
   B) gametophyte production.
   C) alternation of generations.
   D) sporophytic regeneration.
   E) cyclic reproduction.

Answer: C
Topic: 17.3
Skill: Conceptual Understanding

16) Which of the following statements correctly describes the alternation of generations in a plant life cycle?
   A) Diploid sporophytes that produce spores by meiosis alternate with haploid gametophytes that produce gametes by mitosis.
   B) Diploid sporophytes that produce gametes by meiosis alternate with haploid sporophytes that produce gametes by mitosis.
   C) Diploid gametophytes that produce gametes by meiosis alternate with diploid sporophytes that produce spores by mitosis.
   D) Diploid gametophytes that produce spores by mitosis alternate with haploid sporophytes that produce gametes by meiosis.
   E) Diploid gametophytes that produce gametes by meiosis alternate with haploid sporophytes that produce spores by mitosis.

Answer: A
Topic: 17.3
Skill: Factual Recall

17) The dominant stage of mosses is the
   A) sporophyte.
   B) gametangium.
   C) pollen.
   D) ovule.
   E) gametophyte.

Answer: E
Topic: 17.4
Skill: Factual Recall

18) Ferns and mosses are similar because both
    A) produce drought-resistant seeds.
    B) have dominant sporophytes.
    C) have diploid gametophytes.
    D) have flagellated sperm.
    E) have sporophytes that produce diploid spores.

Answer: D
Topic: 17.4, 17.5
Skill: Factual Recall

19) In a moss, most of the plants that we see are _____, while in a fern the most dominant
    stage is the _____.
    A) gametophytes . . . gametophyte
    B) gametophytes . . . sporophyte
    C) sporophytes . . . gametophyte
    D) sporophytes . . . sporophyte
    E) sporangia . . . gametangium

Answer: B
Topic: 17.4, 17.5
Skill: Conceptual Understanding

20) Which of the following organisms has a dominant sporophyte generation and a
    free-living gametophyte generation?
    A) moss
    B) fern
    C) mushroom
    D) conifer
    E) human

Answer: B
Topic: 17.5
Skill: Factual Recall

21) About 95% of all modern plant species
    A) have a dominant sporophyte in their life cycle.
    B) have no sporophyte.
    C) have no gametophyte.
    D) have a gametophyte adapted to house a sporophyte stage.
    E) have flagellated sperm.

Answer: A
Topic: 17.5
Skill: Factual Recall

22) Heavy production and deposition of organic material during the Carboniferous period led to
    A) global warming.
    B) the thinning of the ozone layer.
    C) the production of coal.
    D) the evolution of lycophytes.
    E) the formation of tropical swamps.

Answer: C
Topic: 17.6
Skill: Factual Recall

23) Carboniferous deposition of organic material removed _____ from the atmosphere, which produced a drier, cooler global climate and promoted the success of _____.
    A) oxygen . . . ferns
    B) oxygen . . . seed plants
    C) carbon dioxide . . . lycophytes
    D) carbon dioxide . . . seed plants
    E) water vapor . . . cacti and succulents

Answer: D
Topic: 17.6
Skill: Conceptual Understanding

24) Which part of the life cycle does a pollen grain represent?
    A) a spore
    B) a sperm cell
    C) a male gametophyte
    D) a male sporangium
    E) a male sporophyte

Answer: C
Topic: 17.7
Skill: Factual Recall

25) Which of the following represents the male gametophyte of a conifer?
    A) pollen grain
    B) sperm
    C) spore
    D) tree
    E) ovule

Answer: A
Topic: 17.7
Skill: Factual Recall

26) Which of the following plants has a dominant sporophyte generation and a seed, but no fruit?
    A) fern
    B) pine tree
    C) tulip
    D) lycophyte
    E) moss

Answer: B
Topic: 17.7
Skill: Application

27) The _____ represents the sporophyte generation of a conifer, and the _____ produces gametophytes.
    A) cone . . . tree
    B) tree . . . cone
    C) tree . . . pollen
    D) tree . . . seed
    E) seed . . . tree

Answer: B
Topic: 17.7
Skill: Conceptual Understanding

28) Two characteristics shared by gymnosperms and angiosperms that are absent from earlier plant groups and represent key adaptations to life on dry land are
    A) a vascular system and lignin.
    B) flagellated sperm and gametangia.
    C) gametophyte and sporophyte generations.
    D) flowers and fruits.
    E) pollen and seeds.

Answer: E
Topic: 17.7
Skill: Conceptual Understanding

29) Pollen grains develop in the _____ and are trapped by the _____.
    A) anther . . . stigma
    B) stigma . . . anther
    C) anther . . . ovary
    D) stigma . . . ovary
    E) carpel . . . stamen

Answer: A
Topic: 17.8
Skill: Factual Recall

30) The _____ is the protective chamber that houses the ovule and later matures to become the fruit.
    A) petal
    B) ovary
    C) carpel
    D) sepals
    E) stigma

Answer: B
Topic: 17.8
Skill: Factual Recall

31) To cross-fertilize flowers A and B, one would first remove flower A's immature _____ and later transfer pollen from flower B to flower A's _____.
    A) carpel . . . ovule
    B) anthers . . . stamen
    C) stamens . . . stigma
    D) stigma . . . style
    E) sepals . . . petals

Answer: C
Topic: 17.8
Skill: Application

32) The angiosperm plant we see represents the _____ generation, and the flower produces _____.
    A) sporophyte . . . gametophytes
    B) sporophyte . . . bryophytes
    C) gametophyte . . . sporophytes
    D) gametophyte . . . bryophytes
    E) seed . . . sporophytes

Answer: A
Topic: 17.9
Skill: Factual Recall

33) Some of the unique adaptations of angiosperms include their beneficial relationships with _____ and their relatively _____.
    A) animals . . . well-developed vascular system
    B) animals . . . rapid fertilization and seed production
    C) animals . . . large sporophyte
    D) fungi . . . well-developed vascular system
    E) fungi . . . slow seed maturation

Answer: B
Topic: 17.8, 17.9
Skill: Factual Recall

34) The ripened ovary of a flower, which is adapted to disperse seeds, is called a(n)
    A) ovule.
    B) casing.
    C) fruit.
    D) cone.
    E) sporangium.

Answer: C
Topic: 17.10
Skill: Factual Recall

35) Which structure is found in angiosperms but *not* gymnosperms?
    A) fruit
    B) spores
    C) seeds
    D) ovule
    E) a tube that grows from the pollen to deliver sperm

Answer: A
Topic: 17.9, 17.10
Skill: Factual Recall

36) A cocklebur is dispersed by _____, whereas most fleshy, edible fruits are eaten by animals that _____.
    A) wind . . . defecate the intact seeds
    B) wind . . . fully digest the fruits, including the seeds, which are killed
    C) water currents . . . defecate the intact seeds
    D) hitching rides on mammals . . . fully digest the fruits, including the seeds, which are killed
    E) hitching rides on mammals . . . defecate the intact seeds

Answer: E
Topic: 17.10
Skill: Factual Recall

37) Corn, rice, wheat, fleshy fruits such as apples and berries, and many spices are all produced by
    A) gymnosperms.
    B) ferns.
    C) lycophytes.
    D) angiosperms.
    E) seedless plants.

Answer: D
Topic: 17.11
Skill: Factual Recall

38) Corn, peppers, tomatoes, and cucumbers all contain seeds and are derived from the ovary of a flowering plant. Therefore, in botanical terms, they are _____.
   A) fruits.
   B) gymnosperms.
   C) vegetables.
   D) sporophytes.
   E) seeds.

Answer: A
Topic: 17.11
Skill: Factual Recall

39) Red maples and other wind-pollinated plants invest relatively little in producing _____, but must invest a great deal in producing _____ to achieve good pollination rates.
   A) floral scents . . . showy petals
   B) showy or scented flowers . . . massive amounts of pollen
   C) pollen . . . showy or scented flowers
   D) pollen . . . female flowers
   E) seeds . . . massive amounts of pollen

Answer: B
Topic: 17.12-Evolution Connection
Skill: Factual Recall

40) Which of the following features would you expect to see in the flowers of wind-pollinated grasses?
   A) very large, fragrant, white flowers
   B) petals with UV-absorbing "nectar guides"
   C) very simple flowers that produce massive quantities of pollen
   D) red flowers with long nectar tubes
   E) flowers that smell and look like rotting flesh

Answer: C
Topic: 17.12-Evolution Connection
Skill: Application

41) Plants dependent on nocturnal pollinators typically have flowers that
   A) absorb UV light.
   B) are small.
   C) have long and narrow floral tubes.
   D) are large, light-colored, and highly scented.
   E) are located close to the ground and smell of rotting flesh.

Answer: D
Topic: 17.12-Evolution Connection
Skill: Factual

42) One of the factors that helps animal–pollinated flowering plants target pollen to plants of the same species is
    A) the rapid ability of pollinators to extract nectar from any species of flower, regardless of the pollinators' past or recent experience with a given flower type.
    B) the broad use of many different types of flowers by most pollinators.
    C) the fact that pollinators have limited learning capacities and tend to stick with one type of flower once they have learned to use it.
    D) the tendency of pollinators to avoid visiting the same type of flower more than once, in case its nectar is toxic.
    E) the fact that each species of pollinator typically visits flowers of one and only one plant species.

Answer: C
Topic: 17.12–Evolution Connection
Skill: Conceptual Understanding

43) Many flower traits are specifically attractive to a certain type of pollinator. For example, the scent of rotting flesh is attractive to certain flies and beetles, but not to most other pollinators. What adaptive purpose is served by this kind of "niche marketing" of flowers to specific pollinators?
    A) This adaptation works to reduce pollinator traffic at a flower. Therefore flowers do not have to produce as much nectar to feed big crowds of pollinators.
    B) This adaptation reduces pollinator traffic so that flowers have a chance to develop their pollen fully before it is spread.
    C) This targeting is done because the wrong kind of pollinator might eat all the pollen instead of delivering it to another flower.
    D) This is favored by natural selection because otherwise certain pollinators would starve and die. Specific flowers evolve to give these pollinators a steady, reserved food source to help them survive.
    E) This adaptation helps to assure that pollen will be delivered to another flower of the same species. If less specialized pollinators are used, the odds are greater that pollen will wind up on the stigma of a different species.

Answer: E
Topic: 17.12–Evolution Connection
Skill: Conceptual Understanding

44) More than _____ of prescription drugs are extracted from plants.
    A) 5%
    B) 10%
    C) 15%
    D) 25%
    E) 50%

Answer: D
Topic: 17.13
Skill: Factual Recall

45) In the southeastern United States, almost all of the mature forest had been cleared at least once by 1910. Since then, there has been a dramatic increase in forest cover, largely through the establishment of pine plantations as a source of lumber and pulp for paper making. Compared to the forests they replace, these forests are generally
A) just as biologically diverse, but made up of smaller trees.
B) more hardy and resilient because the trees are younger.
C) less biologically diverse and less hardy and resilient.
D) composed of bigger, healthier trees because the trees are planted in evenly spaced rows and fertilized.
E) more likely to contain a great deal of genetic diversity within a given tree species.

Answer: C
Topic: 17.13
Skill: Conceptual Understanding

46) Generally, forest conservation efforts are designed to
A) stop the cutting of trees entirely so that humans and forests can live in harmony.
B) make sure that all remaining forest are protected from any kind of human use.
C) transform natural forests to more-productive tree plantations that can also be used to reverse global warming.
D) better manage forests so that our uses of trees and other forest products are compatible with the long-term maintenance of forest cover and biological diversity.
E) set the use of trees and other forest products to a level that meets or exceeds the rapid natural regeneration rate.

Answer: D
Topic: 17.13
Skill: Conceptual Understanding

47) Heterotrophic eukaryotes that digest their food externally and absorb the small molecules are referred to as
A) bacteria.
B) protozoans.
C) fungi.
D) plants.
E) multicellular algae.

Answer: C
Topic: 17.14
Skill: Factual Recall

48) Fungi are found associated with the earliest plant fossils. Fungi may have helped plants become terrestrial by
A) forming mycorrhizal associations with plants and by decomposing organic matter.
B) forming lichen–like associations with ancestral plants.
C) stocking the soil with organic matter.
D) providing simple organic compounds in return for sugars.
E) killing the bacterial enemies of plants.

Answer: A
Topic: 17.14
Skill: Factual Recall

49) Threadlike fungal filaments are called
    A) mycelia.
    B) hyphae.
    C) sporangia.
    D) root hairs.
    E) mold.
Answer: B
Topic: 17.14
Skill: Factual Recall

50) A mushroom
    A) is composed of many threadlike filaments called mycorrhizae.
    B) is specialized to obtain most of the nutrients for the fungal mycelium.
    C) is an independent stage in the alternation of generations of the fungal life cycle.
    D) is not actually part of a fungus, but is a member of a related group.
    E) is an above-ground fruiting body connected to a mycelium.
Answer: E
Topic: 17.14
Skill: Factual Recall

51) Fungi
    A) are similar to bacteria because fungi are composed of prokaryotic cells.
    B) are similar to bacteria because fungi use extracellular digestion to obtain their nutrients.
    C) are similar to green plants because fungi produce chlorophyll.
    D) differ from members of the animal kingdom because fungi are autotrophic.
    E) and green plants have cells that are surrounded by a cell wall made of cellulose.
Answer: B
Topic: 17.14
Skill: Conceptual Understanding

52) Fungi contact and absorb food through the _____, a branching network of _____.
    A) mycelium . . . hyphae
    B) hyphae . . . mycelia
    C) mycorrhiza . . . mushrooms
    D) mycelium . . . chitin
    E) mushroom . . . hyphae
Answer: A
Topic: 17.14
Skill: Conceptual Understanding

53) Which of the following structures is an essential part of most fungal reproductive systems?
    A) gametangia
    B) cellulose
    C) flowers
    D) seeds
    E) spores
Answer: E
Topic: 17.15
Skill: Factual Recall

54) The heterokaryotic phase of a fungal life cycle is
    A) a stage in which the hyphae contain only one type of haploid nucleus.
    B) a stage in which hyphae contain two, genetically different, haploid nuclei.
    C) a stage in which hyphae contain two, genetically different, diploid nuclei.
    D) a stage that is diploid but functions as a gametophyte (like the body of an animal).
    E) a triploid stage formed by the fusion of a diploid nucleus with the haploid nucleus of a compatible hypha.

Answer: B
Topic: 17.15
Skill: Factual Recall

55) Which type of reproduction is typical in many fungi, particularly molds and yeast?
    A) sexual reproduction through mating of two diploid parent mycelia
    B) sexual reproduction through fusion of two haploid parent mycelia and subsequent production of haploid spores
    C) asexual reproduction through production of haploid spores by a diploid parent
    D) asexual reproduction through production of haploid spores by a haploid parent
    E) asexual reproduction through production of diploid spores by a haploid parent

Answer: D
Topic: 17.15
Skill: Conceptual Understanding

56) The last common ancestor of animals and fungi was probably _____, like the spores of _____ fungi.
    A) flagellated . . . chytrid
    B) flagellated . . . zygote
    C) prokaryotic . . . glomeromycete
    D) multicellular . . . chytrid
    E) nonflagellated . . . chytrid

Answer: A
Topic: 17.16
Skill: Factual Recall

57) About 90% of plants have mycorrhizae linking them to
    A) chytrids.
    B) glomeromycetes.
    C) ascomycetes (sac fungi).
    D) basidiomycetes (club fungi).
    E) zygote fungi.

Answer: B
Topic: 17.16
Skill: Factual Recall

58) Most familiar types of mushrooms, along with puffballs and shelf fungi, are
 A) chytrids.
 B) ascomycetes (sac fungi).
 C) zygomycetes (zygote fungi).
 D) glomeromycetes.
 E) basidiomycetes (club fungi).

Answer: E
Topic: 17.16
Skill: Factual Recall

59) Most zygomycetes and ascomycetes reproduce _____ when conditions are _____.
 A) sexually . . . constantly moist and food is abundant
 B) sexually . . . favorable, as in the spring of the year
 C) asexually . . . favorable, as in the spring of the year
 D) asexually . . . harsh, as in the fall of the year
 E) by spores . . . windy

Answer: C
Topic: 17.17
Skill: Factual Recall

60) Which of the following occurs in a mushroom, that is, in the fruiting body of a basidiomycete?
 A) Hyphae of two different mating types fuse.
 B) Diploid nuclei form, undergo meiosis, and produce haploid spores.
 C) Heterokaryotic cells separate to re-create the original haploid hyphae.
 D) Spores germinate and form a haploid mycelium.
 E) Asexual reproduction takes place through basidiogenesis.

Answer: B
Topic: 17.17
Skill: Conceptual Understanding

61) Fungal diseases common in _____ include _____ and _____.
 A) animals . . . smuts . . . rusts
 B) plants . . . smuts . . . rusts
 C) animals . . . smuts . . . chytrids
 D) plants . . . ringworm . . . coccidioidomycosis
 E) humans . . . rusts . . . vaginal yeast

Answer: B
Topic: 17.18
Skill: Factual Recall

62) Gangrene, hallucinations, temporary insanity, and even death can result when humans consume grain infested with
 A) corn smut.
 B) chytrids.
 C) coccidioidomycosis.
 D) the yeast *Candida albicans*.
 E) ergots.

Answer: E
Topic: 17.18
Skill: Factual Recall

63) What kind of entity is a lichen?
    A) an association between a fungus and a brown alga
    B) an association between a multicellular protist related to the brown algae and a
       bacterium
    C) an association between a fungus and cyanobacteria or green algae
    D) an association between a bryophyte and a fungus
    E) an association between a bryophyte and a bacterium

Answer: C
Topic: 17.19
Skill: Factual Recall

64) You enjoy learning about history by traveling throughout North America studying
gravestones. You notice that gravestones from 1900 and earlier usually host many types
of lichens. But in one cemetery, lichens are entirely absent, even from old gravestones.
Given what is known about lichens, the cemetery without lichens probably
    A) has an unusually dry climate.
    B) is subject to extremely cold winter temperatures.
    C) gets a great deal of rain, which favors the growth of competing bacteria.
    D) has a high population of fungi that parasitize lichens.
    E) is close to a source of air pollution.

Answer: E
Topic: 17.19
Skill: Application

65) Central American leaf-cutting ants
    A) eat leaves for nutrition.
    B) use the leaves to build their homes.
    C) lay their eggs in decomposing leaves.
    D) cultivate fungal gardens on the leaves.
    E) chew up the leaves and use them for fertilizer to promote the growth of other plants
       that they eat.

Answer: D
Topic: 17.20
Skill: Factual Recall

66) Which of the following statements regarding fungi is *false*?
    A) Fungi are important decomposers in ecosystems.
    B) Fungi can only break down plant material.
    C) The distinctive flavor of certain cheeses is due to fungi.
    D) The first antibiotic discovered came from a fungus.
    E) Fungi are derived from a flagellated protistan ancestor.

Answer: B
Topic: 17.21
Skill: Factual Recall

67) An experimental forest ecosystem is enclosed in a sealed greenhouse. The entire ecosystem, including the air and soil, is treated with an extremely potent fungicide that kills all fungal life stages including spores. What will probably happen next?
   A) Tree growth will increase because the dead fungi will act as a fertilizer.
   B) Plants will enjoy a long-term increase in growth and survival because of the removal of fungal pathogens.
   C) Dead organic matter will accumulate on the forest floor; plant growth will decline because of a lack of nutrients and the loss of mycorrhizal partners.
   D) All of the plants will die immediately when they are poisoned by the death of their mycorrhizal associates.
   E) A few animals will go extinct due to loss of their fungal food sources, but otherwise the forest will be largely unchanged.

Answer: C
Topic: 17.21
Skill: Application

Art Questions

1)

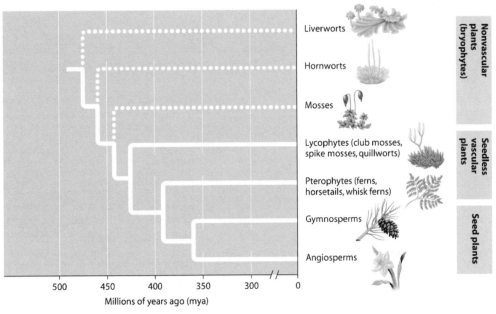

According to this figure, at what time in the evolutionary history of plants did vascular systems likely first evolve?
   A) 475 mya
   B) 460 mya
   C) 425 mya
   D) 360 mya
   E) 50 mya

Answer: C
Topic: 17.2
Skill: Application

2)

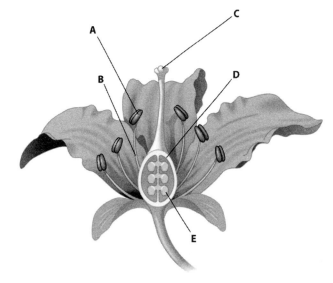

Which part of this figure represents the anther?
   A) structure A
   B) structure B
   C) structure C
   D) structure D
   E) structure E

Answer: A
Topic: 17.8
Skill: Factual Recall

Scenario Questions

After reading the following paragraph, answer the question(s) below.

Scientists believe that a shift from pollination by insects to pollination by birds occurred several times over the course of angiosperm evolution. Two researchers designed an experiment to test this hypothesis using two species of monkey flower (*Mimulus spp.*). *M. lewisii* has violet–pink flowers and is pollinated by bumblebees. *M. cardinalis* has orange–red flowers and is pollinated by hummingbirds.

The researchers switched flower–color genes between the two species. As a result of the gene transfer, they produced a variation of *M. cardinalis* with dark pink flowers (instead of the original orange–red). The new variety of *M. lewisiis* had orange flowers (instead of the original violet–pink). Plants of both genetically altered varieties were placed in their original habitats and observed. The genetically altered variety of *M. cardinalis* was visited by bumblebees 74 times more often than plants with the original color flowers. The genetically altered variety of *M. lewisii* was visited by hummingbirds 68 times more often than plants with the original color flowers.

1) Based on the results of this study, you can conclude that
  A) petal color won't contribute to speciation, since pollinators will select familiar plant species regardless of petal color.
  B) gene mutations that affect petal color will also affect nectar production.
  C) gene mutations that produce larger flowers will cause the species to become more attractive to bird pollinators.
  D) gene mutations affecting petal color can contribute to speciation through a shift in pollinator species.
  E) flower color doesn't appear to be an important factor in the speciation of flowering angiosperms.

Answer: D
Topic: 17.12
Skill: Application

2) The evolution of easily modified flower colors that make plants attractive to animals was an important factor in angiosperm evolution because
  A) plants have no way to cross–pollinate without the intervention of animals.
  B) animals are more effective at delivering pollen to other flowers than is the wind.
  C) flower color attracts animals that can disperse the seeds of the plant.
  D) successful evolution requires interactions between plants and animals.
  E) pollination by animals prevents problems with inbreeding caused by self-pollination.

Answer: B
Topic: 17.10, 17.12
Skill: Factual Recall

Chapter 18 The Evolution of Invertebrate Diversity

Multiple-Choice Questions

1) Which of the following statements about the mimic octopus is *true*?
   A) Octopuses and other invertebrates are simple, primitive life forms.
   B) Octopuses, as invertebrates, have complex chemistry and structure but their behavior is very simple.
   C) Octopuses have only one defense against predators: spraying an ink cloud.
   D) Octopuses can have complex and highly adaptive chemistry, structure, and behaviors.
   E) The mimic octopus sometimes acts like a harmless rock to avoid detection by predators.

   Answer: D
   Topic: Opening Essay
   Skill: Conceptual Understanding

2) All animals
   A) are unicellular.
   B) are prokaryotic.
   C) are heterotrophic.
   D) have cell walls made of chitin.
   E) obtain food by absorption.

   Answer: C
   Topic: 18.1
   Skill: Factual Recall

3) Typical animal embryos have _____, or external cell layer, and _____, which lines the digestive tract.
   A) an ectoderm . . . a blastula
   B) an ectoderm . . . an endoderm
   C) an endoderm . . . an ectoderm
   D) a blastula . . . a gastrula
   E) a mesoderm . . . a gastrula

   Answer: B
   Topic: 18.1
   Skill: Factual Recall

4) Which of the following is true of a typical animal?
   A) *Hox* genes play important roles in the development of the organism from zygote to adult.
   B) The organism requires carbon dioxide as an essential nutrient.
   C) The cell walls are diverse in structure but are composed of chitin.
   D) The main life stage is haploid and produces haploid gametes by mitosis.
   E) The haploid larvae develop into diploid adults.

   Answer: A
   Topic: 18.1
   Skill: Conceptual Understanding

5) Animals probably evolved from
  A) plants.
  B) protists.
  C) fungi.
  D) lichens.
  E) bacteria.

Answer: B
Topic: 18.2
Skill: Factual Recall

6) During the Cambrian explosion approximately 542 million years ago,
  A) all modern species of animals suddenly appeared over a period of about one year.
  B) animals rapidly diversified in the oceans over a period of about 1 million years.
  C) animals rapidly diversified in the oceans over a period of about 15 million years.
  D) a massive volcanic eruption nearly wiped out life on Earth.
  E) great forests produced peat layers that were later transformed into coal.

Answer: C
Topic: 18.2
Skill: Factual Recall

7) Which of the following is considered a likely explanation for the events of the Cambrian explosion?
  A) Complex predator–prey relationships and increased atmospheric oxygen levels promoted animal diversification.
  B) Complex predator–prey relationships and increased atmospheric oxygen levels led to a mass extinction event.
  C) A great surge of volcanic activity was triggered by significant movements of the continental plates and possibly by an asteroid impact.
  D) Solar flares led to increased UV radiation intensity, which in turn promoted a high rate of mutation. This led to rapid diversification of animals.
  E) The massive growth of swamp vegetation depleted the atmosphere's carbon dioxide and eventually cooled the Earth's climate.

Answer: A
Topic: 18.2
Skill: Conceptual Understanding

8) Most of the animals alive today
  A) are vertebrates.
  B) are invertebrates.
  C) are choanoflagellates.
  D) are really colonies of protist cells.
  E) are unicellular.

Answer: B
Topic: 18.2
Skill: Factual Recall

9) Which of the following animals displays radial symmetry?
   A) a worm
   B) a sea anemone
   C) a fish
   D) a lobster
   E) an alligator

Answer: B
Topic: 18.3
Skill: Factual Recall

10) Which of the following items demonstrates radial symmetry?
    A) a glove
    B) a pencil
    C) a tennis racket
    D) a pair of sunglasses
    E) an apple pie

Answer: E
Topic: 18.3
Skill: Application

11) Organisms with true radial symmetry
    A) have their sense organs, mouth, and brain clustered in the head.
    B) tend to be highly mobile.
    C) are capable of directed movement in two dimensions.
    D) do not have a distinct head region and tend to be sedentary or passive drifters.
    E) can be divided into two matching halves along only one plane.

Answer: D
Topic: 18.3
Skill: Factual Recall

12) Which of the following structures *best* represents a hydrostatic skeleton?
    A) an empty coffee mug
    B) a spoon
    C) a piece of M & M candy
    D) a glass marble
    E) a water balloon

Answer: E
Topic: 18.3
Skill: Application

13) A true coelom is best described as
   A) the space between the ectoderm and the endoderm.
   B) a body cavity that is fully lined by tissue derived from the mesoderm.
   C) a body cavity that is lined by tissues derived from the mesoderm on one side and the endoderm on the other.
   D) any body cavity that functions to cushion the internal organs and give them space for growth and movement.
   E) any body cavity that functions to provide a rigid structure against which muscles contract.

Answer: B
Topic: 18.3
Skill: Factual Recall

14) A dog's head is at its _____ end and its belly is its _____ surface.
   A) posterior . . . dorsal
   B) anterior . . . dorsal
   C) posterior . . . ventral
   D) anterior . . . ventral
   E) radial . . . bilateral

Answer: D
Topic: 18.3
Skill: Application

15) In protostomes,
   A) the opening formed during gastrulation becomes the mouth.
   B) the opening formed during gastrulation becomes the anus.
   C) there is no body cavity.
   D) there is no endoderm.
   E) there is no ectoderm.

Answer: A
Topic: 18.3
Skill: Factual Recall

16) Which of the following statements about deuterostomes is *true*?
   A) Deuterostomes lack true tissues.
   B) Deuterostomes have only two tissue layers.
   C) The opening that forms during deuterostome gastrulation becomes the anus.
   D) The opening that forms during deuterostome gastrulation becomes the mouth.
   E) Deuterostomes always lack a body cavity.

Answer: C
Topic: 18.3
Skill: Factual Recall

17) Which of the following are *not* included among the Eumetazoans, which have true tissues?
    A) sea stars (Echinodermata)
    B) earthworms (Annelida)
    C) sea anemones (Cnidaria)
    D) octopus (Mollusca)
    E) sponges (Porifera)

Answer: E
Topic: 18.4
Skill: Factual Recall

18) Which of the following are *not* included among the Bilateria, a clade of animals with bilateral symmetry at some stage of development?
    A) sea stars (Echinodermata)
    B) earthworms (Annelida)
    C) sea anemones (Cnidaria)
    D) octopus (Mollusca)
    E) lizards (Chordata)

Answer: C
Topic: 18.4
Skill: Factual Recall

19) The _____ is a flagellated cell that sweeps water through a sponge's body.
    A) choanocyte
    B) amoebocyte
    C) spicule
    D) spongin
    E) sessile body

Answer: A
Topic: 18.5
Skill: Factual Recall

20) A typical sponge is best described as
    A) a slow-moving suspension feeder with a true coelom.
    B) a sessile suspension feeder with bilateral symmetry.
    C) a slow-moving carnivore with no true tissues or symmetry.
    D) a sessile suspension feeder with no true tissues or body symmetry.
    E) a slow-moving carnivore with bilateral symmetry.

Answer: D
Topic: 18.5
Skill: Factual Recall

21) How do sponges transport nutrients within their bodies?
   A) They have simple digestive and circulatory systems composed of spongin channels.
   B) They rely on diffusion to move nutrients between their cells.
   C) Their mobile amoebocytes transport food molecules from cell to cell.
   D) They are not able to transport nutrients. They are autotrophs, so each cell absorbs its own nutrients and produces its own food.
   E) They are not able to transport nutrients within their bodies, but must independently absorb all necessary nutrients from the surrounding water.

Answer: C
Topic: 18.5
Skill: Factual Recall

22) Which of the following statements regarding cnidarians is *true*?
   A) Cnidarians have three true tissue layers.
   B) The digestive and circulatory compartment of cnidarians is called the gastrovascular cavity.
   C) The more stationary cnidarian body form, which is cylindrical with a ring of tentacles, is the medusa.
   D) The umbrella-shaped cnidarian body form that is able to move about freely in the water is a polyp.
   E) Cnidarians are herbivores and can be destructive grazers on seaweeds.

Answer: B
Topic: 18.6
Skill: Factual Recall

23) Coral reefs are
   A) shells of Mollusca that have been converted to rock by geological processes.
   B) dead bodies of coral animals (Cnidaria).
   C) hard external skeletons secreted by coral animals (Cnidaria).
   D) marine rocks that often are used as attachment places by Cnidaria.
   E) hardened sugars that are secreted by algae.

Answer: C
Topic: 18.6
Skill: Factual Recall

24) While wading in the ocean, you look down into the water and notice an umbrella-shaped, translucent animal. It swims by pulsing its body, and long tentacles trail behind it. One of them brushes your leg. Ouch! You feel a burning sensation where it touched you. To what phylum does this creature probably belong?
   A) Porifera
   B) Cnidaria
   C) Platyhelminthes
   D) Nematoda
   E) Mollusca

Answer: B
Topic: 18.6
Skill: Application

25) Flatworms (Platyhelminthes) are _____ and typically have _____.
   A) radially symmetrical . . . no digestive system
   B) bilaterally symmetrical . . . a true coelom
   C) bilaterally symmetrical . . . a gastrovascular cavity with one opening
   D) bilaterally symmetrical . . . a complete digestive tract with a mouth and anus
   E) all parasites . . . no digestive system

Answer: C
Topic: 18.7
Skill: Factual Recall

26) Tapeworms are similar to fungi because
   A) they have cell walls made of chitin.
   B) they feed by ingestion.
   C) they are sessile autotrophs.
   D) they feed by absorption.
   E) they inhabit marine, damp terrestrial, and freshwater habitats.

Answer: D
Topic: 18.1,18.7
Skill: Factual Recall

27) A bilaterally symmetrical, wormlike animal that has a pseudocoelom, a complete
   digestive tract, and a cuticle could be a member of which one of the following phyla?
   A) Cnidaria
   B) Platyhelminthes
   C) Annelida
   D) Nematoda
   E) Chordata

Answer: D
Topic: 18.8
Skill: Application

28) The digestive tract of a nematode is most like which of the following?
   A) a hot dog
   B) a sock
   C) a soda straw
   D) a cup
   E) a baseball

Answer: C
Topic: 18.8
Skill: Application

29) Which of the following is a typical characteristic of molluscs?
   A) a gastrovascular cavity with only one opening
   B) a sessile lifestyle
   C) an internal skeleton and segmented body plan
   D) three main parts of the body: head, trunk, and tail
   E) a rasping organ called the radula

Answer: E
Topic: 18.9
Skill: Factual Recall

30) Which mollusc group includes primarily sedentary animals that use mucus–coated gills to trap fine food particles as water is pumped through the mantle cavity?

A) cephalopods

B) gastropods

C) chitons

D) bivalves

E) chambered nautilus

Answer: D

Topic: 18.9

Skill: Factual Recall

31) You inflate a balloon and let it go. It shoots away as air exits forcefully through the balloon's narrow opening. This most closely resembles the mode of movement seen in

A) sea anemones.

B) snails.

C) flatworms.

D) squid.

E) nematodes.

Answer: D

Topic: 18.9

Skill: Application

32) Which adaptation is a key characteristic of annelids that greatly increases their flexibility and mobility?

A) complete digestive tract

B) hydrostatic skeleton

C) segmentation

D) hermaphroditic reproductive style

E) three true tissue layers

Answer: C

Topic: 18.10

Skill: Factual Recall

33) _____ are soil-dwellers; _____ are mostly marine; and _____ are mostly freshwater.

A) Earthworms . . . leeches . . . annelids

B) Earthworms . . . leeches . . . polychaetes

C) Earthworms . . . polychaetes . . . leeches

D) Polychaetes . . . leeches . . . earthworms

E) Polychaetes . . . earthworms . . . leeches

Answer: C

Topic: 18.10

Skill: Factual Recall

34) You find a wormlike, soft–bodied adult animal in a mud flat. It is bilaterally symmetrical, is segmented, has a true coelom, and has a complete digestive tract. Based on these characteristics, what phylum does the animal represent?
  A) Cnidaria
  B) Platyhelminthes
  C) Porifera
  D) Nematoda
  E) Annelida

Answer: E
Topic: 18.10
Skill: Application

35) Animals that are segmented and have jointed appendages and an exoskeleton are members of the phylum
  A) Platyhelminthes.
  B) Mollusca.
  C) Annelida.
  D) Cnidaria.
  E) Arthropoda.

Answer: E
Topic: 18.11
Skill: Factual Recall

36) The most numerous, diverse, and widespread animals are the
  A) Arthropoda.
  B) Mollusca.
  C) Annelida.
  D) Nematoda.
  E) Chordata.

Answer: A
Topic: 18.11
Skill: Factual Recall

37) Walking in a basement you hear a crunching noise and notice that you have killed a small animal. You look closely and see a few segmented, jointed appendages twitching around. What phylum does this animal represent?
  A) Cnidaria
  B) Echinodermata
  C) Annelida
  D) Arthropoda
  E) Chordata

Answer: D
Topic: 18.11
Skill: Application

38) Which of the following groups has a series of similar segments that make up most of the body?
   A) millipedes
   B) crustaceans
   C) arachnids
   D) scorpions
   E) insects

Answer: A
Topic: 18.11
Skill: Factual Recall

39) Which of the following groups includes both spiders and horseshoe crabs?
   A) millipedes
   B) crustaceans
   C) centipedes
   D) chelicerates
   E) insects

Answer: D
Topic: 18.11
Skill: Factual Recall

40) Most adult insects have three major body parts or sections. They are the
   A) head, body, and legs.
   B) head, thorax, and abdomen.
   C) antennae, head, and abdomen.
   D) head, legs, and wings.
   E) legs, wings, and body.

Answer: B
Topic: 18.12–Evolution Connection
Skill: Factual Recall

41) An organism that can fly and has an exoskeleton must be
   A) a crustacean.
   B) a member of the Chordata.
   C) an echinoderm.
   D) an insect.
   E) a polychaete.

Answer: D
Topic: 18.12–Evolution Connection
Skill: Conceptual Understanding

42) The traits that are unique to insects and have probably contributed to their diversity and success include
   A) small body size, an exoskeleton, and sexual reproduction.
   B) flight, short generation times, and complex life cycles including complete metamorphosis.
   C) the exoskeleton, an open circulatory system, and jointed appendages.
   D) a closed circulatory system, long adult life spans, and an elaborate central nervous system.
   E) the presence of four or more pairs of legs, an exoskeleton, and a water-resistant cuticle.

Answer: B
Topic: 18.12–Evolution Connection
Skill: Factual Recall

43) Complete metamorphosis is considered to occur in a species
   A) if the larva and adult have different diets.
   B) if the larva and adult live in different habitats.
   C) if the transition from larval to adult stage takes place in a single molt.
   D) if a pupation stage separates the larval and adult stages.
   E) if the adult has wings, but the larva does not.

Answer: D
Topic: 18.12–Evolution Connection
Skill: Conceptual Understanding

44) The insect body plan includes many groups of serially repeated units. For example, there are typically three pairs of legs, one on each of the three segments of the thorax. Which option best describes how these pairs of legs develop and evolve?
   A) A single gene controls the development of all six legs. Thus within a species, all three pairs of legs are identical.
   B) The leg pairs all influence each other during development. Gene products move by diffusion from one segment to the other. Therefore, it is impossible to alter the development and form of one pair of legs without causing similar changes in the other two pairs of legs.
   C) The body parts develop in a modular fashion. Therefore, a genetic change could alter the development of one pair of limbs without noticeably changing the rest of the insect's body plan.
   D) The leg pairs grow under the control of an ancient set of highly conserved genes. Therefore, all insects have more or less identical legs. Other parts of the insect body plan can evolve somewhat more freely.
   E) Insects are a poorly studied group, and their development patterns are completely unknown. There is currently no way to evaluate what kinds of factors may influence the development or evolution of insect legs.

Answer: C
Topic: 18.12–Evolution Connection
Skill: Conceptual Understanding

45) The symmetry of echinoderms generally includes
   A) radially symmetrical larvae and adults.
   B) bilaterally symmetrical larvae and adults.
   C) radially symmetrical larvae and bilaterally symmetrical adults.
   D) bilaterally symmetrical larvae and radially symmetrical adults.
   E) spherically symmetrical larvae and adults.

Answer: D
Topic: 18.13
Skill: Factual Recall

46) Which of the following is a unique feature of echinoderms?
   A) bilateral symmetry
   B) a water vascular system
   C) radial symmetry
   D) a deuterostome pattern of development
   E) free–swimming larvae

Answer: B
Topic: 18.13
Skill: Factual Recall

47) Which of the following phyla is most closely related to echinoderms?
   A) Annelida
   B) Mollusca
   C) Arthropoda
   D) Chordata
   E) Nematoda

Answer: D
Topic: 18.13
Skill: Factual Recall

48) The flexible, longitudinal rod that is located between the digestive tract and the nerve cord in chordates is called the
   A) spinal cord.
   B) notochord.
   C) dorsal, hollow nerve cord.
   D) coelom rod.
   E) spine.

Answer: B
Topic: 18.14
Skill: Factual Recall

49) Which of the following features is unique to chordates?
   A) bilateral symmetry
   B) a coelom
   C) a notochord
   D) segmentation
   E) a complete digestive tract including an anus

Answer: C
Topic: 18.14
Skill: Factual Recall

50) Which of the following is an invertebrate chordate?
   A) lancelets
   B) lampreys
   C) snakes
   D) sharks
   E) sea urchins

Answer: A
Topic: 18.14
Skill: Factual Recall

51) To be characterized as a chordate, an organism must
   A) display all four key characteristics of Chordata in both the larval and adult stages.
   B) possess a backbone in at least one life stage.
   C) possess a backbone in both the larval and adult stages.
   D) display each of the four key characteristics of the chordates at some point in the life cycle.
   E) undergo incomplete metamorphosis.

Answer: D
Topic: 18.14
Skill: Conceptual Understanding

52) Which of the following statements about tunicates indicates that these animals are chordates?
   A) Larvae show segmentation, radial symmetry, and a pseudocoelom.
   B) Larvae have a dorsal hollow nerve cord, a post–anal tail, pharyngeal slits, and a notochord.
   C) Larvae and adults both have a true coelom.
   D) Larvae and adults both feed by filtering water and trapping small food particles.
   E) Tunicates have tube feet and a water vascular system.

Answer: B
Topic: 18.14
Skill: Conceptual Understanding

53) You find a small, elongated animal embedded in the sand with one end sticking out. Among other things, it has segmental musculature, a coelom, a notochord, and a complete digestive tract with an anus located partway down the body. This animal is
   A) an annelid.
   B) either an annelid or a larval echinoderm.
   C) either an annelid, a larval echinoderm, or a chordate.
   D) either a larval echinoderm or a chordate.
   E) a chordate.

Answer: E
Topic: 18.14
Skill: Application

54) Traditional phylogenetic trees and the most recent molecular phylogenetic trees have many similarities. Which is a feature of the recent trees that was *not* present in the traditional phylogeny?
   A) the placement of Echinodermata and Chordata together in a clade of deuterostomes
   B) the status of sponges as the first animals derived from an ancestral protist
   C) the status of choanoflagellates as the probable ancestors of animals
   D) grouping of nematodes and arthropods into a clade called the Ecdysozoa
   E) the grouping of all bilateral animals within a single clade

Answer: D
Topic: 18.15
Skill: Conceptual Understanding

55) According to the "new" revised phylogeny based on genetic analyses, annelids are a member of the Lophotrochozoa and are most closely related to which of the following groups?
   A) echinoderms
   B) molluscs
   C) nematodes
   D) cnidarians
   E) arthropods

Answer: B
Topic: 18.15
Skill: Conceptual Understanding

56) Consider the following analogy. Proteins generated by protein–coding genes are like baking ingredients (chocolate chips, walnuts, flour . . .). Just as an adult organism is put together through the process of development, a cookie is produced according to an ordered set of baking procedures. According to the "evo–devo" perspective of Sean Carroll, which way of producing a new cookie comes closest to matching the process that has produced new types of animal body forms?
   A) New ingredients (that is, new proteins enabled by the evolution of new genes) are added to the existing ingredient list to produce a new type of cookie using existing baking procedures.
   B) Existing ingredients are altered slightly to produce a different cookie using existing baking procedures.
   C) The ingredient list stays about the same, but the baking procedures (processes of development) are changed to produce a very different type of cookie.
   D) All of the existing ingredients are discarded. New ingredients are combined in entirely new ways to produce a new type of cookie.
   E) A slight change in just one of the existing ingredients totally changes the cookie, even using existing baking methods.

Answer: C
Topic: 18.16
Skill: Application

57) According to recent genetic research, the complexity of an organism
  A) is directly correlated with the number of protein–coding genes in its genome.
  B) is inversely related to the number of protein–coding genes in its genome.
  C) results from the total diversity of proteins that are present in the organisms' tissues.
  D) has more to do with how genes are used than with how many genes are present.
  E) is not related to genes or development, so it must have another source.

Answer: D
Topic: 18.16
Skill: Conceptual Understanding

Art Questions

1)

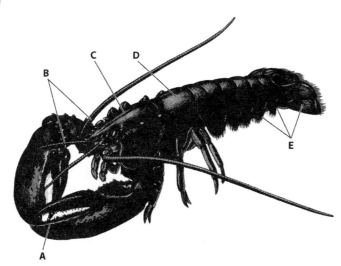

Which part of this figure shows the thorax segment of this lobster?
  A) structure A
  B) structure B
  C) structure C
  D) structure D
  E) structure E

Answer: D
Topic: 18.11
Skill: Factual Recall

2)

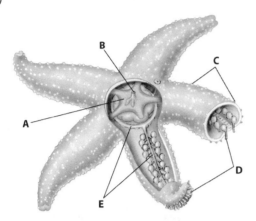

Which part of this figure shows the tube feet of this starfish?
A) structure A
B) structure B
C) structure C
D) structure D
E) structure E

Answer: D
Topic: 18.13
Skill: Factual Recall

Scenario Questions

After reading the following paragraph, answer the question(s) below.

Corals belong to phylum Cnidaria. The reefs themselves are made up of millions of polyps, each of which secretes a calcium carbonate skeleton that becomes part of the reef structure. Coral, which are attached to the reef as adults, have free–swimming larvae that develop into new polyps.

Corals are actually colorless. The brilliant colors that are visible on the reef come from the zooxanthellae (microscopic algae) that live within their body tissues. The zooxanthellae and corals have a symbiotic relationship in which corals provide carbon dioxide and mineral nutrients (released as wastes from coral digestion) to the zooxanthellae. The zooxanthellae perform photosynthesis. Photosynthesis produces nutrients (in the form of sugars) for the coral and also releases oxygen. This relationship supplements energy from predation and allows corals to survive in clear tropical water, even though these areas have very low nutrient levels.

1) What advantage do free–swimming larvae confer on reef–building corals?
A) providing reef–building corals with a defense against fishes and other predators
B) allowing reef–building corals to establish colonies in the deep ocean
C) increasing survival since coral larvae have exoskeletons of chitin
D) allowing reef–building corals to expand their populations into new habitats
E) increasing survival since larvae pass through both vertebrate and invertebrate stages in their life cycles

Answer: D
Topic: 18.6
Skill: Conceptual Understanding

2) Corals supplement the energy they receive from the zooxanthellae by capturing prey with their
   A) amoebocytes.
   B) cnidocytes.
   C) choanocytes.
   D) osteocytes.
   E) melanocytes.

Answer: B
Topic: 18.6, 18.5
Skill: Factual Recall

Chapter 19 The Evolution of Vertebrate Diversity

Multiple-Choice Questions

1) The duck-billed platypus and other monotremes differ from other mammals in that they
    A) are aquatic.
    B) have a backbone and cranium.
    C) lay eggs.
    D) have mammary glands.
    E) have hair.

Answer: C
Topic: Opening Essay
Skill: Factual Recall

2) Mammals exhibit many examples of traits that are shared among species that are adapted to life in similar environments and ecological niches. Examples include several species scattered around the world that resemble anteaters. Like anteaters, they have long snouts and tongues, stout claws, and other features that suit them to eating ants and termites. Yet these species are only distantly related, and each has an ancestor that does not fit the "anteater stereotype." These are examples of
    A) coincidental similarity.
    B) random evolution.
    C) homologous feature.
    D) convergent evolution.
    E) shared derived characters common to all mammals.

Answer: D
Topic: Opening Essay
Skill: Application

3) Which of the following is characteristic of all vertebrates?
    A) a skull and a backbone consisting of vertebrae
    B) a calcified (hard) skeleton and four legs
    C) a hinged jaw
    D) a terrestrially adapted egg or some remnant of it
    E) lungs or lung derivatives

Answer: A
Topic: 19.1
Skill: Factual Recall

4) The first vertebrate with a head and skull probably resembled a
    A) tunicate.
    B) lancelet.
    C) hagfish.
    D) lamprey.
    E) shark.

Answer: C
Topic: 19.1
Skill: Conceptual Understanding

5) The most ancestral extant tetrapods are _____ derived from _____.
   A) reptiles . . . amphibians
   B) amphibians . . . sharks and rays
   C) mammals . . . reptiles
   D) amphibians . . . lobe–finned fishes
   E) amphibians . . . lampreys

Answer: D
Topic: 19.1
Skill: Conceptual Understanding

6) Craniates are chordates that all possess
   A) a skull.
   B) jaws.
   C) a vertebral column.
   D) amniotic eggs.
   E) a notochord.

Answer: A
Topic: 19.1
Skill: Factual Recall

7) Lampreys differ from fishes in that lampreys
   A) lack a backbone.
   B) lack an endoskeleton.
   C) lack jaws and paired fins.
   D) possess opercula.
   E) possess a backbone and skull.

Answer: C
Topic: 19.2
Skill: Factual Recall

8) Key derived characters of sharks and rays include their
   A) jaws and swim bladder.
   B) vertebrae.
   C) calcified (hard) bones.
   D) jaws and paired fins.
   E) ability to filter material from the water.

Answer: D
Topic: 19.3
Skill: Factual Recall

9) Jaws appear to have evolved from
   A) the fusion of many bony elements found in the skin of the neck region of jawless
      ancestors.
   B) a large, bony shield that protruded from between the base of the pectoral fins.
   C) modification of a disk of bones surrounding the mouth in lampreys.
   D) ribs that swung forward into the throat region.
   E) two pairs of skeletal rods that supported gill slits near the mouth.

Answer: E
Topic: 19.3
Skill: Factual Recall

10) Unlike sharks and rays, ray-finned fishes have
   A) an operculum.
   B) a lateral line system.
   C) a flexible skeleton made of cartilage.
   D) hinged jaws.
   E) a series of rod-shaped bones in their muscular pectoral and pelvic fins.

Answer: A
Topic: 19.3
Skill: Factual Recall

11) By far the largest number of extant fish species on Earth have
   A) a cartilaginous skeleton.
   B) a series of rod-shaped bones in their pectoral and pelvic fins.
   C) lungs capable of extracting oxygen from air.
   D) an operculum and swim bladder.
   E) a long tail used for grasping onto structures.

Answer: D
Topic: 19.3
Skill: Conceptual Understanding

12) The key derived character of the lobe-finned fish is
   A) the three pairs of bones in their lower jaw.
   B) the lateral line system.
   C) the series of rod-shaped bones in their pectoral and pelvic fins.
   D) the operculum.
   E) the flattened scales covering their skin.

Answer: C
Topic: 19.3
Skill: Factual Recall

13) Based on *Acanthostega* fossils, scientists now believe the earliest tetrapods
   A) were fully terrestrial.
   B) were amphibians that used their limbs to drag themselves over the land from one waterhole to another.
   C) were fish that used their limbs to raise themselves out of the water to get gulps of air for oxygen.
   D) were reptiles that resembled crocodiles.
   E) were fish that used their limbs to drag themselves from pool to pool during droughts.

Answer: C
Topic: 19.4–Evolution Connection
Skill: Factual Recall

14) Amphibians were diverse and abundant in the lush swamp forests of the _____, which is sometimes referred to as the age of the amphibians.
   A) Precambrian era
   B) Cambrian period
   C) Pleistocene
   D) Mesozoic
   E) Carboniferous

Answer: E
Topic: 19.5
Skill: Factual Recall

15) You are a geologist looking for minerals in a desert during the dry season. While digging for samples, you happen upon a strange organism that seems to be mummified in a membranous sac. You break the sac open to find that the organism has four limbs and is clearly a vertebrate. It has smooth, rather moist skin with no obvious scales, hair, or feathers. You place your specimen in a cardboard box in the shade on the back of your truck. When you check on it after a couple of hours, the creature is dead and as dry as a crust of bread. It is probably
   A) a featherless bird.
   B) an amphibian.
   C) a monotreme.
   D) a reptile.
   E) a hairless mammal.

Answer: B
Topic: 19.5
Skill: Application

16) Recall that cuticle seals plant surfaces and helps plants conserve water and that the seed helps derived plant groups to reproduce effectively on dry land. The analogous adaptations in reptiles are _____ (analogous to cuticle) and _____ (analogous to the seed).
   A) scales . . . jellylike egg masses
   B) scales . . . the amniotic egg
   C) scales . . . aquatic larvae
   D) claws . . . lungs
   E) moist skin . . . jellylike egg masses

Answer: B
Topic: 19.6
Skill: Application

17) Which of the following adaptations allowed reptiles to complete their life cycles on land?
   A) lungs
   B) endothermic metabolism
   C) an amniotic egg
   D) four legs
   E) absence of limbs

Answer: C
Topic: 19.6
Skill: Factual Recall

18) Which animals are or may have been endothermic?
    A) frogs
    B) lizards
    C) turtles
    D) alligators
    E) some small dinosaurs

Answer: E
Topic: 19.6
Skill: Factual Recall

19) Which of the following statements best summarizes the difference between ectothermic and endothermic organisms?
    A) Ectotherms are warm–blooded, but endotherms are cold–blooded.
    B) Endotherms are warm–blooded, but ectotherms are cold–blooded.
    C) Endotherms control their temperature, but ectotherms have no control over their temperature.
    D) Ectotherms obtain body heat from external sources, but endotherms use metabolic heat to maintain a warm, steady body temperature.
    E) Endotherms obtain body heat from external sources, but ectotherms use metabolic heat to maintain a warm, steady body temperature.

Answer: D
Topic: 19.6
Skill: Factual Recall

20) Which of the following statements best describes the current scientific view of birds?
    A) A group of feathered, endothermic dinosaurs that survived the Cretaceous mass extinction.
    B) A group of feathered, ectothermic lizards that lack teeth.
    C) A group of flying, endothermic reptiles that have lost teeth, the amniotic egg, and other heavy body features as an adaptation for flight.
    D) A group of flying mammals whose hairs are modified to feathers.
    E) A group of flying mammals that is derived from monotremes, which also lay amniotic eggs.

Answer: A
Topic: 19.7
Skill: Conceptual Understanding

21) Which bird adaptation is probably less well–developed in flightless birds such as penguins and ostriches?
    A) honeycombed bone structure
    B) amniotic egg
    C) vertebrae
    D) the tetrapod body plan
    E) presence of feathers

Answer: A
Topic: 19.7
Skill: Conceptual Understanding

22) Which of the following statements best describes how flight and feathers are related in the evolution of birds?
    A) The first flying birds did not have feathers, which evolved later.
    B) Feathers and flight both appeared together in the same fossil organism, *Archaeopteryx*.
    C) The first feathered ancestors to birds did not fly, but may have used their feathers for insulation and display.
    D) Feathers are soft and do not leave fossils or fossil traces, so it is unknown which organisms first had feathers.
    E) Feathers were used for flight in many types of dinosaurs, including pterosaurs, and later were used for the same purpose in the first ancestors of birds.

Answer: C
Topic: 19.7
Skill: Conceptual Understanding

23) Mammals
    A) evolved from birds.
    B) all give birth to live young.
    C) all lay eggs.
    D) have hair and mammary glands.
    E) are ectothermic.

Answer: D
Topic: 19.8
Skill: Factual Recall

24) Which part of the body is likely to be much more diverse in mammal fossils compared to those of other groups?
    A) the teeth
    B) the structure of the vertebrae
    C) the structure of the limbs
    D) the jawbone
    E) the eggshells

Answer: A
Topic: 19.8
Skill: Application

25) Compared to other vertebrate groups, mammals have _____ brains relative to body size and a _____ period of parental care.
    A) small . . . brief
    B) small . . . long
    C) large . . . brief
    D) large . . . long
    E) small . . . permanent

Answer: D
Topic: 19.8
Skill: Factual Recall

26) Which of the following organisms is a marsupial?
    A) echidna
    B) kangaroo
    C) whale
    D) zebra
    E) monkey

Answer: B
Topic: 19.8
Skill: Factual Recall

27) Which of the following organisms is a monotreme?
    A) echidna
    B) kangaroo
    C) whale
    D) zebra
    E) monkey

Answer: A
Topic: 19.8
Skill: Factual Recall

28) The forward–facing eyes shared by all primates help them in
    A) manipulating small objects.
    B) depth perception as they navigate through forests.
    C) swinging from tree branches.
    D) intimidating enemies.
    E) seeing in the dark.

Answer: B
Topic: 19.9
Skill: Factual Recall

29) Natural populations of lemurs are currently found only in
    A) Borneo.
    B) North Africa.
    C) New Zealand.
    D) Madagascar.
    E) Tasmania.

Answer: D
Topic: 19.9
Skill: Factual Recall

30) Compared to the earliest primates, anthropoids have
    A) a decreased reliance upon vision.
    B) a stronger reliance upon smell.
    C) a larger brain relative to their body size.
    D) smaller total body size in most cases.
    E) less manual dexterity due to the absence of an opposable thumb.

Answer: C
Topic: 19.9
Skill: Factual Recall

31) A prehensile tail is like an opposable thumb in that both
   A) evolved before the anthropoids.
   B) are used for grasping.
   C) can be fully bent in any direction.
   D) are vestigial organs.
   E) are characteristics of the earliest primates.

   Answer: B
   Topic: 19.9
   Skill: Conceptual Understanding

32) Prehensile tails are found among
   A) most anthropoids.
   B) Old World monkeys.
   C) most hominoids.
   D) New World monkeys.
   E) all primates.

   Answer: D
   Topic: 19.9
   Skill: Factual Recall

33) Old World monkeys are more closely related to _____ than they are to _____.
   A) apes . . . New World monkeys
   B) New World monkeys . . . apes
   C) tarsiers . . . New World monkeys
   D) lemurs . . . New World monkeys
   E) lemurs . . . apes

   Answer: A
   Topic: 19.9
   Skill: Conceptual Understanding

34) Which of the following animals is a hominoid?
   A) New World monkey
   B) Old World monkey
   C) orangutan
   D) lemur
   E) tarsier

   Answer: C
   Topic: 19.9, 19.10
   Skill: Factual Recall

35) Which of the following animal groups is characterized by an absence of tails and forelimbs that are longer than their hind limbs?
   A) apes
   B) Old World monkeys
   C) New World monkeys
   D) lemurs
   E) baboons

   Answer: A
   Topic: 19.10
   Skill: Factual Recall

36) _____ spend almost all of their time on the ground, instead of in trees.
   A) Gorillas
   B) Orangutans
   C) Gibbons
   D) Chimpanzees
   E) Tarsiers

Answer: A
Topic: 19.10
Skill: Factual Recall

37) _____ are known to make and use simple tools.
   A) Gibbons
   B) Gorillas
   C) Chimpanzees
   D) Old World monkeys
   E) Tarsiers

Answer: C
Topic: 19.10
Skill: Factual Recall

38) Our closest relatives, the _____, exhibit several behaviors that closely resemble those of humans.
   A) gibbons
   B) orangutans
   C) gorillas
   D) chimpanzees
   E) baboons

Answer: D
Topic: 19.10
Skill: Factual Recall

39) Human DNA and chimpanzee DNA
   A) differ by about 1%.
   B) differ by about 3%.
   C) differ by more than 10%.
   D) differ by the same amount that human DNA differs from orangutan DNA.
   E) are identical.

Answer: A
Topic: 19.10
Skill: Factual Recall

40) The last common ancestor shared by humans and chimpanzees lived about
   A) 6,000—8,000 years ago.
   B) 1—2 million years ago.
   C) 5—7 million years ago.
   D) 25—40 million years ago.
   E) 1.5—2.5 billion years ago.

Answer: C
Topic: 19.11
Skill: Factual Recall

41) The hominid group includes _____, but the hominoid group includes _____.
A) *Homo sapiens* only . . . humans and all other apes
B) *Homo sapiens* and several extinct human relatives . . . humans and all other apes
C) humans and all other apes . . . *Homo sapiens* only
D) humans and all other apes . . . *Homo sapiens* and several extinct human relatives
E) *Homo sapiens* and several extinct human relatives . . . apes but not humans

Answer: B
Topic: 19.10, 19.11
Skill: Factual Recall

42) Which of the following options lists the major groups or genera from the fossil record in the proper order from earliest to most recent?
A) *Australopithecus, Sahelanthropus, Homo habilis, Homo sapiens*
B) *Sahelanthropus, Australopithecus, Homo habilis, Homo sapiens*
C) *Sahelanthropus, Australopithecus, Homo sapiens, Homo habilis*
D) *Sahelanthropus, Homo habilis, Australopithecus, Homo sapiens*
E) *Australopithecus, Homo habilis, Sahelanthropus, Homo sapiens*

Answer: B
Topic: 19.11
Skill: Factual Recall

43) _____ were the first clearly bipedal hominids.
A) *Australopithecus*
B) *Homo erectus*
C) *Ardipithecus*
D) *Homo habilis*
E) *Homo sapiens*

Answer: A
Topic: 19.12
Skill: Factual Recall

44) Hominid fossil footprints that are obviously bipedal date to about _____ years ago.
A) 50,000
B) 100,000
C) 1 million
D) 3.5 million
E) 12 million

Answer: D
Topic: 19.12
Skill: Factual Recall

45) Which of the following is the first distinctively hominid trait to appear in the fossil record?
A) sophisticated stone tools
B) increased brain size
C) upright walking (bipedalism)
D) a very long period of parental care
E) small teeth and relatively delicate jaws

Answer: C
Topic: 19.12
Skill: Conceptual Understanding

46) _____ appears to have been the first hominid to use stone tools.
  A) *Homo erectus*
  B) *Homo habilis*
  C) *Ardipithecus*
  D) *Homo sapiens*
  E) *Australopithecus*

Answer: B
Topic: 19.13
Skill: Factual Recall

47) Which extinct hominid first appeared about 1.9 million years ago and had a larger brain than *Homo habilis*, its immediate predecessor?
  A) *Homo ergaster*
  B) *Homo neanderthalensis*
  C) *Homo heidelbergensis*
  D) *Homo sapiens*
  E) *Australopithecus*

Answer: A
Topic: 19.13
Skill: Factual Recall

48) According to the fossil record, the genus *Homo* first arose in
  A) North America.
  B) Europe.
  C) Asia.
  D) Africa.
  E) Australia.

Answer: D
Topic: 19.13
Skill: Factual Recall

49) The earliest hominid to be found outside of Africa belongs to which species?
  A) *Ardipithecus ramidus*
  B) *Australopithecus afarensis*
  C) *Homo habilis*
  D) *Homo erectus*
  E) *Homo sapiens*

Answer: D
Topic: 19.13
Skill: Factual Recall

50) Neanderthals are best described as
   A) direct ancestors to modern humans.
   B) direct ancestors to modern Europeans, but not to other human populations.
   C) a localized form or subspecies of *Homo sapiens* that was well–adapted to living in caves and carrying clubs.
   D) a hominid that colonized Europe independently of *Homo sapiens* and did not interbreed with modern humans.
   E) a hominid that colonized Europe and interbred extensively with modern humans.

Answer: D
Topic: 19.14
Skill: Factual Recall

51) The most recent evidence clarifying the relationship between modern humans and Neanderthals comes from analysis of
   A) fossil footprints.
   B) skeletal structure.
   C) the types of tools that were made by Neanderthals.
   D) Neanderthal artwork and burial rites.
   E) Neanderthal mitochondrial DNA.

Answer: E
Topic: 19.14
Skill: Conceptual Understanding

52) Fossil and genetic evidence strongly support the idea that modern humans
   A) independently arose from three different ancestral *Homo* species in Africa and Eurasia.
   B) all derive from a single African lineage that spread from there into other parts of the world starting about 60,000 years ago.
   C) derive from an African lineage but also have genes derived from mixing with several Eurasian descendants of *Homo erectus.*
   D) derive from a hybridization of several African and Eurasian *Homo* species.
   E) derive from Neanderthals that independently evolved the features of modern humans in Europe and Africa.

Answer: B
Topic: 19.15
Skill: Factual Recall

53) All humans alive today have inherited their mitochondrial DNA from some individual female common ancestor. Studies indicate this woman probably lived about _____ years ago, when fossil evidence indicates *Homo sapiens* was restricted to _____.
   A) 20,000 . . . Africa
   B) 50,000 . . . Africa and Asia
   C) 180,000 . . . Africa
   D) 200,000 . . . Africa and Europe
   E) 500,000 . . . Africa, Asia, and Europe

Answer: C
Topic: 19.15
Skill: Factual Recall

54) Compared to other hominids, modern *Homo sapiens* display a particular ability for
   A) symbolic thought.
   B) making stone tools.
   C) upright walking.
   D) manipulating objects with their hands.
   E) long–distance walking.

Answer: A
Topic: 19.15
Skill: Factual Recall

55) _____ is thought to have played a crucial role in the evolution of human speech.
   A) The *FOXP2* gene
   B) Upright posture
   C) Increased parental care
   D) Toolmaking
   E) A shorter nose

Answer: A
Topic: 19.16
Skill: Factual Recall

56) In what animals do we find a *FOXP2* gene that is most similar to humans in structure and function?
   A) alligators
   B) chimpanzees
   C) whales
   D) foxes
   E) song–learning birds

Answer: E
Topic: 19.16
Skill: Factual Recall

57) Human skin color likely represents a locally adapted compromise between
   A) the need to block UV radiation that causes cancer and the need to absorb sunlight for heat.
   B) the need to block UV radiation that causes cancer and the need to synthesize vitamin C.
   C) the need to block UV radiation that destroys folate and the need to synthesize vitamin D.
   D) the need to block UV radiation that destroys folate and the need to absorb sunlight for heat.
   E) the need to blend in with the environment and the need to absorb sunlight for heat.

Answer: C
Topic: 19.17–Evolution Connection
Skill: Conceptual Understanding

58) Which of the following human practices has most seriously threatened the native animal diversity of Australia?
   A) burning of forests
   B) agricultural use of land
   C) elimination of a few native species that supported many others through ecological interactions
   D) introduction of new species from other continents
   E) overharvesting of fish and game

Answer: D
Topic: 19.18
Skill: Factual Recall

59) _____ are considered an introduced species and a widespread threat to native biodiversity in Australia.
   A) Quolls
   B) Cane toads
   C) Bilbies
   D) Kangaroos
   E) Koalas

Answer: B
Topic: 19.18
Skill: Factual Recall

Art Questions

1)

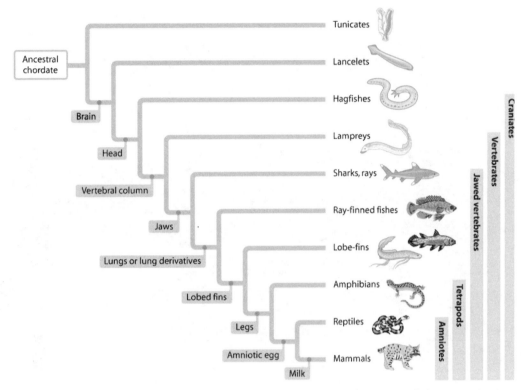

According to this figure, lobe-finned fish are excluded from the tetrapods because they lack which of the following characters?

A) vertebral column
B) jaws
C) lungs or lung derivatives
D) lobed fins
E) legs

Answer: E
Topic: 19.1
Skill: Conceptual Understanding

2)

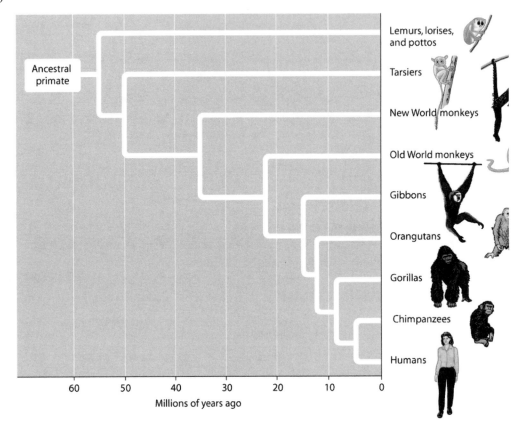

Millions of years ago

According to this figure, which of the following is a monophyletic group?
    A) lemurs, lorises, pottos, tarsiers, New World monkeys, and Old World monkeys
    B) New World monkeys and Old World monkeys
    C) gibbons, orangutans, gorillas, and chimpanzees
    D) orangutans, gorillas, and chimpanzees
    E) gorillas, chimpanzees, and humans

Answer: E
Topic: 19.9
Skill: Application

3)

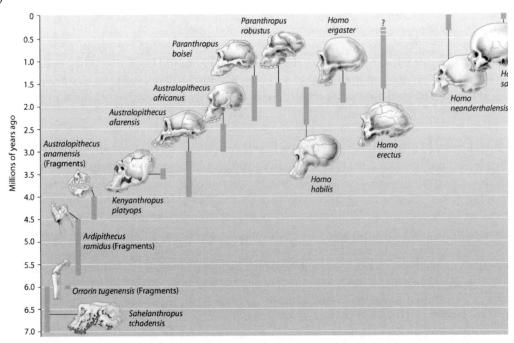

Drawn from photos of fossils: *O. tugenensis* photo in Michael Balter, Early hominid sows division, *ScienceNow*, Feb. 22, 2001, © 2001 American Association for the Advancement of Science. *A. ramidus* [...]
photo by Timothy White, 1999/Brill Atlanta. *A. anamensis*, *A. garhi*, and *H. neanderthalensis* adapted from *The Human Evolution Coloring Book*. *K platyops* drawn from photo in Maeve Leakey et al., New [...]
genus from eastern Africa shows diverse middle Pliocene lineages, *Nature*, March 22, 2001, 410:433. *P. boisei* drawn from a photo by David Bill. *H. ergaster* drawn from a photo at www.inhandmuseum [...]
S. tchadensis drawn from a photo in Michel Brunet et al., A new hominid from the Upper Miocene of Chad, Central Africa, *Nature*, July 11, 2002, 418:147, fig. 1b.

According to this figure, which species lived concurrently with *Homo ergaster*?

A) *Australopithecus anamensis*

B) *Australopithecus africanus*

C) *Paranthropus boisei*

D) *Homo neanderthalensis*

E) *Homo sapiens*

Answer: C
Topic: 19.11
Skill: Conceptual Understanding

Scenario Questions

After reading the following paragraph, answer the question(s) below.

Bipedalism is one of the most important characteristics of hominid evolution. The appearance of bipedalism led to anatomical changes that are considered to be distinguishing characteristics among hominid fossils. The evidence for bipedalism is supported by fossil evidence from more than 4 million years ago and a trackway of footprints in volcanic ash 3.6 million years old.

Recently, however, scientists have focused on the link between tooth structure and diet in the evolution of the early hominids, specifically in *Australopithecus* species. Detailed studies of hominid dental features have provided evidence of an important dietary shift that led to adaptive radiation within this genus. Most of the evidence comes from analyses of tooth size and shape, microscopic wear patterns on teeth, and jaw structure. The evidence suggests that fibrous plant materials became more important through the Pliocene, perhaps as critical components in the diet of some species.

1) What is the most likely evolutionary link between bipedalism and changes in the diet of early hominids?
    A) Bipedal species would be more likely to remain in one type of habitat.
    B) Bipedalism led to new farming practices.
    C) It's easier to escape predators with an upright posture.
    D) The greater ability to move to new habitats facilitated exploitation of new foods.
    E) Bipedalism enabled early hominids to gather fruit from the trees.
  Answer: D
  Topic: 19.11, 19.12, 19.13
  Skill: Conceptual Understanding

2) Evidence from fossil dentition suggests that *Australopithecus* species
    A) evolved specifically to eat meat.
    B) experienced a decrease in both tooth size and brain size.
    C) had larger teeth than earlier hominids.
    D) were direct ancestors of modern humans.
    E) were adapted to function successfully in a wide range of habitats.
  Answer: E
  Topic: 19.11, 19.12, 19.13
  Skill: Conceptual Understanding

Chapter 20 Unifying Concepts of Animal Structure and Function

Multiple-Choice Questions

1) Geckos are able to walk up walls and across ceilings because of
    A) the little suction cups on their toes.
    B) the sticky adhesive secretions on their feet.
    C) the sticky saliva licked onto the regions where the gecko is about to walk.
    D) the many setae on their toes that form molecular bonds with the wall and ceiling
       surface.
    E) their sharp toenails that grasp surfaces.
Answer: D
Topic: Opening Essay
Skill: Factual Recall

2) The connection between structure and _____ is a basic concept of biology.
    A) species
    B) adaptation
    C) function
    D) sex
    E) strength
Answer: C
Topic: 20.1
Skill: Conceptual Understanding

3) A physiologist is a biologist who studies
    A) the structure of living things.
    B) the structure of body parts.
    C) the evolution of animals.
    D) the physics of living things.
    E) the function of body parts.
Answer: E
Topic: 20.1
Skill: Conceptual Understanding

4) An organ system consists of
    A) organs that collectively perform a vital body function.
    B) a group of coordinated tissues.
    C) a collection of similar cells.
    D) organs that serve as a backup for a vital nonfunctioning body system.
    E) blood, lymph, and other body fluids.
Answer: A
Topic: 20.1
Skill: Factual Recall

5) Structure in the living world is organized into hierarchical levels. Which of the following lists these from *least* inclusive to *most* inclusive?
   A) cell, molecule, organ, organ system, tissue, organism
   B) molecule, cell, tissue, organ, organ system, organism
   C) molecule, cell, organ, organ system, tissue, organism
   D) cell, molecule, tissue, organ, organ system, organism
   E) molecule, cell, tissue, organ system, organ, organism

Answer: B
Topic: 20.1
Skill: Conceptual Understanding

6) Tuna, sharks, and penguins have adapted to their environment by becoming fast swimmers. They are fast swimmers due to
   A) the oily secretion on their skins.
   B) their streamlined, tapered bodies.
   C) their oversized fins and flippers.
   D) their exceptional capacity for energy storage.
   E) the Frisbee–like turning motion of their bodies.

Answer: B
Topic: 20.2–Evolution Connection
Skill: Factual Recall

7) Some animals have evolved a body form that allows them to run very fast, while others run more slowly. Whereas a cheetah can run at speeds over 50 mph, an elephant can barely run at 15 mph. The most important physical factor behind this variance is the difference in
   A) the ratio of muscle to their total body mass.
   B) the ratio of body length to body height.
   C) the shape of their feet.
   D) their diets.
   E) the length of their legs.

Answer: A
Topic: 20.2–Evolution Connection
Skill: Application

8) Which of the following is an example of a tissue?
   A) heart muscle
   B) heart
   C) red blood cell
   D) circulatory system
   E) liver

Answer: A
Topic: 20.3
Skill: Application

9) Which of the following is a major category of animal tissue?
   A) epithelium
   B) heart
   C) lymph
   D) blood serum
   E) biceps

Answer: A
Topic: 20.3
Skill: Factual Recall

10) Stratified squamous epithelium is well–suited for
   A) exchanging materials by diffusion.
   B) exchanging materials by active transport.
   C) lining our lungs.
   D) lining body surfaces subject to abrasion.
   E) secreting mucus.

Answer: D
Topic: 20.4
Skill: Conceptual Understanding

11) Epithelial tissues
   A) transmit impulses.
   B) cause body movements.
   C) cover both external and internal body surfaces.
   D) sense stimuli.
   E) form a framework that supports the body.

Answer: C
Topic: 20.4
Skill: Factual Recall

12) Which of the following items has a shape most like a squamous epithelial cell?
   A) a watermelon
   B) a cupcake
   C) a fried egg
   D) a spoon
   E) the letter "S"

Answer: C
Topic: 20.4
Skill: Application

13) Which of the following statements about the cells of the mucous membrane lining your air tubes is *false?*
   A) They manufacture secretory products.
   B) They are stratified squamous epithelial cells.
   C) They have a large volume of cytoplasm.
   D) They are cuboidal or columnar in shape.
   E) They carry cilia that sweep mucus up and out of the respiratory system.

Answer: B
Topic: 20.4
Skill: Factual Recall

14) The liquid part of the blood that consists of water, salts, and dissolved proteins is known as
A) serum.
B) interstitial fluid.
C) lymph.
D) plasma.
E) platelets.

Answer: D
Topic: 20.5
Skill: Factual Recall

15) Which of the following is a type of connective tissue?
A) plasma
B) adipose tissue
C) spinal fluid
D) epithelial tissue
E) muscle tissue

Answer: B
Topic: 20.5
Skill: Factual Recall

16) Which of the following is formed from a matrix of collagen fibers embedded in a hard mineral substance?
A) blood
B) cartilage
C) bone
D) adipose tissue
E) fibrous connective tissue

Answer: C
Topic: 20.5
Skill: Factual Recall

17) What kind of connective tissue has an extracellular liquid matrix called plasma?
A) cartilage
B) nerve tissue
C) loose connective tissue
D) adipose tissue
E) blood

Answer: E
Topic: 20.5
Skill: Factual Recall

18) Connective tissue is different from the other major tissue types in that
A) it is made of cells.
B) the cells are sparsely scattered through a nonliving matrix.
C) it is not made of cells.
D) it has no essential function in an animal's body.
E) it is found only in humans.

Answer: B
Topic: 20.5
Skill: Conceptual Understanding

19) The most common type of connective tissue in the human body is
   A) fibrous connective tissue.
   B) adipose tissue.
   C) loose connective tissue.
   D) bone.
   E) loose adipose tissue.

Answer: C
Topic: 20.5
Skill: Factual Recall

20) Smooth muscle is responsible for
   A) voluntary body activities.
   B) the pumping action of the heart.
   C) an athlete's ability to run a 100-meter dash.
   D) involuntary body activities.
   E) transmission of information.

Answer: D
Topic: 20.6
Skill: Factual Recall

21) Which is the most abundant kind of tissue in an animal, such as a gorilla?
   A) connective
   B) epithelial
   C) blood
   D) muscle
   E) nerve

Answer: D
Topic: 20.6
Skill: Conceptual Understanding

22) Which of the following statements regarding skeletal muscle is *true*?
   A) Individual skeletal muscle cells are visible to the naked eye.
   B) Skeletal muscle is attached to bones by tendons.
   C) Skeletal muscle cells do not contain nuclei.
   D) Skeletal muscle is largely responsible for involuntary body motions.
   E) Skeletal muscle coordinates movement of nutrients and oxygen throughout the body.

Answer: B
Topic: 20.6
Skill: Factual Recall

23) Unlike both smooth and skeletal muscle, cardiac muscle
   A) has cells that contact one another.
   B) has cells that are striped.
   C) generally cannot be contracted at will.
   D) generally can be contracted at will.
   E) has branched cells.

Answer: E
Topic: 20.6
Skill: Factual Recall

24) The main function of muscle tissue is
    A) sensation.
    B) support.
    C) contraction.
    D) covering surfaces.
    E) absorption.

Answer: C
Topic: 20.6
Skill: Factual Recall

25) Which type of tissue forms a communication and coordination system within the body?
    A) nervous
    B) blood
    C) epithelial
    D) connective
    E) muscle

Answer: A
Topic: 20.7
Skill: Factual Recall

26) The structural and functional unit of nervous tissue is the
    A) dendrite.
    B) axon.
    C) cell body.
    D) neuron.
    E) nerve.

Answer: D
Topic: 20.7
Skill: Factual Recall

27) An organ represents a higher level of structure than the tissue composing it and performs functions that the tissues cannot perform alone. This is an example of the principle of
    A) structural adaptations.
    B) cellular regulation.
    C) emergent properties.
    D) biotechnology.
    E) protein scaffolding.

Answer: C
Topic: 20.8
Skill: Conceptual Understanding

28) Which of the following statements about organs is *false?*
    A) An organ represents a higher level of structure than the tissues composing it.
    B) An organ consists of several tissues.
    C) An organ can only carry out the functions of its component tissues.
    D) An organ consists of many cells.
    E) Organs are found in virtually all animals except sponges and some cnidarians.

Answer: C
Topic: 20.8
Skill: Conceptual Understanding

29) Which of the following tissues would likely be found in the small intestine?
    A) cardiac muscle
    B) nervous tissue
    C) bone tissue
    D) tendons
    E) cartilage

Answer: B
Topic: 20.8
Skill: Conceptual Understanding

30) Which of the following tissues can currently be produced artificially and has been successfully used in human transplants?
    A) heart muscle
    B) esophageal lining
    C) lining of the small intestine
    D) skin
    E) urinary bladder

Answer: D
Topic: 20.9
Skill: Factual Recall

31) Which of the following statements about artificial skin is *false*?
    A) Artificial skin has been used on burn victims.
    B) Artificial skin is grown from human fibroblasts.
    C) Artificial skin is inexpensive and easy to use.
    D) Artificial skin has shown such success that other artificial tissues are under investigation.
    E) Artificial skin may not be used on any animal, just humans.

Answer: C
Topic: 20.9
Skill: Factual Recall

32) The respiratory system includes all of the following structures *except* the
    A) esophagus.
    B) bronchus.
    C) trachea.
    D) larynx.
    E) lung

Answer: A
Topic: 20.10
Skill: Factual Recall

33) Which organ system removes nitrogen–containing waste products from blood?
    A) lymphatic system
    B) integumentary system
    C) muscular system
    D) excretory system
    E) reproductive system

Answer: D
Topic: 20.10
Skill: Factual Recall

34) Fingernails are a component of the _____ system.
   A) respiratory
   B) integumentary
   C) muscular
   D) skeletal
   E) excretory

Answer: B
Topic: 20.10
Skill: Conceptual Understanding

35) Which of the following is a part of the immune system?
   A) bone marrow
   B) liver
   C) pancreas
   D) lungs
   E) endocrine system

Answer: A
Topic: 20.10
Skill: Factual Recall

36) Suppose your doctor decides to X-ray your hip. Which would show up more distinctly, the muscles or the bones?
   A) the muscles, because they are rich in hydrogen
   B) the muscles, because they are metabolically more active
   C) the muscles, because they are softer
   D) the bones, because they are denser
   E) the bones, because they are rich in hydrogen

Answer: D
Topic: 20.11
Skill: Application

37) X-ray imaging is routinely used to check for all of the following *except*
   A) broken bones.
   B) dense tumors.
   C) tooth cavities.
   D) brain disorders.
   E) bone tumors.

Answer: D
Topic: 20.11
Skill: Factual Recall

38) Which of the following imaging techniques is best suited for visualizing fine anatomic detail in the brain?
   A) electrocardiogram
   B) X-ray imaging
   C) magnetic resonance imaging (MRI)
   D) positron-emission tomography (PET)
   E) X-ray tomography

Answer: C
Topic: 20.11
Skill: Application

39) Which of the following imaging techniques is used for visualizing areas of high or low metabolic activity?
   A) computerized tomography (CT)
   B) X-ray imaging
   C) magnetic resonance imaging (MRI)
   D) positron-emission tomography (PET)
   E) X-ray tomography

Answer: D
Topic: 20.11
Skill: Factual Recall

40) Assume you have scratched a mosquito bite and, in the process, damaged some of your stratified squamous epithelial cells. What will happen?
   A) The damaged cells will heal themselves.
   B) The cells near the base of the epithelium will rapidly replicate to replace the damaged cells.
   C) Sensory receptors in the skin will become activated.
   D) Vitamin D synthesis will begin, thus encouraging cell replacement.
   E) The function of the skin will be totally lost.

Answer: B
Topic: 20.12
Skill: Application

41) Which of the following is closely associated with the digestive, respiratory, and excretory systems?
   A) the skeletal system
   B) the circulatory system
   C) the reproductive system
   D) the muscular system
   E) the lymphatic system

Answer: B
Topic: 20.13
Skill: Conceptual Understanding

42) Which of the following best represents an adaptation to increase surface-to-volume ratio?
   A) the long bones of a giraffe
   B) the smooth skin of an earthworm
   C) the multilobed sacs in the lungs
   D) the striations of skeletal muscle
   E) the smooth muscle inside the intestine

Answer: C
Topic: 20.13
Skill: Conceptual Understanding

43) Mouse lung cells are much more active metabolically than frog lung cells. What is the consequence of this?
    A) The frog must eat insects for energy.
    B) The mouse lung cells must have a large cell surface area.
    C) The mouse can survive longer and colder winters.
    D) There is a salt imbalance in the frog.
    E) The internal environment of the frog fluctuates significantly.

Answer: B
Topic: 20.13
Skill: Conceptual Understanding

44) Cells receive material such as food, minerals, and oxygen from the outside world through
    A) water.
    B) interstitial fluid.
    C) matrix fibers.
    D) cytoplasm.
    E) neurons.

Answer: B
Topic: 20.13
Skill: Factual Recall

45) Imagine an invertebrate that lives in an estuary where salinity varies cyclically with the tides. If this individual is able to adjust the salt concentration of its body fluids, its salt concentration will have
    A) adjustments within the cell to equal salt concentration outside the cell.
    B) slight fluctuations that are kept within a narrow range.
    C) regular variations that range from large to small.
    D) a cyclic variation similar to that of the surrounding water.
    E) a cyclic variation depending upon when the animal drinks.

Answer: B
Topic: 20.14
Skill: Conceptual Understanding

46) Homeostasis
    A) is the maintenance of a constant internal state.
    B) results from hormone imbalance.
    C) is a pathological condition.
    D) results from a hormone imbalance.
    E) is the way the internal environment influences the external environment.

Answer: A
Topic: 20.14
Skill: Conceptual Understanding

47) The vertebrate kidney helps to keep the acidity of the body fluids constant by varying the amount of hydrogen ions (H^+) it secretes into the urine. You can confidently predict that this aspect of kidney function will be controlled by
  A) a positive feedback mechanism.
  B) a negative feedback mechanism.
  C) nerve impulses from the brain.
  D) a hormone ultimately controlled by the brain.
  E) a hormone produced in the kidney itself.

Answer: B
Topic: 20.15
Skill: Application

48) Which of the following is most likely to be responsible if, when your blood sugar level rises, the level of sugar goes back down?
  A) diabetes insipidus
  B) the use of the sugar for energy by your cells
  C) a homeostatic mechanism based on negative feedback
  D) type II diabetes
  E) a homeostatic mechanism based on positive feedback

Answer: C
Topic: 20.15
Skill: Conceptual Understanding

49) Most homeostasis depends on
  A) positive feedback control.
  B) negative feedback control.
  C) hormonal regulation.
  D) predictable environmental conditions.
  E) predictable internal conditions.

Answer: B
Topic: 20.15
Skill: Conceptual Understanding

50) When body temperature is too high, which of the following occurs?
  A) The brain sends out distress signals.
  B) Blood vessels in the skin dilate.
  C) Blood glucose rises significantly.
  D) Capillaries contract.
  E) The internal lining of the intestine increases in surface area.

Answer: B
Topic: 20.15
Skill: Conceptual Understanding

Art Questions

1)

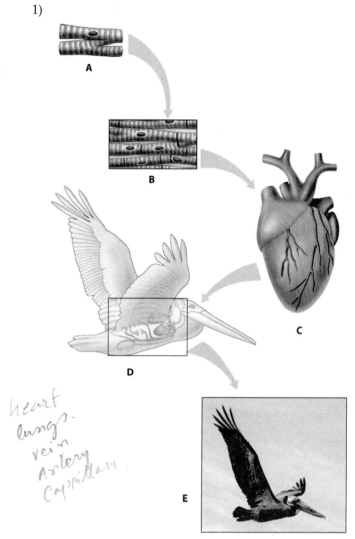

handwritten: heart
lungs.
vein
Artery
Capillary.

Which part of this figure shows a complete organ system?
A) part A
B) part B
C) part C
D) part D
E) part E

Answer: D
Topic: 20.1
Skill: Application

2)

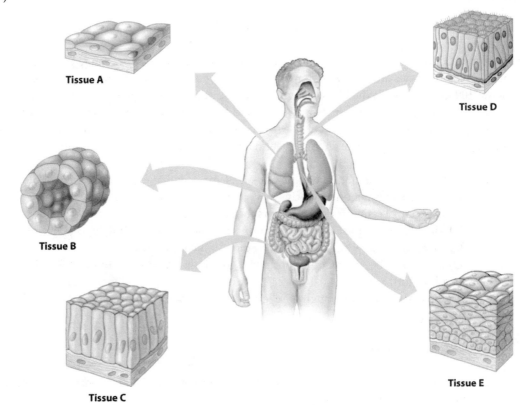

Tissue A

Tissue D

Tissue B

Tissue C

Tissue E

Which type of epithelial tissue shown is a stratified tissue?
   A) tissue A
   B) tissue B
   C) tissue C
   D) tissue D
   E) tissue E

Answer: E
Topic: 20.4
Skill: Application

Scenario Questions

After reading the following paragraph, answer the question(s) below.

Under normal conditions, blood sugar levels are controlled within a narrow range by negative feedback. Two hormones are involved in maintaining blood sugar levels at the set point (about 90 mg of glucose/100 ml of blood). When blood sugar levels rise above the set point, the hormone insulin signals the liver to absorb the excess sugar. When blood sugar levels drop below the set point, the hormone glucagon signals the liver to release its stored glucose to the bloodstream. In juvenile onset diabetes, the body doesn't produce enough insulin and insulin supplements are required.

1) Based on your understanding of homeostasis, for negative feedback control of blood glucose levels to function properly
   A) the control center for glucose must be somewhere in the digestive system.
   B) glucose levels must be able to rapidly rise and fall depending on dietary intake.
   C) there must be sensors that monitor blood glucose levels.
   D) there must be several other hormones involved (in addition to insulin and glucagon).
   E) the body must prevent glucose levels from changing even slightly.
   Answer: C
   Topic: 20.15
   Skill: Conceptual Understanding

2) If you hadn't eaten for several hours, which hormone would be responsible for returning your glucose levels to the set point?
   A) insulin
   B) glucagon
   C) liver
   D) pancreas
   E) glycogen
   Answer: B
   Topic: 20.15
   Skill: Factual Recall

Chapter 21 Nutrition and Digestion

Multiple-Choice Questions

1) Humpback whales
    A) use a bubble net system to capture krill for food.
    B) catch and eat salmon and seals throughout the year.
    C) use baleen to blow bubbles for capturing krill.
    D) eat nothing but kelp.
    E) use baleen to catch salmon.

Answer: A
Topic: Opening Essay
Skill: Factual Recall

2) Which of the following statements regarding animals is *false?*
    A) Animals that eat plants are called herbivores.
    B) Animals that eat meat are called carnivores.
    C) Animals that live in or on their food source and eat their way through it are called substrate feeders.
    D) Animals that eat plants and meat are called omnivores.
    E) Animals that extract food particles suspended in the surrounding water are called fluid feeders.

Answer: E
Topic: 21.1
Skill: Factual Recall

3) Most animals are
    A) bulk feeders.
    B) substrate feeders.
    C) suspension feeders.
    D) fluid feeders.
    E) parasites.

Answer: A
Topic: 21.1
Skill: Factual Recall

4) Digestion is the
    A) absorption of nutrients suspended in water.
    B) conversion of glycogen to glucose.
    C) chemical and mechanical breakdown of food for absorption into the body.
    D) churning of food in the stomach and intestine.
    E) process of building proteins from amino acids.

Answer: C
Topic: 21.2
Skill: Factual Recall

5) During which of the following stages of food processing is undigested material removed from the digestive tract?
   A) absorption
   B) elimination
   C) digestion
   D) gestation
   E) ingestion

Answer: B
Topic: 21.2
Skill: Factual Recall

6) What happens to nutrient macromolecules in an animal's digestive tract?
   A) They are absorbed whole and are broken down into monomers in cells that ultimately use them.
   B) Proteins and nucleic acids are digested into monomers before absorption; energy–storage macromolecules (starch and fat) are absorbed whole.
   C) The digestive breakdown of macromolecules is keyed to the body's need for monomers; only the monomers that are immediately needed are produced.
   D) Nutrient macromolecules are digested into monomers before absorption.
   E) Nucleic acids and triglycerides (which diffuse across the plasma membrane) are not digested into monomers, but other macromolecules are.

Answer: D
Topic: 21.2
Skill: Conceptual Understanding

7) Through digestion, polysaccharides are broken down into
   A) fatty acids.
   B) monosaccharides.
   C) glycerols.
   D) nucleotides.
   E) amino acids.

Answer: B
Topic: 21.2
Skill: Factual Recall

8) Through digestion, nucleic acids are broken down into
   A) fatty acids.
   B) monosaccharides.
   C) glycerols.
   D) nucleotides.
   E) amino acids.

Answer: D
Topic: 21.2
Skill: Factual Recall

9) Which of the following organisms has a gastrovascular cavity?
    A) hydra
    B) earthworm
    C) clam
    D) grasshopper
    E) bird

Answer: A
Topic: 21.3
Skill: Factual Recall

10) An animal digestive tract that consists of two openings (a mouth and anus) is called
    A) an excretory system.
    B) the alimentary canal.
    C) the digestive enzyme center.
    D) an intestine.
    E) a mammalian crop.

Answer: B
Topic: 21.3
Skill: Factual Recall

11) An alimentary canal is best defined as
    A) the compartment in which an animal temporarily stores its food.
    B) a digestive cavity in which food is churned and mixed.
    C) a tube-shaped compartment with either one or two openings.
    D) a tube-shaped compartment for the transport, digestion, and absorption of food.
    E) an organ designed for regulation of food passage.

Answer: D
Topic: 21.3
Skill: Conceptual Understanding

12) The main function of an earthworm's gizzard is to
    A) moisten food.
    B) store food.
    C) digest vitamins.
    D) absorb nutrients.
    E) grind food.

Answer: E
Topic: 21.3
Skill: Factual Recall

13) Which of the following choices lists the organs of the bird digestive system in the correct order, from first to last contact with food material?
    A) esophagus, stomach, gizzard, crop, intestine, anus
    B) esophagus, gizzard, crop, stomach, intestine, anus
    C) esophagus, crop, stomach, gizzard, intestine, anus
    D) esophagus, crop, gizzard, stomach, intestine, anus
    E) esophagus, gizzard, stomach, crop, intestine, anus

Answer: C
Topic: 21.3
Skill: Factual Recall

14) The main function of the hindgut in the grasshopper is to
    A) absorb water and compact wastes.
    B) digest food.
    C) absorb nutrients.
    D) absorb vitamins and pulverize the food.
    E) store food.

Answer: A
Topic: 21.3
Skill: Factual Recall

15) Digestion takes place in specialized compartments for all of the following reasons *except* that
    A) the environment of digestion must favor the action of digestive enzymes.
    B) the environment of digestion must protect the food.
    C) the environment of digestion must be contained.
    D) the animal's body must be protected from its own digestive enzymes.
    E) specialization of the sites of digestion promotes efficiency.

Answer: B
Topic: 21.3
Skill: Conceptual Understanding

16) Which of the following correctly lists the order of the parts of the human digestive system, from first to last contact with food matter?
    A) pharynx, oral cavity, esophagus, stomach, large intestine
    B) oral cavity, pharynx, esophagus, stomach, small intestine, large intestine
    C) esophagus, pharynx, stomach, small intestine, large intestine
    D) esophagus, pharynx, stomach, large intestine, small intestine
    E) oral cavity, esophagus, stomach, large intestine, small intestine

Answer: B
Topic: 21.4
Skill: Factual Recall

17) Smooth muscle propels food through the alimentary canal by a process called
    A) circular contractions.
    B) diffusion.
    C) active transport.
    D) peristalsis.
    E) progurgitation.

Answer: D
Topic: 21.4
Skill: Factual Recall

18) Regulation of the passage of food from the stomach is accomplished by
    A) peristalsis.
    B) reverse peristalsis.
    C) sphincters.
    D) the stomach lining.
    E) the pharynx.

Answer: C
Topic: 21.4
Skill: Factual Recall

19) Digestion begins in the
    A) tongue.
    B) oral cavity.
    C) esophagus.
    D) pharynx.
    E) stomach.

Answer: B
Topic: 21.5
Skill: Factual Recall

20) The digestion of carbohydrates begins in the mouth. What is the name given to the starch–digesting enzyme secreted by salivary glands?
    A) bile salts
    B) lipase
    C) pepsin
    D) amylase
    E) trypsin

Answer: D
Topic: 21.5
Skill: Factual Recall

21) Human saliva performs all of the following functions *except*
    A) lubricating food.
    B) neutralizing food acids.
    C) controlling bacterial populations.
    D) hydrolyzing starch.
    E) hydrolyzing proteins.

Answer: E
Topic: 21.5
Skill: Factual Recall

22) The epiglottis is a
    A) muscle that moves the esophagus into line with the pharynx during swallowing.
    B) muscle that moves the trachea out of line with the pharynx during swallowing.
    C) flap of cartilage that flips down to cover the entry to the trachea during swallowing.
    D) muscle sphincter that closes off the entry to the trachea during swallowing.
    E) flap of skin that covers the entry to the trachea except during breathing.

Answer: C
Topic: 21.6
Skill: Factual Recall

23) The tongue does all of the following *except*
    A) taste food.
    B) manipulate food.
    C) shape food into a ball called a bolus.
    D) secrete saliva.
    E) push food into the pharynx.

Answer: D
Topic: 21.5
Skill: Factual Recall

24) The structure of the esophagus fits its function in that
    A) it can direct food to the lungs or stomach.
    B) it has smooth muscle for peristalsis.
    C) it is regulated by contractions in the pharynx.
    D) it is regulated by the composition of the bolus entering the esophagus.
    E) its length determines the volume of food an animal can ingest.

Answer: B
Topic: 21.6
Skill: Factual Recall

25) The Heimlich maneuver is performed to forcibly
    A) elevate the diaphragm.
    B) depress the diaphragm.
    C) squeeze the ribs.
    D) compress the intestines.
    E) straighten the back.

Answer: A
Topic: 21.7
Skill: Factual Recall

26) The mucous-producing cells that line the stomach
    A) increase the surface of the stomach for faster digestion.
    B) stimulate production of hydrochloric acid.
    C) lubricate and protect the stomach lining.
    D) move food upward in the stomach to prolong digestion.
    E) increase stomach acidity.

Answer: C
Topic: 21.8
Skill: Factual Recall

27) The secretory parietal cells of the stomach are responsible for producing
    A) mucus.
    B) pepsinogen.
    C) pepsin.
    D) hydrochloric acid.
    E) lactic acid.

Answer: D
Topic: 21.8
Skill: Factual Recall

28) Which of the following mechanisms helps prevent the gastric juice from destroying the stomach lining?
    A) digestion of protein by pepsin
    B) secretion of acid-neutralizing compounds
    C) generation through mitosis of new cells to replace the stomach lining
    D) protection of the cells of the stomach-lining by a bone-like substance
    E) dilution of the acid by food passing through the stomach

Answer: C
Topic: 21.8
Skill: Factual Recall

29) The stomach mixes food with secretions of the stomach wall to form
    A) gastric juice.
    B) a parietal bolus.
    C) gastrin.
    D) chyme.
    E) acid gastrin.

Answer: D
Topic: 21.8
Skill: Factual Recall

30) The function of the pyloric sphincter is to
    A) retain chyme in the stomach until pepsin digestion is complete.
    B) periodically release chyme into the duodenum in periodic squirts.
    C) release bile into the duodenum when chyme is present.
    D) release bile and pancreatic secretions into the duodenum when chyme is present.
    E) release pancreatic secretions into the duodenum when chyme is present.

Answer: B
Topic: 21.8
Skill: Factual Recall

31) Heartburn is usually caused by the
    A) secretion of acid by the lining of the lower esophagus.
    B) reflux of chyme from the stomach into the lower esophagus.
    C) retention of food at the bottom of the esophagus by a sphincter that is reluctant to open.
    D) irritation of the lower esophagus by substances in spicy food.
    E) compression of the lower esophagus by an overfilled stomach.

Answer: B
Topic: 21.9
Skill: Factual Recall

32) When the wall of the stomach cannot protect the organ from the effects of digestion, the result is
    A) heartburn.
    B) reverse peristalsis.
    C) a duodenal ulcer.
    D) nausea.
    E) a gastric ulcer.

Answer: E
Topic: 21.9
Skill: Factual Recall

33) Most gastric ulcers are caused by
    A) overconsumption of coffee.
    B) overuse of aspirin and/or ibuprofen.
    C) excessive mental stress.
    D) spiral–shaped bacteria.
    E) overconsumption of alcohol.

Answer: D
Topic: 21.9
Skill: Factual Recall

34) In the digestive system, most nutrient absorption occurs in the
   A) stomach.
   B) liver.
   C) pancreas.
   D) small intestine.
   E) large intestine.

Answer: D
Topic: 21.10
Skill: Application

35) Epithelial cells lining the intestine have surface projections that increase nutrient absorption. These projections are called
   A) villi.
   B) cilia.
   C) microvilli.
   D) rugae.
   E) flagella.

Answer: C
Topic: 21.10
Skill: Factual Recall

36) What is the main digestive function of the pancreas?
   A) to produce digestive enzymes and bile salts
   B) to produce bile
   C) to produce digestive enzymes and a bicarbonate buffer
   D) to produce bicarbonate-containing mucus
   E) to aid in the control of cholesterol

Answer: C
Topic: 21.10
Skill: Factual Recall

37) Which of the following is important in the digestion of lipids?
   A) pepsin
   B) amylase
   C) bile salts
   D) trypsin
   E) nucleases

Answer: C
Topic: 21.10
Skill: Factual Recall

38) Which of the following digestive enzymes is present in children but often absent in adults?
   A) sucrase
   B) lactase
   C) maltase
   D) lipase
   E) amylase

Answer: B
Topic: 21.10
Skill: Application

39) Bile produced in the liver is stored in the _____ before entering the intestine.
    A) pancreas
    B) blood
    C) gallbladder
    D) intestinal wall
    E) common bile duct

Answer: C
Topic: 21.10
Skill: Factual Recall

40) Which enzyme breaks large polypeptides into smaller polypeptides?
    A) amylase
    B) nuclease
    C) lipase
    D) lactase
    E) chymotrypsin

Answer: E
Topic: 21.10
Skill: Factual Recall

41) Which of the following nutrients is digested only after it reaches the small intestine?
    A) fat
    B) protein
    C) starch
    D) complex carbohydrate
    E) polypeptide

Answer: A
Topic: 21.10
Skill: Factual Recall

42) Nutrients absorbed by the intestines move directly to the liver, which
    A) converts the nutrients into monomers.
    B) converts excess glucose to glycogen.
    C) produces platelets for blood clotting.
    D) manages the amount of glucose that is converted to polysaccharides.
    E) converts glucose to alcohol.

Answer: B
Topic: 21.11
Skill: Factual Recall

43) Absorption of water is a major function of the
    A) cecum.
    B) esophagus.
    C) colon.
    D) rectum.
    E) appendix.

Answer: C
Topic: 21.12
Skill: Factual Recall

44) Altogether, the body secretes about 7 liters of water into the alimentary canal each day. About what percentage of this water gets reabsorbed?
   A) 30%
   B) 40%
   C) 50%
   D) 75%
   E) 90%

Answer: E
Topic: 21.12
Skill: Factual Recall

45) Which of the following statements regarding animal digestive systems is *false*?
   A) We expect that an herbivore will have a longer alimentary canal than a carnivore of similar body size.
   B) Meat is more difficult to digest than vegetable matter because of its protein content.
   C) Many herbivorous animals have cellulose–digesting microbes in their colon and cecum.
   D) Prokaryotes in the colon and cecum digest plant material.
   E) Rumination helps to soften and break down plant fibers, making them more accessible to digestion by microbes.

Answer: B
Topic: 21.13–Evolution Connection
Skill: Conceptual Understanding

46) Lions are not always successful hunters, and may go days between meals. What evolutionary adaptation helps the lion survive periods of famine?
   A) production of amylase
   B) formation of a two–chambered stomach
   C) an extended cecum
   D) an expandable stomach
   E) a rich microbial flora in the colon

Answer: D
Topic: 21.13–Evolution Connection
Skill: Conceptual Understanding

47) Interestingly, most herbivorous animals do not have the ability to digest the cellulose in plants. However, in the absence of this ability, they have evolved a mechanism that allows them to survive despite eating only plant matter, namely
   A) production of saliva containing amylase.
   B) digestion by symbiotic microorganisms.
   C) avoidance of plants containing cellulose.
   D) drinking large volumes of water.
   E) converting cellulose to other carbohydrates.

Answer: B
Topic: 21.13–Evolution Connection
Skill: Application

48) Which of the following digestive system structures is greatly expanded in size in koalas, resulting in a very large surface area for prokaryotes to digest plant material?
  A) liver
  B) stomach
  C) rumen
  D) cecum
  E) gall bladder

Answer: D
Topic: 21.13–Evolution Connection
Skill: Factual Recall

49) All animals must obtain _____ from outside sources.
  A) preformed ATP
  B) fuel to power body activities
  C) enzymes
  D) kilocalories
  E) chyme

Answer: B
Topic: 21.14
Skill: Conceptual Understanding

50) Which of the following statements regarding metabolism is *false*?
  A) The basal metabolic rate is the amount of energy a person needs just to stay alive, and does not include the energy needed for activities.
  B) Cells usually use carbohydrates and fats as fuel sources.
  C) Humans store some extra energy in the form of glycogen reserves in the pancreas and spleen.
  D) The average basal metabolic rate for humans is 1300–1800 kcal per day.
  E) One dietary calorie is actually a kilocalorie.

Answer: C
Topic: 21.15
Skill: Factual Recall

51) The rate of energy consumption by the body is called
  A) metabolism.
  B) digestion.   *aerobic respiration*
  C) metabolic rate.
  D) consumption.
  E) glycolysis.

Answer: C
Topic: 20.15
Skill: Factual Recall

52) Organisms suffering from malnourishment have a diet deficient in
    A) one or more essential nutrients.
    B) bile and acids needed for digestion.
    C) calories.
    D) protein.
    E) water.

Answer: A
Topic: 21.16
Skill: Factual Recall

53) A material that must be ingested in preassembled form because the animal cannot synthesize it is
    A) an end product.
    B) adenosine triphosphate.
    C) an enzyme.
    D) glucose.
    E) an essential nutrient.

Answer: E
Topic: 21.16
Skill: Factual Recall

54) Essential fatty acids, which are required in the human diet, are
    A) those fatty acids that humans are unable to synthesize.
    B) the fatty acids that humans can synthesize from simpler molecules.
    C) the fatty acids used in the construction of the phospholipids of cell membranes.
    D) required in order to synthesize most vitamins.
    E) stored in the gallbladder.

Answer: A
Topic: 21.16
Skill: Factual Recall

55) The essential amino acids
    A) are required for making carbohydrates.
    B) must be obtained from the food we eat.
    C) are found only in green, leafy vegetables.
    D) are essential as an energy source.
    E) are required for making nucleic acids.

Answer: B
Topic: 21.16
Skill: Conceptual Understanding

56) Vegetarians who rely upon a single type of plant food
    A) may become severely dehydrated.
    B) run the risk of depleting their liver of glycogen.
    C) are soon unable to produce sufficient quantities of bile.
    D) may become protein-deficient.
    E) live longer than people who ingest animal protein.

Answer: D
Topic: 21.17
Skill: Factual Recall

57) Which of the following vitamins is fat-soluble and consequently, can be stored in body fat?
   A) biotin
   B) pantothenic acid
   C) niacin
   D) K
   E) pyridoxine

Answer: D
Topic: 21.18
Skill: Factual Recall

58) Which of the following statements regarding vitamins is *true*?
   A) They are simple inorganic compounds.
   B) They must be ingested in large quantities.
   C) They can serve as coenzymes or parts of coenzymes.
   D) They are major sources of dietary calories.
   E) They lower the activation energy required for biochemical reactions.

Answer: C
Topic: 21.18
Skill: Factual Recall

59) Which of the following choices correctly pairs a mineral with one of its major functions in the body?
   A) calcium = used in amino acid metabolism
   B) phosphorus = maintaining water balance
   C) sulfur = component of vitamins
   D) iron = component of the nucleic acid backbone
   E) sodium = maintaining osmotic balance of cells

Answer: E
Topic: 21.18
Skill: Factual Recall

60) If a person on a fad diet experiences muscle cramps and reduced appetite, a physician would suspect that this individual is likely suffering from a deficiency of
   A) table salt.
   B) zinc.
   C) iodine.
   D) iron.
   E) calcium.

Answer: A
Topic: 21.18
Skill: Application

61) The minimal amount of nutrients needed every day by healthy people to prevent nutrient deficiencies is called the
   A) RDA, Recommended Dietary Allowances.
   B) MDA, Minimal Daily Allowances.
   C) RMA, Recommended Minimal Allowances.
   D) MNR, Minimal Nutrition Requirements.
   E) DNR, Daily Nutritional Requirements.

Answer: A
Topic: 21.19
Skill: Factual Recall

62) A food label indicates that the contents of a product contain 12 grams of total carbohydrate per serving, 7 grams of sugar per serving (simple carbohydrate), and 2 grams of fiber per serving. How many grams of digestible complex carbohydrate are there per serving?
   A) 5
   B) 3
   C) 9
   D) 2
   E) 12

Answer: B
Topic: 21.20
Skill: Application

63) Which of the following diseases is associated with obesity?
   A) chicken pox
   B) multiple sclerosis
   C) cardiovascular disease
   D) rheumatoid arthritis
   E) cancer

Answer: C
Topic: 21.21–Evolution Connection
Skill: Factual Recall

64) Which of the following is a hormone produced by adipose cells that helps to control appetite?
   A) insulin
   B) bile
   C) glucagon
   D) leptin
   E) pepsinogen

Answer: D
Topic: 21.21–Evolution Connection
Skill: Factual Recall

65) Which of the following is widely regarded as a healthy approach to losing weight?
    A) gastric bypass surgery
    B) regularly engaging in exercise in addition to monitoring food intake
    C) consuming at least 5,000 kcal/day
    D) substituting fatty acids for carbohydrates
    E) trimming daily carbohydrates back to less than 20 grams per day

Answer: B
Topic: 21.22
Skill: Factual Recall

66) Which of the following is associated with a *reduced* risk of cardiovascular disease?
    A) high blood pressure
    B) high levels of HDL
    C) high levels of LDL
    D) high consumption of trans fats
    E) high consumption of dietary cholesterol

Answer: B
Topic: 21.23
Skill: Application

67) To reduce the risk of cancer, it has been suggested that a diet high in _____ is beneficial.
    A) moldy foods
    B) bacon
    C) red meat
    D) cured and smoked foods
    E) antioxidants

Answer: E
Topic: 21.23
Skill: Application

Art Questions

1)

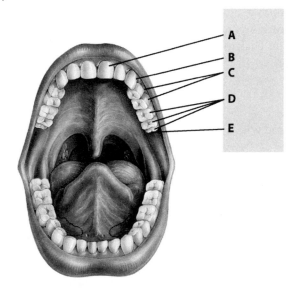

Which of these teeth is an incisor?
   A) tooth A
   B) tooth B
   C) tooth C
   D) tooth D
   E) tooth E

Answer: A
Topic: 21.5
Skill: Factual Recall

2)

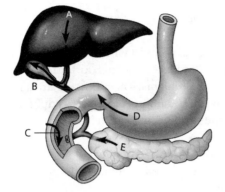

Orgun
digestive system
stomach, liver
Pancreas
Small intestine

Which arrow shows the release of digestive enzymes by the pancreas?

   A) arrow A

   B) arrow B

   C) arrow C

   D) arrow D

   E) arrow E

Answer: E
Topic: 21.10
Skill: Factual Recall

3)

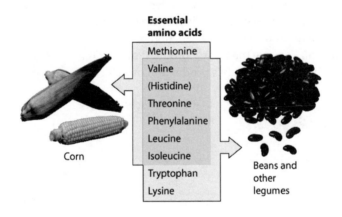

According to this figure, which amino acid is found in corn but not in beans?

   A) methionine

   B) valine

   C) threonine

   D) arginine

   E) lysine

Answer: A
Topic: 21.17
Skill: Application

Scenario Questions

After reading the following paragraph, answer the question(s) below.

Fred is a 24-year-old college student whose father was just diagnosed with cardiovascular disease. Since he knows that these problems often run in families, Fred has asked his doctor to recommend a plan so that he can minimize his risk of developing similar problems. The following are a few of the doctor's recommendations: quit smoking, exercise for at least 30 minutes per day, reduce saturated fats and trans fats in his diet, and increase the number of fruits and vegetables in his diet.

1) Which of the following would match his doctor's recommendations?
   A) eat less of foods that contain partially hydrogenated vegetable oils
   B) eat less of foods that contain antioxidants
   C) avoid cooking with olive oil
   D) consume more beef and less fish
   E) switch to a low-carb diet

Answer: A
Topic: 21.22, 21.23
Skill: Conceptual Understanding

2) Fred was explaining to his family how the doctor's advice would help prevent cardiovascular disease, but he made a mistake in his explanation. Which of the following statements is *incorrect*?
   A) A diet high in saturated fats is associated with a higher risk of heart disease.
   B) A diet high in saturated fats tends to increase LDL levels.
   C) Exercise increases the body's production of LDL.
   D) Smoking will increase the body's production of LDL.
   E) Trans fats increase the body's production of LDL.

Answer: C
Topic: 21.23
Skill: Factual Recall

Chapter 22 Gas Exchange

Multiple-Choice Questions

1) High-flying birds are able to obtain enough oxygen even when the air is very thin because
    A) they have more efficient lungs than other vertebrates.
    B) they have reduced amounts of hemoglobin in their blood.
    C) their mitochondria are more efficient than those of other vertebrates.
    D) their heart can increase or decrease in size as altitude changes.
    E) they are able to store oxygen in oxygen chambers within muscle cells.

Answer: A
Topic: Opening Essay
Skill: Conceptual Understanding

2) If you were to move from around sea level to a much higher altitude, your body would respond with
    A) profuse sweating.
    B) a decrease in the diameter and number of capillaries close to your body's surface.
    C) an increase in energy production.
    D) a decrease in the affinity of hemoglobin for oxygen.
    E) an increase in the number of your red blood cells.

Answer: E
Topic: Opening Essay
Skill: Conceptual Understanding

3) The reason animals need a continuous supply of oxygen is to
    A) make carbon dioxide.
    B) synthesize protein.
    C) dispose of carbon dioxide.
    D) carry out glycolysis.
    E) obtain energy from their food.

Answer: E
Topic: Opening Essay
Skill: Conceptual Understanding

4) A waste product of respiration is
    A) water.
    B) electrons.
    C) hydrogen peroxide.
    D) carbon dioxide.
    E) glucose.

Answer: D
Topic: 22.1
Skill: Factual Recall

5) When you exhale, you
    A) release oxygen and carbon dioxide.
    B) exchange CO_2 for O_2.
    C) take up oxygen and release carbon dioxide to the blood.
    D) take up carbon dioxide and release oxygen.
    E) remove CO_2 from the body.

Answer: E
Topic: 22.1
Skill: Conceptual Understanding

6) In the final phase of respiration, body cells
    A) release CO_2 to red blood cells.
    B) take up O_2 from red blood cells.
    C) increase in size to accommodate the reuptake of O_2.
    D) migrate to the circulatory system.
    E) release CO_2 and take up O_2.

Answer: E
Topic: 22.1
Skill: Conceptual Understanding

7) The body structure where gas exchange occurs is called the
    A) integumentary surface.
    B) respiratory surface.
    C) capillary surface.
    D) exchange network.
    E) capillary network.

Answer: B
Topic: 22.2
Skill: Factual Recall

8) Animals that effectively use their body surface for gas exchange must
    A) be terrestrial.
    B) have a high ratio of body surface area to volume.
    C) have a low ratio of body surface area to volume.
    D) be aquatic and nearly spherical.
    E) have a special kind of hemoglobin.

Answer: B
Topic: 22.2
Skill: Conceptual Understanding

9) Which of the following organisms has a respiratory system that does not require a circulatory system?
    A) grasshopper
    B) mouse
    C) earthworm
    D) carp
    E) crayfish

Answer: A
Topic: 22.2
Skill: Conceptual Understanding

10) Which of the following is likely to have the lowest concentration of O_2?

    A) warm salt water
    B) cool salt water
    C) warm fresh water
    D) cool fresh water
    E) air

Answer: A
Topic: 22.3
Skill: Conceptual Understanding

11) The organization of blood and water flow in a fish's gills increases the fish's ability to

    A) extract oxygen from the water.
    B) extract carbon dioxide from the water.
    C) detect toxic materials in the water.
    D) transport blood throughout the fish's body.
    E) regulate fluid excretion from the body.

Answer: A
Topic: 22.3
Skill: Conceptual Understanding

12) Which of the following statements about fish gills is *true*?

    A) They have a surface area that is much greater than the body surface.
    B) They aid in reproduction.
    C) Because of their efficiency, they only need a small surface area.
    D) They have a poor blood supply.
    E) Like lungs, they have an exhale/inhale function.

Answer: A
Topic: 22.3
Skill: Conceptual Understanding

13) The chief advantage of gas exchange in water is that

    A) water can contain more oxygen than air.
    B) carbon dioxide is easier to eliminate in water than in air.
    C) no energy is used to keep the exchange surface wet.
    D) less energy is required to ventilate gills as compared to lungs.
    E) contact between the respiratory surface and the gas–containing medium is more efficient in water than in air.

Answer: C
Topic: 22.3
Skill: Conceptual Understanding

14) Gills are unsuitable for animals living on land because

    A) the large surface area of gills would allow dehydration of the animal.
    B) air cannot diffuse across the gill surface.
    C) there is no way to get air into the gills.
    D) gills require high blood pressure.
    E) gills do not function well in animals that have a diaphragm.

Answer: A
Topic: 22.3
Skill: Conceptual Understanding

15) In the countercurrent exchange system of fish gills,
    A) blood and water flow in the same direction.
    B) blood and water flow in opposite directions.
    C) blood and water are separated by a thick polysaccharide barrier.
    D) blood flow in the gills reverses direction with every heartbeat.
    E) water flow over the gills reverses direction with every inhalation.

Answer: B
Topic: 22.3
Skill: Factual Recall

16) Which of the following statements regarding breathing and circulation is *false*?
    A) Insects lose very little water by using a tracheal system to breathe.
    B) Air–breathing animals lose water by evaporation.
    C) The tracheal system of insects consists of a series of branching air tubes that extend from the surface to deep inside the body.
    D) A terrestrial animal spends much more energy than an aquatic animal ventilating its respiratory surface.
    E) The circulatory system of insects is not involved in transporting oxygen.

Answer: D
Topic: 22.4
Skill: Conceptual Understanding

17) The tracheal system of an insect is most like which of the following?
    A) the exhaust system of an automobile
    B) the electrical wiring in a home
    C) the air duct system in a building
    D) a river system draining a large region
    E) leaves on a tree

Answer: C
Topic: 22.4
Skill: Conceptual Understanding

18) Which of the following statements is *false*?
    A) Most amphibians use lungs and skin for gas exchange.
    B) Unlike the tracheal system of insects, vertebrate lungs are restricted to one location in the body.
    C) Vocal cords in our bronchi allow us to speak.
    D) It is easier to use the O_2 in air than in water because air is easier to move.
    E) Gas exchange in the human lungs occurs in the alveoli.

Answer: C
Topic: 22.5-Evolution Connection
Skill: Conceptual Understanding

19) Evolutionary movement of aquatic animals to land involved an intermediate individual that
    A) could fly.
    B) is called a "podafish."
    C) evolved a tracheal system of branching internal tubes.
    D) had both gills and lungs.
    E) had ribs to protect the heart and lungs.

Answer: D
Topic: 22.5–Evolution Connection
Skill: Conceptual Understanding

20) Evolutionary adaptations for survival on land produced tetrapods, which later evolved into
    A) snakes and skinks.
    B) amphibians, reptiles, and mammals.
    C) frogs and toads.
    D) migratory birds.
    E) humans.

Answer: B
Topic: 22.5–Evolution Connection
Skill: Factual Recall

21) Which of the following animals requires the largest and most complex lungs proportional to its overall body size?
    A) frog
    B) snake
    C) turtle
    D) bear
    E) newt

Answer: D
Topic: 22.5–Evolution Connection
Skill: Conceptual Understanding

22) Which of the following options correctly lists the direction of carbon dioxide travel as it leaves the body?
    A) alveoli, bronchioles, bronchi, trachea, pharynx, larynx
    B) alveoli, bronchi, bronchioles, trachea, larynx, pharynx
    C) alveoli, bronchioles, bronchi, trachea, larynx, pharynx
    D) alveoli, bronchi, bronchioles, trachea, pharynx, larynx
    E) alveoli, trachea, bronchioles, bronchi, pharynx, larynx

Answer: C
Topic: 22.6
Skill: Factual Recall

23) Which of the following is a function of the nasal cavities in humans?
   A) secreting enzymes for digestion
   B) warming inhaled air
   C) secreting excess carbon dioxide into exhaled air
   D) determining O_2 content in inhaled air
   E) providing a tract for nerve distribution

Answer: B
Topic: 22.6
Skill: Conceptual Understanding

24) What name is given to the sheet of muscle that helps move air in and out of the lungs?
   A) trachea
   B) alveolus
   C) larynx
   D) diaphragm
   E) bronchus

Answer: D
Topic: 22.6
Skill: Factual Recall

25) Within the lungs, gas exchange occurs across
   A) alveoli.
   B) tracheae.
   C) bronchioles.
   D) diaphragms.
   E) bronchi.

Answer: A
Topic: 22.6
Skill: Factual Recall

26) The _____ is a passageway shared by both food and air.
   A) alveolus
   B) trachea
   C) pharynx
   D) larynx
   E) nasal cavity

Answer: C
Topic: 22.6
Skill: Factual Recall

27) Cigarette smoke can affect macrophages that reside in our lungs for the purpose of
   A) preventing emphysema.
   B) engulfing particles and microorganisms.
   C) enhancing oxygen and carbon dioxide exchange.
   D) producing antibodies.
   E) maintaining the appropriate pH and moisture content within the lungs.

Answer: B
Topic: 22.7
Skill: Conceptual Understanding

28) Labored breathing, coughing, lung infection, and respiratory failure are characteristics defining
   A) tuberculosis.
   B) meningitis.
   C) chronic obstructive pulmonary disease.
   D) multiple sclerosis.
   E) myasthenia gravis

Answer: C
Topic: 22.6
Skill: Factual Recall

29) Why do cigarette smokers cough more than nonsmokers?
   A) The tar in cigarette smoke tends to make alveoli stick together, and coughing separates them.
   B) Cigarette smoke harms the cilia that normally move debris out of the lungs, and coughing is the remaining way to clean the lungs.
   C) Cigarette smoking partially paralyzes the muscles in the lungs, resulting in an increased residual volume, and coughing exchanges this "dead air."
   D) Coughing stimulates blood flow to the lungs.
   E) By raising the pressure in the lungs, coughing forces more oxygen into the blood.

Answer: B
Topic: 22.7
Skill: Conceptual Understanding

30) Cigarette smoking and secondhand smoke cause cancer due to the
   A) effects they have on our breathing mechanisms.
   B) toxins in the smoke.
   C) resistance they have for products of our immune system.
   D) immunosuppressive effects they display.
   E) lack of antioxidants in smoke.

Answer: B
Topic: 22.7
Skill: Factual Recall

31) The maximum amount of air that a human can inhale and exhale is called the
   A) tidal volume.
   B) vital capacity.
   C) maximum capacity.
   D) physiological volume.
   E) inhalation capacity.

Answer: B
Topic: 22.8
Skill: Factual Recall

32) Inhalation in humans is achieved by
   A) contraction of muscles in the lungs.
   B) contraction of the diaphragm.
   C) relaxation of the diaphragm and chest muscles.
   D) relaxation of the diaphragm.
   E) contraction of the diaphragm and chest muscles.

Answer: E
Topic: 22.8
Skill: Conceptual Understanding

33) When you are breathing normally, exhalation results mainly from
   A) the contraction of muscles in the chest.
   B) the contraction of the diaphragm.
   C) the contraction of muscles in the lungs.
   D) the relaxation of the chest muscles and diaphragm.
   E) low pressure in the lungs.

Answer: D
Topic: 22.8
Skill: Conceptual Understanding

34) Compared to the vital capacity, how much air can lungs actually hold?
   A) always less
   B) sometimes less
   C) always more
   D) sometimes more
   E) always the same amount

Answer: C
Topic: 22.8
Skill: Conceptual Understanding

35) The function of passageways for gas exchange in birds is to
   A) lighten the bird.
   B) adjust the temperature of air.
   C) clean the air.
   D) permit one-way ventilation of the lungs.
   E) store air for times of physical exertion.

Answer: D
Topic: 22.8
Skill: Conceptual Understanding

36) Air leaving human lungs during exhalation contains
   A) no oxygen.
   B) no carbon dioxide.
   C) mostly carbon dioxide and carbon monoxide.
   D) carbon dioxide and unused oxygen.
   E) one-half oxygen and one-half carbon dioxide.

Answer: D
Topic: 22.8
Skill: Conceptual Understanding

37) When you hold your breath, which of the following blood gas changes leads initially to the urge to breathe again?
   A) rising oxygen concentration
   B) rising carbon dioxide concentration
   C) falling oxygen concentration
   D) falling carbon dioxide concentration
   E) falling nitrogen concentration

Answer: B
Topic: 22.9
Skill: Conceptual Understanding

38) What part of the human brain contains the primary breathing control center?
   A) neocortex
   B) hippocampus
   C) cerebellum
   D) medulla oblongata
   E) thalamus

Answer: D
Topic: 22.9
Skill: Factual Recall

39) Medullary breathing centers directly sense and respond to
   A) blood pH and CO_2 concentration.
   B) blood O_2 concentration.
   C) alveolar CO_2 concentration.
   D) alveolar O_2 concentration.
   E) blood pH and O_2 concentration.

Answer: A
Topic: 22.9
Skill: Conceptual Understanding

40) In a mammal, blood leaving the lungs goes to
   A) the kidneys.
   B) the heart.
   C) the limbs.
   D) the liver.
   E) the brain.

Answer: B
Topic: 22.10
Skill: Factual Recall

41) Oxygen moves from blood into the interstitial fluid and then to body cells because
   A) it diffuses from a region of higher partial pressure to a region of lower partial pressure.
   B) it diffuses from a region of lower partial pressure to a region of higher partial pressure.
   C) it descends down an osmotic gradient, following the movement of water.
   D) the cells of the body create molecular attractions that pull the oxygen to them.
   E) oxygen diffuses from a higher to a lower pH.

Answer: A
Topic: 22.10
Skill: Factual Recall

42) An oxygen molecule enters an alveolus. If it is to reach a red blood cell, its next step must be to
   A) pass down a bronchiole to an air sac.
   B) diffuse across the alveolar epithelium.
   C) dissolve in the fluid lining the alveolus.
   D) dissolve in the plasma of blood surrounding the alveolus.
   E) diffuse across a capillary epithelium.

Answer: C
Topic: 21.10
Skill: Conceptual Understanding

43) Oxygen is mostly transported through the body
   A) dissolved in the blood.
   B) dissolved in red blood cells.
   C) bound to hemoglobin.
   D) bound to dissolved iron.
   E) bound to carbon.

Answer: C
Topic: 22.11
Skill: Factual Recall

44) The oxygen–carrying component in red blood cells is
   A) carbon dioxide.
   B) hemoglobin.
   C) bicarbonate ions.
   D) iron.
   E) the cell membrane.

Answer: B
Topic: 22.11
Skill: Factual Recall

45) Most CO_2 is transported to the lungs
    A) dissolved in the plasma.
    B) attached to hemoglobin.
    C) as carbonic anhydrase.
    D) as carboxyl.
    E) as bicarbonate ions.

Answer: E
Topic: 22.11
Skill: Factual Recall

46) In the capillaries of the body, oxygen released from hemoglobin first diffuses into the
    A) blood plasma.
    B) pulmonary veins.
    C) pulmonary arteries.
    D) interstitial fluid.
    E) alveoli.

Answer: A
Topic: 22.11
Skill: Factual Recall

47) Which of the following contributes to gas exchange in the human fetus?
    A) lower blood pH of the embryo
    B) lack of turbulence in the fetal blood
    C) lower pressure of the gases O_2 and CO_2
    D) high oxygen levels maintained in the amniotic fluid by the placenta
    E) the increased oxygen binding capability of fetal hemoglobin

Answer: E
Topic: 22.12
Skill: Conceptual Understanding

48) What prompts a newborn baby to start to breathe?
    A) an increase in the concentration of carbon dioxide in the baby's blood
    B) a decrease in the concentration of oxygen in the baby's blood
    C) a change in the temperature on the surface of the skin
    D) exposure to air
    E) an increase in the pH of the baby's blood

Answer: A
Topic: 22.12
Skill: Factual Recall

Art Questions

1)

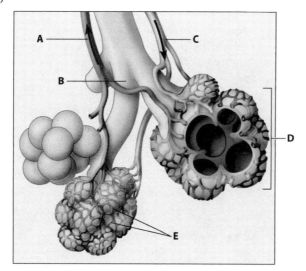

Which part of the diagram above shows alveoli?
   A) part A
   B) part B
   C) part C
   D) part D
   E) part E

Answer: D
Topic: 22.6
Skill: Factual Recall

2)

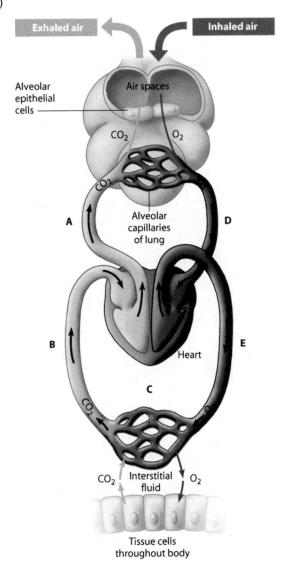

At which point is oxygen–rich blood traveling through a vein?

A) point A
B) point B
C) point C
D) point D
E) point E

Answer: D
Topic: 22.10
Skill: Conceptual Understanding

Scenario Questions

After reading the following paragraph, answer the question(s) below.

Amphibians (for example, frogs, toads, and salamanders) spend the early part of their lives in water, but may live on land as adults. Regardless of whether the adults live on land or in the water, they return to water to breed and lay their eggs. Frogs have small lungs and supplement their oxygen intake by breathing through the skin. Although large frogs have more total surface area than smaller frogs, the larger frogs have a lower surface/volume ratio (less skin surface relative to their total body volume). To keep their respiratory surfaces moist, frogs are only found in wet or very moist locations.

In an experiment designed to investigate oxygen consumption in relation to body size, frogs from five different species were weighed and placed in a respirometer (a machine that measures oxygen consumption) for one hour. The table below shows the results of the experiment.

Species	Average Weight (grams)	Oxygen Consumption in One Hour (cc)
A	7	0.35
B	11	0.55
C	15	0.75
D	21	1.05
E	37	1.85

1) From the data in the table, it's reasonable to conclude that
   A) smaller frogs consume less oxygen per gram of body weight.
   B) frogs kept at warm temperatures consume more oxygen than in colder temperatures.
   C) each tested species consumes a different amount of oxygen per gram of body weight.
   D) oxygen consumption per gram of body weight is the same for all tested species.
   E) oxygen consumption per gram of body weight for the largest species is much higher than for the smallest species.

Answer: D
Topic: 22.2
Skill: Application

2) If you could alter the shape of a frog so that it was long and thin instead of compact, the frog's oxygen transfer efficiency would
   A) increase, because the frog would be larger.
   B) decrease, because there's more skin area to keep moist.
   C) increase, because the frog would have more surface area in relation to body volume.
   D) decrease, because a long body has more contact with the soil or water.
   E) not change at all, because the body volume would remain constant.

Answer: C
Topic: 22.2
Skill: Conceptual Understanding

Chapter 23 Circulation

Multiple-Choice Questions

1) Which of the following statements regarding circulation is *true*?
   A) Muscle contraction tends to pull blood downward into the lower parts of the body of a terrestrial vertebrate.
   B) A standing giraffe requires a great deal more pressure to pump blood to its head than an animal with a shorter neck.
   C) Valves in veins and muscle contractions pressing against veins slow down the return of blood to the heart.
   D) When a corn snake climbs up a tree, its heart beats slower but with greater force.
   E) Gravity significantly affects blood moving through the circulatory system.

   Answer: B
   Topic: Opening Essay
   Skill: Conceptual Understanding

2) Which of the following statements regarding circulatory systems is *true*?
   A) The smallest blood vessels in the body are veins.
   B) A circulatory system is necessary in any animal whose body is too large or too complex for vital chemicals to reach all parts of the body by diffusion.
   C) Red blood cells are too large to pass single file through capillaries.
   D) Materials are exchanged directly between the blood and body cells.
   E) The circulatory system transports gases and nutrients, but the lymphatic system transports metabolic wastes.

   Answer: B
   Topic: 23.1
   Skill: Conceptual Understanding

3) Which of the following is a function of the circulatory system?
   A) maintaining an optimal red blood cell count
   B) transporting nerve impulses throughout the body
   C) governing nutrient concentration in the blood
   D) transporting nutrients to body cells
   E) mounting a response to invading microorganisms

   Answer: D
   Topic: 23.1
   Skill: Factual Recall

4) The two basic types of circulatory systems that have evolved over time are
   A) flat and circular.
   B) open and closed.
   C) transverse and repetitive.
   D) horizontal and vertical.
   E) single and double.

   Answer: B
   Topic: 23.1
   Skill: Factual Recall

5) Which of the following is characteristic of the circulatory system of arthropods?
    A) lack of a heart
    B) lack of blood
    C) lack of blood vessels.
    D) blood flowing out of the body
    E) lack of distinction between blood and interstitial fluid

Answer: E
Topic: 23.1
Skill: Conceptual Understanding

6) Adaptation to terrestrial life required major evolutionary changes, not just in the respiratory system, but also in the
    A) reproductive system.
    B) cardiovascular system.
    C) manufacture of blood cells.
    D) maintenance of body temperature.
    E) association of blood and interstitial fluid.

Answer: B
Topic: 23.2–Evolution Connection
Skill: Conceptual Understanding

7) Which of the following animals has a single circuit of blood flow and two heart chambers?
    A) salamander
    B) salmon
    C) snake
    D) swan
    E) squirrel

Answer: B
Topic: 23.2–Evolution Connection
Skill: Factual Recall

8) Which of the following animals has a three-chambered heart?
    A) snake
    B) crocodile
    C) human
    D) cow
    E) bird

Answer: A
Topic: 23.2–Evolution Connection
Skill: Factual Recall

9) Which of the following is a likely advantage of a three-chambered heart?
    A) greater separation of oxygenated and deoxygenated blood
    B) greater blood pressure
    C) the ability to divert deoxygenated blood away from the lungs when diving underwater
    D) the ability to generate more body heat than a mammal
    E) greater mixing of blood in the ventricle

Answer: C
Topic: 23.2–Evolution Connection
Skill: Conceptual Understanding

10) Although birds and mammals descended from different ancestors, they both have a four-chambered heart. This is the result of
    A) the simplification of the cardiovascular system.
    B) the necessity for rapid movement of blood.
    C) the importance of entirely filling the chest cavity.
    D) nature selecting adaptations of two unrelated individuals in response to similar environmental challenges.
    E) genetic aberrations that resulted from mistakes in somatic cell division.

Answer: D
Topic: 23.2–Evolution Connection
Skill: Conceptual Understanding

11) Which of the following statements about mammalian circulatory systems is *false?*
    A) The pulmonary circuit carries blood between the heart and the lungs.
    B) The systemic circuit carries blood between the heart and the rest of the body.
    C) Mammals have two atria and two ventricles in their hearts.
    D) A mammal uses about ten times as much oxygen as a lizard of the same size.
    E) The left side of a mammal's heart sends blood to the lungs.

Answer: E
Topic: 23.3
Skill: Factual Recall

12) In mammals, blood returning from the head will pass through the _____ just before entering the right atrium.
    A) right ventricle
    B) left atrium
    C) superior vena cava
    D) inferior vena cava
    E) aorta

Answer: C
Topic: 23.3
Skill: Factual Recall

13) In mammals, which of the following vessels transports oxygenated blood from the lung back to the heart?
    A) pulmonary artery
    B) pulmonary vein
    C) aorta
    D) vena cava
    E) coronary artery
Answer: B
Topic: 23.3
Skill: Factual Recall

14) Oxygen-poor blood is carried from the heart of a mammal to the lungs via the
    A) pulmonary arteries.
    B) pulmonary veins.
    C) venae cavae.
    D) aorta.
    E) coronary veins.
Answer: A
Topic: 23.3
Skill: Factual Recall

15) Blood is pumped from the heart to the lungs by the
    A) pulmonary artery.
    B) left atrium.
    C) right atrium.
    D) left ventricle.
    E) right ventricle.
Answer: E
Topic: 23.3
Skill: Factual Recall

16) From the left ventricle, oxygen-rich blood flows through the
    A) superior vena cava.
    B) inferior vena cava.
    C) aorta.
    D) pulmonary artery.
    E) pulmonary vein.
Answer: C
Topic: 23.3
Skill: Factual Recall

17) The largest blood vessel in the human body is the
    A) superior vena cava.
    B) vena cava.
    C) arteria maxima.
    D) aorta.
    E) pulmonary artery.
Answer: D
Topic: 23.3
Skill: Factual Recall

18) During which phase of the heartbeat does the heart fill with blood?
   A) interphase
   B) resting phase
   C) diastole
   D) atrial phase
   E) systole

Answer: C
Topic: 23.4
Skill: Factual Recall

19) Cardiac output is defined as the volume of blood pumped by a(n) _____ each time it contracts.
   A) heart
   B) atrium
   C) aorta
   D) atrioventricular valve
   E) ventricle

Answer: E
Topic: 23.4
Skill: Factual Recall

20) During ventricular systole, the _____ valves _____.
   A) AV . . . open
   B) semilunar . . . close
   C) AV . . . close
   D) semilunar . . . open
   E) AV and semilunar . . . close

Answer: D
Topic: 23.4
Skill: Factual Recall

21) Heart rate is least influenced by
   A) emotional cues.
   B) hormones.
   C) exercise.
   D) a pacemaker in the right atrium.
   E) the number of cells per unit of blood.

Answer: E
Topic: 23.4
Skill: Conceptual Understanding

22) Using a stethoscope, you listen to a beating heart and hear "lub–dup, lub–dup." These sounds are created by
   A) muscles in the left ventricle.
   B) blood flowing through the aorta.
   C) muscles in the right atrium.
   D) blood pressure differentials from chamber to chamber.
   E) valves in the heart closing.

Answer: E
Topic: 23.4
Skill: Factual Recall

23) The location of the heart's pacemaker is a specialized region of cardiac muscle called the
   A) atrioventricular node.
   B) sinoatrial node.
   C) Purkinje fibers.
   D) heart center of the brain.
   E) aorta.

Answer: B
Topic: 23.5
Skill: Factual Recall

24) The main function of the AV node is to
   A) initiate the heartbeat.
   B) set the rhythm of the heartbeat.
   C) relay the signal for the heart to contract from the right ventricle to the right atrium.
   D) relay the signal for the heart to contract from the right heart to the left heart.
   E) relay a signal for the ventricles to contract.

Answer: E
Topic: 23.5
Skill: Factual Recall

25) Myocardial infarction, also called a heart attack,
   A) is caused by excessive blood pressure in the heart.
   B) actually causes no permanent damage to the heart.
   C) is the result of angina pectoris.
   D) is unrelated to cigarette smoking.
   E) results from the death of cardiac muscle cells.

Answer: E
Topic: 23.6
Skill: Factual Recall

26) Which of the following is the cause of 40% of all deaths in the United States?
   A) cardiovascular disease
   B) HIV
   C) flu
   D) cancer
   E) diabetes

Answer: A
Topic: 23.6
Skill: Factual Recall

27) Arteries are distinguished from veins based on all of the following features *except*
   A) the direction of blood flow relative to the heart.
   B) the structure of their walls.
   C) the amount of oxygen present in the blood.
   D) the blood pressure.
   E) the number of red blood cells.

Answer: C
Topic: 23.7
Skill: Factual Recall

28) Which blood vessels have the thinnest walls?
   A) arteries
   B) arterioles
   C) veins
   D) venules
   E) capillaries

Answer: E
Topic: 23.7
Skill: Conceptual Understanding

29) In humans, which blood vessels have valves?
   A) arteries in the neck
   B) arterioles
   C) capillaries
   D) venules
   E) veins

Answer: E
Topic: 23.7
Skill: Factual Recall

30) As blood moves away from the heart, the relative size and number of blood vessels
   _____, the blood pressure _____, and the velocity of blood flow _____.
   A) decreases . . . drops. . . slows
   B) decreases. . . increases . . . increases
   C) decreases. . . drops . . . increases
   D) increases. . . increases. . . increases
   E) increases. . . drops . . . slows

Answer: A
Topic: 23.8
Skill: Conceptual Understanding

31) In which of the following human blood vessels is the blood pressure lowest?
   A) arteries in the head
   B) arterioles in the legs
   C) capillaries in the feet
   D) the aorta
   E) veins in the head

Answer: E
Topic: 23.8
Skill: Conceptual Understanding

32) Which kind of vessel has the lowest blood velocity?
   A) artery
   B) arteriole
   C) capillary
   D) venule
   E) vein

Answer: C
Topic: 23.8
Skill: Factual Recall

33) Which of the following factors contributes to the flow of blood in veins?
    A) skeletal muscle contractions
    B) the number of red blood cells in venous blood
    C) the diameter of capillaries
    D) blood pressure generated by the heart
    E) cardiac output

Answer: A
Topic: 23.8
Skill: Conceptual Understanding

34) Which of the following statements regarding blood pressure is *false?*
    A) Normal blood pressure for adult humans is usually at or below 120/80.
    B) Hypertension is defined as persistent systolic pressure above 120 and/or diastolic above 80.
    C) High blood pressure can lead to an enlarged and weakened heart, increased risk of heart attack, stroke, and kidney failure.
    D) The higher number in a blood pressure reading measures the force of a heart contraction.
    E) The lower number in a blood pressure reading measures the force during heart relaxation.

Answer: B
Topic: 23.9
Skill: Conceptual Understanding

35) Which of the following can contribute to high blood pressure?
    A) regular exercise
    B) eating a heart-healthy diet
    C) avoiding excess alcohol
    D) smoking
    E) maintaining proper weight

Answer: D
Topic: 23.9
Skill: Factual Recall

36) At any given time, what percentage of the body's capillaries have blood flowing through them?
    A) 5—10%
    B) 20—25%
    C) 40—50%
    D) 60—70%
    E) 85—90%

Answer: A
Topic: 23.10
Skill: Factual Recall

37) Blood flow through capillaries is controlled by
   A) one–way valves.
   B) precapillary sphincters.
   C) smooth muscle in the walls of arterioles.
   D) precapillary sphincters and smooth muscle in the walls of arterioles.
   E) blood pressure.

   Answer: D
   Topic: 23.10
   Skill: Factual Recall

38) What type of blood vessel is solely responsible for exchange between the blood and the interstitial fluid?
   A) artery
   B) arteriole
   C) capillary
   D) venule
   E) vein

   Answer: C
   Topic: 23.11
   Skill: Factual Recall

39) The diameter of a capillary is about the same as that of
   A) a nerve.
   B) a red blood cell.
   C) an arteriole.
   D) a valve.
   E) a venule.

   Answer: B
   Topic: 23.11
   Skill: Factual Recall

40) One way that substances move between blood and interstitial fluid is by
   A) alternatively breaking and regenerating membranes of cells lining capillaries.
   B) osmosis.
   C) diffusion through clefts between the epithelial cells of the capillary wall.
   D) active transport utilizing ATP.
   E) activating pressure differentials.

   Answer: C
   Topic: 23.11
   Skill: Factual Recall

41) Whether there is a net flow of fluid into or out of a capillary at a given point along its length depends upon
   A) whether the fluid contains nutrients or wastes.
   B) whether or not the fluid contains oxygen.
   C) whether or not the fluid contains carbon dioxide.
   D) the balance between blood pressure and osmotic pressure.
   E) the needs of the tissue.

   Answer: D
   Topic: 23.11
   Skill: Conceptual Understanding

42) The liquid part of blood is called
    A) water.
    B) plasma.
    C) serum.
    D) extrastitial fluid.
    E) anionic fluid.

Answer: B
Topic: 23.12
Skill: Factual Recall

43) Cells make up about what percentage of total blood volume?
    A) 10%
    B) 25%
    C) 45%
    D) 65%
    E) 80%

Answer: C
Topic: 23.12
Skill: Factual Recall

44) Blood proteins are involved in all of the following activities *except*
    A) fighting infection.
    B) maintaining osmotic balance.
    C) acting as buffers.
    D) maintaining salinity.
    E) blood clotting.

Answer: D
Topic: 23.12
Skill: Conceptual Understanding

45) Which of these statements about erythrocytes is *true?*
    A) The main function of erythrocytes is to carry nutrients.
    B) Erythrocytes are shaped like biconcave disks.
    C) Each erythrocyte contains about 250 million molecules of iron.
    D) Erythrocytes in adult humans have nuclei.
    E) Oxygen is transported on the surface of leukocytes.

Answer: B
Topic: 23.12
Skill: Factual Recall

46) Which of the following cells are phagocytes?
    A) monocytes and neutrophils
    B) basophils and eosinophils
    C) lymphocytes only
    D) lymphocytes, basophils, and eosinophils
    E) basophils, lymphocytes, and neutrophils

Answer: A
Topic: 23.12
Skill: Factual Recall

47) How long do human red blood cells circulate in the blood before they wear out and have to be replaced?
   A) 1 to 2 weeks
   B) 1 month
   C) 3 to 4 months
   D) 6 to 8 months
   E) 10 to 12 months

Answer: C
Topic: 23.13
Skill: Factual Recall

48) What is the most common cause of anemia?
   A) vitamin deficiency
   B) low blood pressure
   C) iron deficiency
   D) inefficient hemoglobin production
   E) bone marrow cancer

Answer: C
Topic: 23.13
Skill: Factual Recall

49) An adult human's red blood cells are formed in the
   A) spleen.
   B) liver.
   C) bone marrow.
   D) abdominal cavity.
   E) thoracic cavity.

Answer: C
Topic: 23.13
Skill: Factual Recall

50) Which of the following can increase red blood cell concentration in a unit of blood?
   A) training at low altitudes
   B) reducing blood levels of EPO
   C) blood doping
   D) hydration
   E) a condition called anemia

Answer: C
Topic: 23.13
Skill: Factual Recall

51) Blood clots are formed by platelets and the plasma protein
   A) thrombin.
   B) sealin.
   C) hemophilin.
   D) fibrinogen.
   E) thrombus.

Answer: D
Topic: 23.14
Skill: Factual Recall

52) Which of the following statements about blood clotting is *true*?
    A) The first response to an injury is dilation of the damaged blood vessels.
    B) During the clotting response, platelets rapidly congregate in the interstitial fluid.
    C) Fibrin is enzymatically converted to fibrinogen.
    D) Threads of fibrin trap blood cells and platelets.
    E) Chemicals released by platelets prevent cell division in smooth muscle and connective tissues.

Answer: D
Topic: 23.14
Skill: Factual Recall

53) Multipotent stem cells
    A) phagocytize bacterial cells.
    B) are primarily important in blood clotting.
    C) are responsible for an immune response.
    D) are isolated from adult blood.
    E) can differentiate into all blood cells and platelets.

Answer: E
Topic: 23.15
Skill: Factual Recall

54) Stem cell research may eventually result in a cure for blood cell diseases, such as
    A) monocyte differentiation.
    B) leukemia.
    C) anemia.
    D) metastatic cancer.
    E) hemophilia.

Answer: B
Topic: 23.15
Skill: Conceptual Understanding

Art Questions

1)

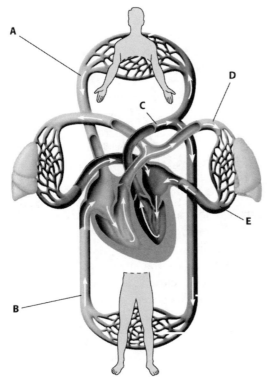

*Blood circulary System
artery, vain, Capillari
heart-*

Which part of this figure depicts a pulmonary artery?
  A) part A
  B) part B
  C) part C
  D) part D
  E) part E

Answer: D
Topic: 23.3
Skill: Factual Recall

2)

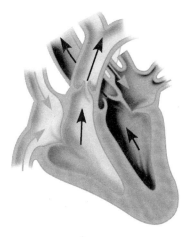

Which of the following describes the stage of the cardiac cycle shown?
  A) AV and SL valves both open, ventricles contracting
  B) AV valves open, SL valves closed, ventricles contracting
  C) AV valves closed, SL valves open, ventricles contracting
  D) AV valves closed, SL valves open, ventricles relaxed
  E) AV valves closed, SL valves closed, ventricles relaxed

Answer: C
Topic: 23.4
Skill: Application

3)

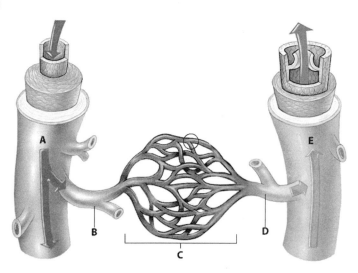

Which part of this figure depicts an arteriole?
  A) part A
  B) part B
  C) part C
  D) part D
  E) part E

Answer: B
Topic: 23.7
Skill: Factual Recall

Scenario Questions

After reading the following paragraph, answer the question(s) below.

Ron and Tiffany are studying circulatory system function. They designed an experiment to test whether the diameter of a tube would affect the rate of flow through the tube. They ran water from a large container through five tubes with different diameters for exactly 30 seconds for each tube. They measured the volume of liquid that passed through the tube in the 30–second period. They tested each tube three times and poured the water back into the container after each test. The results of the experiment are shown in the following table.

	Diameter of Tube (cm)	Average Volume of Fluid (ml)
Tube A	0.5	210
Tube B	0.6	350
Tube C	0.7	480
Tube D	0.8	600
Tube E	0.9	975

1) Which statement best summarizes the results of the experiment?
   A) The larger the tube diameter, the greater the flow volume.
   B) The larger the tube diameter, the smaller the flow volume.
   C) The tube diameter shows no clear relationship to flow volume.
   D) The smaller the tube, the greater the flow volume.
   E) The flow rate through the largest tube is approximately twice that of the smallest.
   Answer: A
   Topic: 23.8
   Skill: Conceptual Understanding

2) The rate of flow in the smallest diameter tube is comparable to that found in the _____ of the human body.
   A) arteries
   B) veins
   C) capillaries
   D) arterioles
   E) venules
   Answer: C
   Topic: 23.8
   Skill: Application

Chapter 24 The Immune System

Multiple-Choice Questions

1) The Epstein–Barr virus causes the symptoms of mononucleosis by
    A) damaging both male and female gametes.
    B) causing the production of excessive mucus.
    C) infecting B cells and weakening the immune system.
    D) destroying phagocytic cells within the bloodstream.
    E) preventing the production of saliva.

Answer: C
Topic: Opening Essay
Skill: Factual Recall

2) The body's innate defenses against infection include
    A) several nonspecific antibodies.
    B) several nonspecific amino acid toxins.
    C) barriers such as dead skin cells and mucus.
    D) increased production of certain hormones and changes in microcirculation.
    E) memory cells.

Answer: C
Topic: 24.1
Skill: Factual Recall

3) Which of the following wander through the interstitial fluid eating any bacteria and virus–infected cells they encounter?
    A) erythrocytes
    B) megakaryocytes
    C) leukocytes
    D) macrophages
    E) interferons

Answer: D
Topic: 24.1
Skill: Factual Recall

4) Natural killer cells
    A) are phagocytes that attack and kill pathogenic microorganisms.
    B) attack virus–infected cells by releasing chemicals that promote programmed cell death.
    C) are phagocytes that attack virus–infected cells.
    D) tag pathogenic microorganisms with antibodies.
    E) phagocytize microorganisms that have been tagged with antibodies.

Answer: B
Topic: 24.1
Skill: Factual Recall

5) What substance, produced by virus-infected cells, diffuses to neighboring cells to help them fight a viral infection?
  A) lysozyme
  B) interferon
  C) histamine
  D) antigen
  E) interleukin-2

Answer: B
Topic: 24.1
Skill: Factual Recall

6) A researcher who detects a higher-than-normal amount of interferon in a laboratory rat would correctly conclude that
  A) the rat has, or recently had, a viral infection.
  B) cancerous cells are present in the rat.
  C) the rat's diet is deficient in calcium.
  D) the complement system is activated.
  E) monocytes are differentiating into macrophages in the rat's bloodstream.

Answer: A
Topic: 24.1
Skill: Application

7) Some complement proteins
  A) induce antibody formation by phagocytic cells.
  B) help trigger the inflammatory response.
  C) trigger the production of lysozyme by monocytes.
  D) are released by natural killer cells to attack cancer and virus-infected cells.
  E) replace T cells in the cell-mediated response.

Answer: B
Topic: 24.1
Skill: Factual Recall

8) Which of the following helps activate our nonspecific (innate) defense system?
  A) active immunity
  B) inflammation
  C) passive immunity
  D) cell-mediated immunity
  E) mobilization of erythrocytes

Answer: B
Topic: 24.2
Skill: Factual Recall

9) When you cut yourself, the damaged cells immediately release chemical alarm signals, such as
   A) interferon.
   B) complement.
   C) histamine.
   D) antihistamine.
   E) anti–interferon.
Answer: C
Topic: 24.2
Skill: Application

10) Which of the following is an immediate effect of histamine release?
   A) dilation of local blood vessels
   B) blocking of a response to ragweed pollen
   C) conversion of histamine to histidine
   D) increase in blood pressure
   E) metabolic production of energy molecules
Answer: A
Topic: 24.2
Skill: Conceptual Understanding

11) The major result of the inflammatory response is to
   A) initiate the production of antibodies.
   B) remove contaminating microorganisms and initiate repair of damaged tissues.
   C) initiate cell–mediated immune responses.
   D) initiate humoral–mediated immune responses.
   E) initiate the production of killer cells.
Answer: B
Topic: 24.2
Skill: Conceptual Understanding

12) Bacterial infections can cause a serious, potentially fatal systemic inflammatory response called
   A) anaphylaxis.
   B) pelvic inflammatory disease.
   C) bacterial sepsis.
   D) septic shock.
   E) pneumonia.
Answer: D
Topic: 24.2
Skill: Factual Recall

13) The human lymphatic system consists of all of the following structures *except* the
   A) thymus.
   B) tonsils.
   C) spleen.
   D) pancreas.
   E) appendix.
Answer: D
Topic: 24.3
Skill: Factual Recall

14) The two main functions of the lymphatic system are
    A) coagulating blood and fighting infections.
    B) producing hormones that regulate the immune system and coagulating blood.
    C) producing hormones that regulate the immune system and fighting infections.
    D) returning tissue fluid to the circulatory system and coagulating blood.
    E) returning tissue fluid to the circulatory system and fighting infections.

Answer: E
Topic: 24.3
Skill: Conceptual Understanding

15) A substance that can elicit an immune response is called
    A) a complement.
    B) an interferon.
    C) histamine.
    D) an antibody.
    E) an antigen.

Answer: E
Topic: 24.4
Skill: Factual Recall

16) Antibodies are
    A) amino acids.
    B) lipids.
    C) carbohydrates.
    D) proteins.
    E) nucleic acids.

Answer: D
Topic: 24.4
Skill: Factual Recall

17) One kind of vaccine consists of
    A) buffered antibodies.
    B) horse erythrocytes.
    C) B cells.
    D) a harmless variant strain of a disease–causing microbe.
    E) antibiotics.

Answer: D
Topic: 24.4
Skill: Conceptual Understanding

18) Which of the following diseases cannot currently be prevented by vaccination?
    A) AIDS
    B) polio
    C) mumps
    D) measles
    E) tetanus

Answer: A
Topic: 24.4
Skill: Factual Recall

19) The transfer of antibodies in breast milk to an infant is an example of _____ immunity.
   A) nonspecific
   B) passive
   C) humoral
   D) active
   E) cell-mediated

Answer: B
Topic: 24.4
Skill: Conceptual Understanding

20) Passive immunity depends upon
   A) a person's own immune system producing antibodies.
   B) antibodies made by another organism.
   C) antibody-producing cells from another organism.
   D) antigens from a person's own body.
   E) isoantibodies.

Answer: B
Topic: 24.4
Skill: Factual Recall

21) Which of the following cell types is responsible for humoral immunity?
   A) C lymphocytes
   B) B cells
   C) neutrophils
   D) natural killer cells
   E) macrophages

Answer: B
Topic: 24.5
Skill: Factual Recall

22) Which of the following statements about humoral immunity is *true*?
   A) Humoral immunity primarily defends against bacteria and viruses by activating T cells.
   B) Humoral immunity can be passively transferred by injecting plasma from an immune individual into a nonimmune individual.
   C) Humoral immunity plays a major role in protecting the body from cancerous cells.
   D) Humoral immunity is the result of macrophages producing antibodies.
   E) Humoral immunity does not require chemical signals, such as growth factors.

Answer: B
Topic: 24.5
Skill: Application

23) Which of the following cell types is responsible for cell-mediated immunity?
   A) T cells
   B) B cells
   C) leukocytes
   D) natural killer cells
   E) lymphocytes

Answer: A
Topic: 24.5
Skill: Factual Recall

24) The immune system is capable of mounting specific responses to particular microorganisms because
    A) lymphocytes are able to change their antigen specificity as required to fight infection.
    B) stem cells determine which type of B and T cells to make.
    C) the body contains an enormous diversity of lymphocytes, each with the ability to respond to a different antigen.
    D) stem cells make different antigen receptors depending on the invading microorganism.
    E) stem cells are able to change their antigen specificity as required to fight infection.

Answer: C
Topic: 24.5
Skill: Conceptual Understanding

25) Which of the following statements regarding antigens and antibodies is *false?*
    A) An antibody usually recognizes and binds to an antigenic determinant.
    B) An antigen usually has several different antigenic determinants.
    C) A single antigen may stimulate the immune system to make several distinct antibodies to it.
    D) Most antigens are proteins or large polysaccharides on the surfaces of viruses or foreign cells.
    E) Each antibody has only one antigen–binding site.

Answer: E
Topic: 24.6
Skill: Factual Recall

26) A primary immune response is
    A) the production of primary–type antibodies in the first day of exposure to a microorganism.
    B) the immune response elicited by the primary antigen of a disease–causing microorganism.
    C) the immune response elicited by the primary antibodies of a disease–causing microorganism.
    D) the immune response elicited by the first exposure of lymphocytes to a particular antigen.
    E) the immune response elicited by the first exposure of memory cells to a particular antigen.

Answer: D
Topic: 24.7
Skill: Conceptual Understanding

27) Clonal selection
    A) determines the pool of mature leukocytes that will be stimulated by macrophages.
    B) requires activation of natural killer cells.
    C) indicates that only a particular B or T lymphocyte will be stimulated by a particular antigen.
    D) does not require effector cells.
    E) requires the presence and activation of complement.

Answer: C
Topic: 24.7
Skill: Factual Recall

28) When a B cell first interacts with its particular antigen, the B cell
    A) dies after destroying the antigen.
    B) engulfs the antigen and digests it.
    C) differentiates and develops into a clone of antibody–producing cells.
    D) sticks to other cells with attached antigens to form a large clot.
    E) alters the chemical configuration of the antigen.

Answer: C
Topic: 24.7
Skill: Conceptual Understanding

29) Which of the following choices best describes a plasma cell?
    A) It is a differentiated T cell.
    B) It is a differentiated B cell.
    C) It responds to an antigen and differentiates into a B cell.
    D) It is produced during a primary immune response, persists, and multiplies in response to a reappearance of the antigen.
    E) It is generated from bone marrow stem cells in response to an antigen.

Answer: B
Topic: 24.7
Skill: Conceptual Understanding

30) The secondary immune response occurs when memory cells bind to
    A) hormones.
    B) antibodies.
    C) antigens.
    D) plasma cells.
    E) clones.

Answer: C
Topic: 24.7
Skill: Factual Recall

31) Which of the following distinguishes the secondary immune response from the primary immune response?
    A) The primary response is specific; the secondary one is not.
    B) The secondary response produces higher levels of antibodies.
    C) The primary response involves B cells; the secondary one involves T cells.
    D) The secondary response allows additional antigens to be recognized faster.
    E) The secondary response only functions with the help of complement.

Answer: B
Topic: 24.7
Skill: Conceptual Understanding

32) Which of the following statements about antibodies is *false*?
   A) Antibody molecules are constructed from four polypeptide chains.
   B) Antibodies recognize and bind to particular antigens.
   C) Antibodies assist in eliminating particular antigenic particles.
   D) The polypeptide chains of an antibody molecule have both a V region and a C region.
   E) The antibodies of mammals can be divided into two major classes.

   Answer: E
   Topic: 24.8
   Skill: Factual Recall

33) An important effector function of antibody molecules is the
   A) destruction of complement proteins.
   B) agglutination of antigenic particles.
   C) phagocytosis of antigenic particles.
   D) solubilization of antigenic particles.
   E) crystallization of antigenic particles.

   Answer: B
   Topic: 24.9
   Skill: Factual Recall

34) Complement can be activated by
   A) inflammatory mediators.
   B) antigen–antibody complexes.
   C) B cell plasma membrane.
   D) T cells.
   E) blocking antibodies.

   Answer: B
   Topic: 24.9
   Skill: Factual Recall

35) All effector mechanisms of the immune system involve a specific recognition and attack phase, followed by a
   A) short phase of antibody release.
   B) nonspecific destruction phase.
   C) short phase of nonspecific antibody release.
   D) phase of specific killer cell activation.
   E) resting phase.

   Answer: B
   Topic: 24.9
   Skill: Factual Recall

36) Monoclonal antibodies are produced
   A) by cells that are formed when an activated B cell is fused to a tumor cell.
   B) when a female is pregnant.
   C) when an animal is infected by a single type of pathogen.
   D) by cells that are formed when a B cell is fused to a T cell.
   E) by cancerous tumors.

   Answer: A
   Topic: 24.10
   Skill: Factual Recall

37) Which of the following statements regarding monoclonal antibodies is *false*?
   A) Monoclonal antibodies are used in some home pregnancy tests.
   B) Monoclonal antibodies are used to bind toxins to tumor cells.
   C) Monoclonal antibodies can be used to identify bacteria that cause sexually transmitted disease.
   D) Monoclonal antibodies usually cross-react with other antigenic determinants.
   E) Monoclonal antibodies are specific for a single antigenic determinant and can be produced in large amounts.

Answer: D
Topic: 24.10
Skill: Conceptual Understanding

38) The basic function of activated T cells is to identify
   A) pathogens in blood or lymph.
   B) pathogens in interstitial fluid.
   C) body cells that have been invaded by pathogens.
   D) chemical mediators of immunity.
   E) activated macrophages.

Answer: C
Topic: 24.11
Skill: Conceptual Understanding

39) When an antigen–presenting cell interacts successfully with a helper T cell, the antigen–presenting cell secretes a signal molecule that assists in the activation of the helper T cell. This signal molecule is
   A) interferon.
   B) complement.
   C) an antibody.
   D) interleukin-1.
   E) perforin.

Answer: D
Topic: 24.11
Skill: Factual Recall

40) What type of cell acts as an intermediary between humoral and cell–mediated immunity?
   A) plasma cell
   B) cytotoxic T cell
   C) B cell
   D) helper T cell
   E) macrophage

Answer: D
Topic: 24.11
Skill: Factual Recall

41) Which of the following is an effect of interleukin-2?
    A) stimulating helper T cells to divide
    B) stimulating mass cells to release histamine
    C) stimulating antigen-presenting cells
    D) modulating macrophage phagocytosis
    E) governing the rate of hormone production by the endocrine system

Answer: A
Topic: 24.11
Skill: Factual Recall

42) After binding to an infected cell, the cytotoxic T cell
    A) releases interleukin-1.
    B) becomes a phagocytic cell.
    C) neutralizes the infecting bacteria or viruses.
    D) becomes activated.
    E) releases a protein called perforin.

Answer: E
Topic: 24.12
Skill: Factual Recall

43) _____ can destroy infected cells.
    A) Macrophages
    B) Plasma cells
    C) Monocytes
    D) B cells
    E) Cytotoxic T cells

Answer: E
Topic: 24.12
Skill: Application

44) Which of the following statements about HIV is *false*?
    A) The genome of HIV consists of RNA.
    B) HIV attacks mast cells.
    C) New HIV are produced inside helper T cells.
    D) HIV is transmitted by body fluids containing infected cells.
    E) Some drugs have proven effective in combating the spread of HIV from mothers to
       their children.

Answer: B
Topic: 24.13
Skill: Factual Recall

45) Which of the following types of cells does HIV preferentially infect?
    A) cytotoxic T cells
    B) natural killer cells
    C) helper T cells
    D) plasma cells
    E) memory cells

Answer: C
Topic: 24.13
Skill: Factual Recall

46) Which of the following statements about AIDS is *true*?
A) The human immunodeficiency virus also infects non-human primates.
B) The AIDS vaccine can prevent the spread of HIV.
C) AIDS patients usually die from cancer rather than bacterial or fungal infections.
D) Using condoms during sex prevents the spread of the virus that causes AIDS.
E) AIDS patients live no longer than 2 to 3 years.

Answer: D
Topic: 24.13
Skill: Conceptual Understanding

47) What enzyme enables an HIV virus to make DNA from an RNA template?
A) reverse transcriptase
B) DNA polymerase
C) DNA ligase
D) restriction enzyme
E) RNA polymerase

Answer: A
Topic: 24.13
Skill: Factual Recall

48) HIV is a virus that is particularly difficult to eradicate
A) because of its DNA genome.
B) since it is transmitted in water.
C) because it rarely mutates.
D) because it mutates to produce new drug-resistant strains.
E) due to its small size.

Answer: D
Topic: 24.14–Evolution Connection
Skill: Conceptual Understanding

49) Why has it been so difficult for researchers to develop effective antivirals for HIV?
A) because the virus is able to produce DNA as an intermediate in viral replication
B) because HIV has a high mutation rate
C) due to the damaged helper T cells that are targets for HIV
D) because evolution favors a rapidly expanding viral population
E) because HIV is a sexually transmitted viral disease

Answer: B
Topic: 24.14–Evolution Connection
Skill: Conceptual Understanding

50) HIV has a high mutation rate and can use this to its advantage to develop resistance to antivirals because
A) frequent mutations provide greater opportunity for survival of selective pressures.
B) viral agents infect specific cells, which enhances mutations.
C) antivirals target viral DNA.
D) helper T cells prevent antivirals from reaching HIV.
E) mutation in RNA viruses is always an advantage to the virus.

Answer: A
Topic: 24.14–Evolution Connection
Skill: Conceptual Understanding

51) _____ genes are responsible for coding for self-proteins.
   A) STR
   B) MHC
   C) RFLP
   D) PCR
   E) SCID

Answer: B
Topic: 24.15
Skill: Factual Recall

52) Which of the following diseases is thought to be an autoimmune disease?
   A) cancer of the bone marrow
   B) insulin-dependent diabetes mellitus
   C) measles and mumps
   D) myocardial infarction
   E) duodenal ulcer

Answer: B
Topic: 24.16
Skill: Factual Recall

53) What type of immune response is always disadvantageous to a person?
   A) cell-mediated
   B) inflammatory
   C) humoral-mediated
   D) autoimmune
   E) complement-mediated

Answer: D
Topic: 24.16
Skill: Conceptual Understanding

54) Which of the following statements best explains why people with Hodgkin's disease often show signs of immunodeficiency?
   A) The Hodgkin's disease virus infects and destroys B cells.
   B) Hodgkin's disease involves the deposition of immune complexes in the kidneys.
   C) Hodgkin's disease affects lymphocytes, resulting in immune suppression.
   D) Hodgkin's disease consists of a cancerous proliferation of epithelial cells.
   E) Hodgkin's disease occurs when an immune response elicited by bacteria kill normal heart cells as well as bacteria.

Answer: C
Topic: 24.16
Skill: Application

55) Which of the following compounds is produced and secreted by mast cells?
   A) interferon
   B) complement
   C) allergens
   D) histamine
   E) perforin

Answer: D
Topic: 24.17
Skill: Factual Recall

56) Anaphylactic shock is an example of an
    A) autoimmune disease.
    B) immunodeficiency disease.
    C) allergic response.
    D) acquired immunodeficiency disease.
    E) acquired autoimmune disease.

Answer: C
Topic: 24.17
Skill: Factual Recall

Art Questions

1)

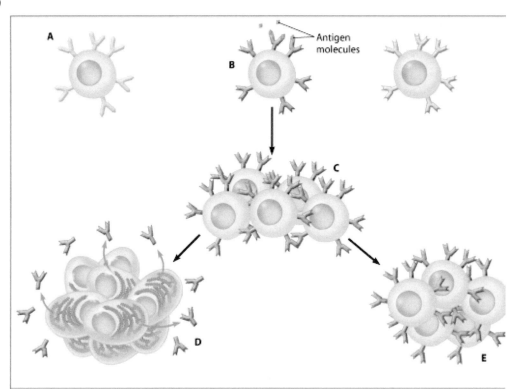

Which part of this figure shows an active plasma B cell?
    A) part A
    B) part B
    C) part C
    D) part D
    E) part E

Answer: D
Topic: 24.7
Skill: Factual Recall

2)

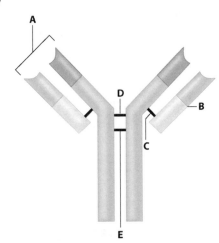

Where is the antigen–binding site of this antibody?
  A) site A
  B) site B
  C) site C
  D) site D
  E) site E

Answer: A
Topic: 24.6, 24.8
Skill: Factual Recall

Scenario Questions

After reading the following paragraph, answer the question(s) below.

To protect U.S. soldiers serving overseas, each soldier receives vaccinations against several diseases, including smallpox, before deployment. Following intelligence about an imminent smallpox threat, the Army wants to ensure that soldiers stationed in Iraq are fully protected from exposure to the disease, so all the soldiers in the threat zone are given a second vaccination against smallpox.

  1) The first vaccination provides immunity because
      A) the vaccine confers acquired immunity by triggering a localized inflammatory response.
      B) the vaccine contains manufactured antibodies against smallpox.
      C) antigenic determinants in the vaccine activate B cells and effectors form antibodies to counter the antigen in the vaccine.
      D) antigenic determinants in the vaccine activate T cells, which produce antibodies to counter the antigen in the vaccine.
      E) the vaccine contains antibiotics and other drugs that kill the smallpox virus.

  Answer: C
  Topic: 24.4, 24.7
  Skill: Conceptual Understanding

2) The second vaccination is beneficial because
   A) it contains plasma cells that survive longer than 4–5 days.
   B) it stimulates production of a higher concentration of antibodies in the bloodstream.
   C) it requires two injections to stimulate antibody formation.
   D) it keeps previously produced plasma cells circulating in the bloodstream.
   E) it renews the primary immune response.

Answer: B
Topic: 24.7
Skill: Conceptual Understanding

Chapter 25 Control of Body Temperature and Water Balance

Multiple-Choice Questions

1) You are repairing the roof one cool September morning, and you find a bat behind a shingle. The bat appears to be asleep but will not rouse. It finally begins to shiver and eventually wakes up and flies off. What is the probable explanation for its behavior?
   A) The bat was hibernating.
   B) The bat was estivating.
   C) The bat was deeply asleep, but the cold woke it up.
   D) The bat was exhibiting torpor.
   E) The bat had rabies.

Answer: D
Topic: Opening Essay
Skill: Application

2) Torpor is
   A) a 24-hour period of sleeping and waking.
   B) weekly periods of sleeping in the summertime.
   C) a state where body temperature and metabolic activity is reduced.
   D) a sharp rise in body temperature.
   E) a period where metabolic activity is reduced but energy requirements remain high.

Answer: C
Topic: Opening Essay
Skill: Conceptual Understanding

3) Which of the following statements about hibernation is *true*?
   A) Hibernation is a long period of torpor in cold weather.
   B) Whales hibernate at the surface of the oceans.
   C) During hibernation, the body temperature can increase considerably.
   D) Metabolic rates increase during the winter and decrease during the summer.
   E) Hibernating animals will use stored proteins to survive the winter.

Answer: A
Topic: Opening Essay
Skill: Factual Recall

4) Thermoregulation, an important part of homeostasis, is defined as
   A) a mechanism for utilizing body fat.
   B) reduced blood flow to an animal's extremities.
   C) the maintenance of internal body temperature within narrow limits.
   D) the mechanisms that allow an animal to hibernate without food or drink.
   E) regulation of nitrogen-containing wastes that prevents a need to urinate.

Answer: C
Topic: Opening Essay
Skill: Factual Recall

5) Animals that maintain internal body temperature using heat generated by their own metabolism are called
　　A) endotherms.
　　B) aerophiles.
　　C) thermoregulators.
　　D) hibernators.
　　E) dormants.

Answer: A
Topic: 25.1
Skill: Factual Recall

6) It is a cool winter evening, and you are feeling a little chilled. To warm yourself up, you sip some warm tea. As you swallow, you can feel the tea warm your mouth and throat. This tea is warming you up by the process of
　　A) convection.
　　B) induction.
　　C) conduction.
　　D) evaporation.
　　E) radiation.

Answer: A
Topic: 25.2
Skill: Application

7) Which of the following processes involves heat exchange between an animal and its environment?
　　A) irradiation
　　B) exchange conduction
　　C) suppuration
　　D) induction
　　E) evaporation

Answer: E
Topic: 25.2
Skill: Factual Recall

8) Which of the following physiological responses occurs in the human body when it becomes overheated?
　　A) slowing of the heart rate
　　B) constriction of blood vessels in the skin
　　C) contraction of muscles
　　D) increased blood flow to the skin
　　E) retention of water

Answer: D
Topic: 25.3
Skill: Conceptual Understanding

9) The transfer of heat from arteries carrying warm blood past veins returning cooler blood is an example of
   A) insulation.
   B) a countercurrent heat exchanger.
   C) evaporative cooling.
   D) behavioral thermoregulation.
   E) metabolic heat production.

Answer: B
Topic: 25.3
Skill: Application

10) To enhance heat loss, humans sweat, an adaptation known as
   A) a behavioral response.
   B) evaporative cooling.
   C) the maintenance principle.
   D) internal evaporation.
   E) homeostasis.

Answer: B
Topic: 25.3
Skill: Conceptual Understanding

11) Marine animals that have body fluids with a solute concentration equal to that of the surrounding seawater are
   A) osmoregulators.
   B) osmoconformers.
   C) osmoinformers.
   D) hypertonic.
   E) hypotonic.

Answer: B
Topic: 25.4
Skill: Factual Recall

12) Which of the following statements regarding freshwater fish is *true*?
   A) Freshwater fish frequently drink to obtain salt ions.
   B) Freshwater fish use their gills to actively take up salt ions.
   C) Freshwater fish lose water through their gills by osmosis.
   D) Freshwater fish do not produce urine.
   E) Freshwater fish cannot directly exchange water with the environment by osmosis.

Answer: B
Topic: 25.4
Skill: Conceptual Understanding

13) To conserve precious salts, freshwater fish
   A) produce small amounts of urine.
   B) significantly dilute their urine.
   C) do not take up water.
   D) drink through their gills.
   E) eliminate water by osmosis.

Answer: B
Topic: 25.4
Skill: Factual Recall

14) Which of the following statements regarding saltwater fish is *true*?
   A) Saltwater fish frequently dilute their body fluids.
   B) The concentration of solutes in the internal fluids of saltwater fish is much lower than in the surrounding water.
   C) The concentration of solutes in the internal fluids of saltwater fish is higher than in the surrounding environment.
   D) Saltwater fish produce large amounts of diluted urine.
   E) Saltwater fish must visit freshwater streams and rivers entering the ocean to maintain the correct concentration of solutes in their internal fluids.

Answer: B
Topic: 25.4
Skill: Conceptual Understanding

15) Which of the following by-products of metabolism is most toxic?
   A) carbon monoxide
   B) ammonia
   C) urea
   D) carbonic acid
   E) lactic acid

Answer: B
Topic: 25.5-Evolution Connection
Skill: Factual Recall

16) Which of the following kinds of animals excrete their nitrogenous waste entirely as ammonia?
   A) birds
   B) tropical insects
   C) fish
   D) garden snails
   E) insects

Answer: C
Topic: 25.5-Evolution Connection
Skill: Factual Recall

17) What is the advantage of excreting nitrogenous waste in the form of ammonia?
   A) Ammonia is less toxic than uric acid.
   B) Ammonia is less soluble than uric acid.
   C) Ammonia excretion conserves energy.
   D) Ammonia does not diffuse across cell membranes.
   E) Ammonia contains more nitrogen atoms per molecule than uric acid.

Answer: C
Topic: 25.5-Evolution Connection
Skill: Factual Recall

18) The land animals that evolved from earlier aquatic forms had to change their mechanisms for excreting nitrogenous wastes because
   A) land animals concurrently developed a more efficient reproduction system.
   B) land animals found better food sources.
   C) aquatic animals metabolized fewer amino acids than land animals.
   D) land animals had a more difficult time with water balance than aquatic species since water was not always available on land.
   E) aquatic animals did not have as much protein in their diets as did land animals.

Answer: D
Topic: 25.5–Evolution Connection
Skill: Conceptual Understanding

19) Natural selection is nature's mechanism for selecting characteristics that best adapt the animal to its environment. Mammals have evolved a sophisticated mechanism for eliminating nitrogenous wastes that involves
   A) secretion through cell membranes.
   B) forming urea and storing it in concentrated solution.
   C) producing uric acid and excreting it with feces.
   D) recycling urea and using it as an energy source.
   E) converting ammonia to urea in the pancreas.

Answer: B
Topic: 25.5–Evolution Connection
Skill: Conceptual Understanding

20) Birds, like other animals, must eliminate ammonia or urea, and do so by converting them to
   A) amino acids.
   B) ammonium ions.
   C) lactic acid.
   D) sodium chloride.
   E) uric acid.

Answer: E
Topic: 25.5–Evolution Connection
Skill: Factual Recall

21) Which of the following statements about uric acid is *true*?
   A) Animals that excrete uric acid avoid the problem of dehydration associated with excretion of urea.
   B) Uric acid is more soluble in water than urea.
   C) The darker material in bird droppings is mostly uric acid.
   D) Uric acid cannot be excreted because of its toxicity.
   E) Uric acid is a less complex molecule than urea.

Answer: A
Topic: 25.5–Evolution Connection
Skill: Factual Recall

22) Which of the following is a function of the vertebrate liver?
    A) combining ammonia and carbon dioxide
    B) synthesizing ammonia from uric acid
    C) excreting urea
    D) helping with water excretion
    E) producing urea from uric acid and carbon dioxide
Answer: A
Topic: 25.5–Evolution Connection
Skill: Factual Recall

23) Which of the following is a function of the excretory system?
    A) detoxification
    B) blood maintenance
    C) elimination of undigested foods
    D) maintenance of water balance
    E) production of urea
Answer: D
Topic: 25.6
Skill: Conceptual Understanding

24) What is the name of the functional unit of the kidney?
    A) renal unit
    B) Bowman's capsule
    C) nephron
    D) glomerulus
    E) tubule
Answer: C
Topic: 25.6
Skill: Factual Recall

25) Through which of the following structures does urine leave the bladder?
    A) ureter
    B) urethra
    C) renal artery
    D) renal medulla
    E) distal convoluted tubule
Answer: B
Topic: 25.6
Skill: Factual Recall

26) Which of the following statements regarding the urinary system is *true*?
    A) Bowman's capsule envelops the glomerulus.
    B) Most glomeruli are located in the renal medulla.
    C) The functional unit of the kidney is the renal cortex.
    D) The urinary bladder receives ammonia for excretion.
    E) The urethra is responsible for transporting urea from the kidney to the urinary
       bladder.
Answer: A
Topic: 25.6
Skill: Factual Recall

27) Which of the following options correctly lists the structures in the kidney in the order in which fluid flows through them?
- A) proximal tubule, Bowman's capsule, loop of Henle, distal tubule, glomerulus
- B) Bowman's capsule, proximal tubule, loop of Henle, distal tubule, glomerulus
- C) Bowman's capsule, glomerulus, proximal tubule, loop of Henle, distal tubule
- D) glomerulus, Bowman's capsule, proximal tubule, loop of Henle, distal tubule
- E) glomerulus, proximal tubule, distal tubule, Bowman's capsule, loop of Henle

Answer: D
Topic: 25.6
Skill: Factual Recall

28) During filtration in the glomerulus, which of the following will enter Bowman's capsule from the bloodstream?
- A) ammonia
- B) nucleic acids
- C) lymphocytes
- D) plasma proteins
- E) water

Answer: E
Topic: 25.6
Skill: Factual Recall

29) The first step in the formation of urine is the
- A) secretion of hydrogen ions into the kidney tubules.
- B) reabsorption of poisons by the kidney tubules.
- C) formation of filtrate that accumulates in Bowman's capsule.
- D) secretion of urea into the renal pelvis.
- E) reabsorption of nutrients by Bowman's capsule.

Answer: C
Topic: 25.6
Skill: Factual Recall

30) Urine flows from the collecting duct into the
- A) ureter.
- B) urethra.
- C) renal pelvis.
- D) distal tubule.
- E) proximal tubule.

Answer: C
Topic: 25.6
Skill: Factual Recall

31) The overall process that refines the filtrate and ultimately returns water and valuable solutes to the blood is known as
   A) reabsorption.
   B) excretion.
   C) collection.
   D) filtration.
   E) purification.
   Answer: A
   Topic: 25.7
   Skill: Factual Recall

32) Secretion is the movement of substances such as glucose, amino acids, ions, and vitamins from the _____ into the _____.
   A) nephron tubule . . . glomerulus
   B) filtrate . . . blood
   C) glomerulus . . . nephron tubule
   D) blood . . . filtrate
   E) urinary bladder . . . outside
   Answer: D
   Topic: 25.7
   Skill: Factual Recall

33) During production of urine, a major function of the kidney is
   A) water conservation.
   B) amino acid production.
   C) osmosis.
   D) detoxification.
   E) uric acid production.
   Answer: A
   Topic: 25.8
   Skill: Factual Recall

34) Water moves out of filtrate in the nephron tubule into the interstitial fluid by
   A) reabsorption.
   B) capillary action.
   C) refinement.
   D) secretion.
   E) osmosis.
   Answer: E
   Topic: 25.8
   Skill: Factual Recall

35) Where along the nephron is glucose reabsorbed from the filtrate back into the blood?
   A) distal tubule
   B) collecting duct
   C) loop of Henle
   D) proximal tubule
   E) Bowman's capsule
   Answer: D
   Topic: 25.8
   Skill: Factual Recall

36) Why must water that has moved to the interstitial fluid in the medulla be quickly removed from the interstitial fluid?
  A) to prevent dilution of urine
  B) to prevent destruction of the concentration gradient necessary for water reabsorption
  C) to equilibrate the concentration of solutes in the cortex and medulla
  D) to maintain an environment for transport of nutrients
  E) to eliminate wastes in the blood

Answer: B
Topic: 25.8
Skill: Factual Recall

37) What is the function of urea reabsorption in the collecting ducts of the kidney?
  A) It restores the correct concentration of blood urea.
  B) It increases the osmotic concentration of the interstitial fluid in the renal medulla so that more water can be extracted from the urine.
  C) It reduces the salinity of the renal medulla and thus helps regulate how much water is reabsorbed from the urine.
  D) It induces NaCl to move into the capillaries and thus helps maintain blood salinity.
  E) It moves the urea into the ascending limb of the loop of Henle so that it can be excreted from there in the urine.

Answer: B
Topic: 25.8
Skill: Conceptual Understanding

38) What is the function of the antidiuretic hormone?
  A) to increase urination
  B) to increase water reabsorption
  C) to stimulate sodium reabsorption
  D) to decrease endocrine function
  E) to modulate urine production

Answer: B
Topic: 25.8
Skill: Factual Recall

39) ADH acts on
  A) the collecting duct.
  B) the loop of Henle.
  C) the proximal tubule.
  D) the distal tubule.
  E) Bowman's capsule.

Answer: A
Topic: 25.8
Skill: Factual Recall

40) The dialyzing solution used during kidney dialysis functions much like a fluid associated with a nephron. What is the fluid?
    A) interstitial fluid
    B) the filtrate in the proximal tubule
    C) the filtrate in the Loop of Henle
    D) the filtrate in the distal tubule
    E) the filtrate in the collecting duct

Answer: A
Topic: 25.9
Skill: Factual Recall

41) In a dialysis machine, wastes are removed from blood plasma by a process of
    A) filtration and reabsorption.
    B) diffusion.
    C) reabsorption and diffusion.
    D) absorption.
    E) absorption and reabsorption.

Answer: B
Topic: 25.9
Skill: Conceptual Understanding

Art Questions

1)

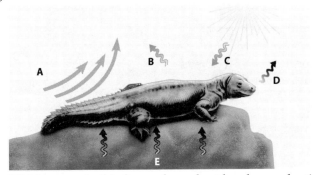

Which arrow in this figure shows heat loss by conduction?
    A) arrow A
    B) arrow B
    C) arrow C
    D) arrow D
    E) arrow E

Answer: E
Topic: 25.2
Skill: Factual Recall

2)

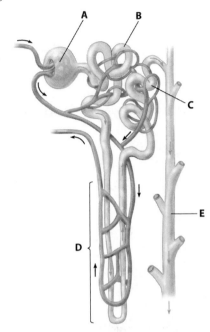

Which part of the nephron shown is its proximal tubule?
   A) part A
   B) part B
   C) part C
   D) part D
   E) part E

Answer: B
Topic: 25.6
Skill: Factual Recall

3)

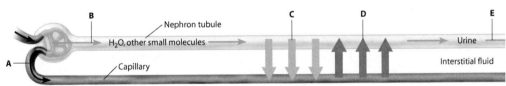

Which arrow in this schematic view of the nephron shows reabsorption?
   A) arrow A
   B) arrow B
   C) arrow C
   D) arrow D
   E) arrow E

Answer: C
Topic: 25.6, 25.7
Skill: Factual Recall

Scenario Questions

After reading the following paragraph, answer the question(s) below.

Most fishes can live either in freshwater or saltwater habitats, but not both. If you move a marine fish from the ocean to a lake, it will quickly die, and vice versa. However, a small number of fish species are capable of moving between the two environments. Salmon are osmoregulators that hatch in rivers, spend most of their lives in the ocean, and return to the river where they were born in order to breed.

1) When a salmon moves from the ocean to a freshwater environment, you would expect its urine volume to _____ and its rate of salt absorption to _____.
   A) remain the same . . . decrease
   B) increase . . . remain the same
   C) increase . . . increase
   D) decrease . . . decrease
   E) decrease . . . increase
   Answer: C
   Topic: 25.4
   Skill: Conceptual Understanding

2) When a salmon leaves the river and moves out to sea, you would expect _____ to enter its body by osmosis and excess _____ to be pumped out.
   A) salt . . . water
   B) water . . . salt
   C) salt . . . salt
   D) water . . . water
   E) both salt and water . . . water
   Answer: B
   Topic: 25.4
   Skill: Conceptual Understanding

Chapter 26 Hormones and the Endocrine System

Multiple-Choice Questions

1) Hormones are chemicals produced by the endocrine system that
   A) control the formation of urine.
   B) regulate a variety of body functions, such as metabolism.
   C) are stimulated by the action of metabolic enzymes.
   D) play a role in digestion of fats.
   E) function to prevent a variety of diseases, such as diabetes.

   Answer: B
   Topic: Opening Essay
   Skill: Factual Recall

2) How are hormones distributed to tissues, and what determines which cells hormones will affect?
   A) They are carried throughout the body in the bloodstream, and each hormone affects target cells responsive to it.
   B) They are carried to specific organs by lymphatic vessels and affect the cells in those organs.
   C) They are carried to specific organs by ducts and affect the cells in those organs.
   D) They are delivered by neurosecretory cells to specific tissues and cells, which are affected.
   E) They are distributed locally in the interstitial fluid and affect nearby responsive target cells.

   Answer: A
   Topic: 26.1
   Skill: Conceptual Understanding

3) Compared to the endocrine system, the nervous system
   A) has a faster response, but the signal does not last as long.
   B) has a slower response and a signal that does not last as long.
   C) has a faster response with a longer-lasting signal.
   D) has a slower response with a longer-lasting signal.
   E) has a slower response, but a signal that lasts roughly the same amount of time.

   Answer: A
   Topic: 26.1
   Skill: Conceptual Understanding

4) Chemical signals secreted into the interstitial fluid that only affect target cells near the secretory cell are called
   A) hormones.
   B) local regulators.
   C) neurotransmitters.
   D) pheromones.
   E) second messengers.

   Answer: B
   Topic: 26.1
   Skill: Factual Recall

5) Neurosecretory cells
   A) are local regulators.
   B) are restricted to the endocrine system.
   C) participate in the nervous and endocrine systems.
   D) transmit electrical signals.
   E) produce hormones that will regulate nontarget cells.

Answer: C
Topic: 26.1
Skill: Factual Recall

6) Nonsteroid hormones are synthesized from
   A) amino acids.
   B) cholesterol.
   C) nucleic acids.
   D) carbohydrates.
   E) long–chain fatty acids.

Answer: A
Topic: 26.2
Skill: Factual Recall

7) Which of the following options lists the sequence of events in the cell–signaling process in the correct order?
   A) reception, cell response, transduction
   B) transduction, reception, cell response
   C) transduction, cell response, reception
   D) reception, transduction, cell response
   E) cell response, transduction, reception

Answer: D
Topic: 26.2
Skill: Factual Recall

8) Why must some hormones bind to a membrane receptor on a target cell's surface in order to activate it?
   A) for activation by ATP
   B) because they are not water–soluble
   C) to distinguish between the many types of cells
   D) because they cannot cross cell membranes
   E) to stimulate endocytosis to internalize the hormone

Answer: D
Topic: 26.2
Skill: Conceptual Understanding

9) The result of binding a signal molecule to its receptor is
   A) production of a protein by the target cell, followed by death.
   B) cell division.
   C) signal transduction.
   D) dehydration, followed by sodium release.
   E) partitioning of the nucleus within the target cell.

Answer: C
Topic: 26.2
Skill: Conceptual Understanding

10) A target cell that is affected by a particular steroid hormone would be expected to have
   A) DNA sites that interact with the hormone.
   B) an intracellular receptor protein that binds the hormone.
   C) a cell–surface receptor protein that binds the hormone.
   D) enzymes that are activated or inactivated by the intracellular hormone–receptor complex.
   E) enzymes that are activated or inactivated by the hormone's second messenger.

Answer: B
Topic: 26.2
Skill: Conceptual Understanding

11) Steroid hormones are lipids made from
   A) amino acids.
   B) cholesterol.
   C) nucleic acids.
   D) carbohydrates.
   E) carbohydrates and amino acids.

Answer: B
Topic: 26.2
Skill: Factual Recall

12) Which of the following statements about steroid hormones is *true*?
   A) Steroid hormones cause the production of cAMP.
   B) Steroid hormones are polar molecules that cannot pass through the cell membrane.
   C) Steroid hormones activate a transcription factor.
   D) Steroid hormones do not have the ability to turn genes on or off.
   E) Steroid hormones bind to specific receptor proteins and the complex acts as a gene activator.

Answer: E
Topic: 26.2
Skill: Conceptual Understanding

13) A single steroid hormone can cause different effects in different cells by
   A) sticking to different parts of the cellular membrane.
   B) binding to different receptors.
   C) acting on different organelles.
   D) activating different second messengers.
   E) activating different enzymes.

Answer: B
Topic: 26.2
Skill: Conceptual Understanding

14) Which of the following statements regarding endocrine glands is *true*?
   A) Some endocrine glands, like the pituitary, have other endocrine glands as their targets.
   B) The sex organs and the thyroid gland produce steroid hormones.
   C) The pancreas has only nonendocrine functions.
   D) The thyroid gland begins to shrink at puberty in humans.
   E) Most of the endocrine glands produce steroid hormones.

Answer: A
Topic: 26.3
Skill: Factual Recall

15) Which of the following endocrine glands synthesizes melatonin?
   A) thymus
   B) pineal
   C) adrenal cortex
   D) thyroid
   E) parathyroid

Answer: B
Topic: 26.3
Skill: Factual Recall

16) Which of the following hormones stimulates and maintains metabolic processes?
   A) calcitonin
   B) thyroxine
   C) thymosin
   D) oxytocin
   E) melatonin

Answer: B
Topic: 26.3
Skill: Factual Recall

17) Which of the following options correctly pairs an endocrine gland or hormone with an aspect of metabolism that it regulates?
   A) parathyroid = stimulates the adrenal cortex to secrete glucocorticoids
   B) pancreas = stimulates growth of the uterine lining
   C) insulin = regulates blood glucose levels
   D) prolactin = manages blood potassium levels
   E) thyroid = stimulates T lymphocyte development

Answer: C
Topic: 26.3
Skill: Factual Recall

18) Which of the following is an endocrine gland that raises blood calcium levels?
   A) parathyroid
   B) thyroid gland
   C) salivary gland
   D) pituitary gland
   E) testes

Answer: A
Topic: 26.3
Skill: Factual Recall

19) Which of the following statements about glands and hormones is *true*?
   A) The anterior pituitary is composed of endocrine cells.
   B) The posterior pituitary is composed of lymphatic tissue.
   C) The pituitary is the master control center of the entire endocrine system.
   D) Growth hormone is produced by the thymus gland.
   E) The hypothalamus is an endocrine gland responsible for producing the hormone, calcitonin.

Answer: A
Topic: 26.4
Skill: Factual Recall

20) Which of the following hormones is released by neurosecretory cells extending from the hypothalamus?
   A) estrogen
   B) growth hormone
   C) oxytocin
   D) insulin
   E) calcitonin

Answer: C
Topic: 26.4
Skill: Factual Recall

21) Which of the following hormones affects the greatest variety of cell types?
   A) prolactin
   B) endorphin
   C) melatonin
   D) growth hormone
   E) calcitonin

Answer: D
Topic: 26.4
Skill: Factual Recall

22) TRH is a type of _____ hormone secreted by the _____.
   A) steroid . . . thyroid gland
   B) releasing . . . hypothalamus
   C) peptide . . . thymus
   D) releasing . . . anterior pituitary
   E) releasing . . . posterior pituitary

Answer: B
Topic: 26.4
Skill: Factual Recall

23) Which gland requires the element iodine to produce its hormones?
   A) adrenal medulla
   B) thyroid
   C) pineal
   D) pituitary
   E) ovary

Answer: B
Topic: 26.5
Skill: Factual Recall

24) An excess of T$_3$ and T$_4$ in the blood is hyperthyroidism, which in its most common form is called
  A) goiter.
  B) sterility.
  C) Graves' disease.
  D) botulism.
  E) vitamin deficiency.

Answer: C
Topic: 26.5
Skill: Factual Recall

25) Which of the following processes depends on the presence of appropriate calcium levels in the blood and interstitial fluid?
  A) transmission of nerve signals from cell to cell
  B) synthesis of interferons
  C) capillary dilation
  D) goiter formation
  E) movement of hormones throughout the body

Answer: A
Topic: 26.6
Skill: Factual Recall

26) Which of the following may be a consequence of excessive secretion of parathyroid hormone?
  A) convulsive contractions of skeletal muscles
  B) gigantism
  C) loss of calcium from the blood
  D) exhaustion of the immune system
  E) loss of calcium from the bone

Answer: E
Topic: 26.6
Skill: Conceptual Understanding

27) Which of the following pairs of hormones have opposite effects?
  A) testosterone and melatonin
  B) follicle–stimulating hormone and luteinizing hormone
  C) progesterone and insulin
  D) parathyroid hormone and calcitonin
  E) oxytocin and prolactin

Answer: D
Topic: 26.6
Skill: Factual Recall

28) Which gland exerts primary control over the concentration of sugar in the blood?
   A) liver
   B) pituitary
   C) pineal
   D) pancreas
   E) parathyroid

Answer: D
Topic: 26.7
Skill: Conceptual Understanding

29) Which of the following is a nonsteroid hormone?
   A) glucagon
   B) a mineralocorticoid
   C) a glucocorticoid
   D) estrogen
   E) androgen

Answer: A
Topic: 26.7
Skill: Factual Recall

30) Which of the following statements best describes the relationship of insulin to glucagon?
   A) They work together to prepare the body to deal with stress.
   B) Insulin stimulates the pancreas to secrete glucagon.
   C) High levels of insulin inhibit pancreatic secretion of glucagon.
   D) They are antagonistic hormones.
   E) Insulin is a steroid hormone; glucagon is a protein hormone.

Answer: D
Topic: 26.7
Skill: Conceptual Understanding

31) When the concentration of glucose in the blood rises following digestion of a meal, what is the hormonal response?
   A) Both glucagon and insulin are released.
   B) Glucagon is released but not insulin.
   C) Insulin is released but not glucagon.
   D) Neither glucagon nor insulin is released.
   E) The total amount of insulin in the blood decreases.

Answer: C
Topic: 26.7
Skill: Factual Recall

32) Which of the following hormones causes glucose release and, consequently, a rise in the concentration of sugar in the blood?
   A) insulin
   B) glucagon
   C) melatonin
   D) calcitonin
   E) oxytocin

Answer: B
Topic: 26.7
Skill: Factual Recall

33) What is the metabolic abnormality that underlies the characteristic symptoms of diabetes mellitus?
   A) a failure of the kidney tubules to reabsorb enough glucose from the urine
   B) a failure of the gastrointestinal epithelium to absorb enough glucose from the food
   C) an inability of the body's cells to switch from glucose metabolism to fat metabolism between meals
   D) an inability of the body's cells to retain glucose they have absorbed from the blood
   E) an inability of the body's cells to absorb enough glucose from the blood

Answer: E
Topic: 26.8
Skill: Conceptual Understanding

34) Which of the following is associated with obesity, often does not show up until after the age of 40, and occurs because cells of the body fail to respond adequately to insulin?
   A) type 1 diabetes
   B) type 2 diabetes
   C) type 3 diabetes
   D) hyperglycemia
   E) hypoglycemia

Answer: B
Topic: 26.8
Skill: Factual Recall

35) Which of the following glands is located nearest the kidneys?
   A) ovaries
   B) pancreas
   C) pineal glands
   D) parathyroid glands
   E) adrenal glands

Answer: E
Topic: 26.9
Skill: Factual Recall

36) Which of the following glands secretes hormones that enable the body to respond to stress?
   A) pancreas
   B) adrenal
   C) pineal
   D) salivary
   E) parathyroid

Answer: B
Topic: 26.9
Skill: Factual Recall

37) Which of the following is a function of epinephrine?
    A) release of glucose from the liver
    B) decreased heart rate
    C) increase in urine output
    D) increased absorption of glucose by the digestive tract
    E) increased sensitivity to light

Answer: A
Topic: 26.9
Skill: Factual Recall

38) Which of the following act mainly to regulate salt and water balance?
    A) mineralocorticoids
    B) glucocorticoids
    C) androgens
    D) melatonin
    E) oxytocin

Answer: A
Topic: 26.9
Skill: Factual Recall

39) Which of the following hormones can suppress the body's immune system when administered for extended periods of time?
    A) glucagon
    B) mineralocorticoids
    C) glucocorticoids
    D) antidiuretic hormone
    E) androgens

Answer: C
Topic: 26.9
Skill: Factual Recall

40) Which of the following is one of the three major categories of sex hormones?
    A) glucocorticoids
    B) estrogens
    C) glucagons
    D) prolactins
    E) follicle–stimulating hormones

Answer: B
Topic: 26.10
Skill: Factual Recall

41) Androgens stimulate
    A) the female reproductive system.
    B) release of glucose into the blood system.
    C) growth of breasts in mammals.
    D) growth of facial hair in humans.
    E) ovulation.

Answer: D
Topic: 26.10
Skill: Factual Recall

42) The hormone prolactin, found in distantly related vertebrates, exerts different effects in different species. From an evolutionary standpoint, this is an indication that hormonal regulation
   A) is not critical to all animals.
   B) is required only of nonsteroid hormones.
   C) is an ancient process whose function diversified through evolution.
   D) was a recent evolutionary adaptation.
   E) was not required in fish and amphibians.

Answer: C
Topic: 26.11–Evolution Connection
Skill: Conceptual Understanding

43) Prolactin is a hormone whose molecular structure has remained stable over evolutionary time, but whose hormonal role has changed dramatically in different animal species. This is an excellent example of how evolution
   A) is responsible for mutation in vertebrates.
   B) occurs rapidly at the molecular level to keep up with changing environmental influences.
   C) is governed by the molecular biology of cells.
   D) has stayed within narrow boundaries in regard to regulation of homeostasis.
   E) can both preserve unity and promote diversity.

Answer: E
Topic: 26.11–Evolution Connection
Skill: Conceptual Understanding

Art Questions

1)

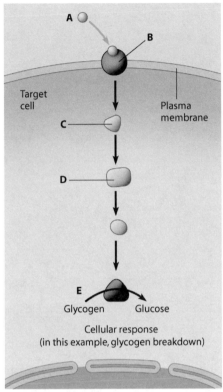

Which molecule in this figure portraying water–soluble hormone action is the receptor protein?
- A) molecule A
- B) molecule B
- C) molecule C
- D) molecule D
- E) molecule E

Answer: B
Topic: 26.2
Skill: Factual Recall

2)

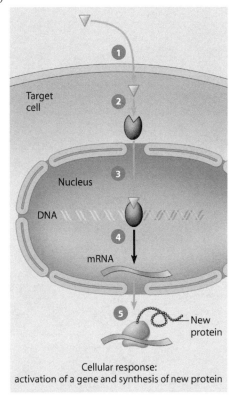

Target
cell

1

2

Nucleus

3

DNA

4

mRNA

5 — New
protein

Cellular response:
activation of a gene and synthesis of new protein

Which step in this figure portraying lipid–soluble hormone action shows transcription in
response to the bound hormone–receptor complex?

    A) step 1
    B) step 2
    C) step 3
    D) step 4
    E) step 5

Answer: D
Topic: 26.2
Skill: Application

Scenario Questions

After reading the following paragraph, answer the question(s) below.

Recent studies have shown that the onset of puberty in American girls has decreased from an average of 12–13 years of age to as young as 8–10. Many scientists that study premature puberty suggest that steroids in our food and in the environment may be contributing factors, since steroids are known to cross cell membranes and bind to receptors inside cells.

Why are hormones present in our foods? Synthetic testosterone compounds (similar to those used by some athletes) make young animals gain weight faster so they are ready for market sooner. Female animals receive synthetic estrogen to inhibit the reproductive cycle and divert all energy into weight gain. In the United States, up to two–thirds of meat animals are raised using hormones. In addition, hormones are used to increase milk production in dairy cattle.

Scientific investigation of the exact effects of environmental steroids on humans is extremely difficult since there are multiple sources of hormones in the environment. A valid study would require a control group who hasn't been exposed to the chemicals being studied. Since everyone has had some exposure to environmental hormones, no control group is available to use as a reference.

1) When environmental estrogens trigger premature puberty, the main organs affected are the
   A) ovaries and uterus.
   B) thymus.
   C) thyroid gland and pituitary gland.
   D) adrenal cortex.
   E) pituitary gland and parathyroid glands.

Answer: A
Topic: 26.3, 26.4
Skill: Factual Recall

2) How are steroids able to cross cell membranes and enter cells?
   A) Steroids and cell membranes both contain receptor proteins.
   B) Steroids are polar, and the cell membrane is polar on the inside of the lipid bilayer.
   C) Steroids are nonpolar lipids, and the cell membrane is lipid based.
   D) Steroids can diffuse through open channel proteins in the membrane.
   E) Steroids move through cell membranes, such as water, by osmosis.

Answer: C
Topic: 26.2
Skill: Conceptual Understanding

Chapter 27 Reproduction and Embryonic Development

Multiple-Choice Questions

1) Between 1980 and 2003, the rate of multiple births in the United States rose by 87%, primarily as a result of
   A) better nutrition available for potential mothers.
   B) increased use of fertility drugs.
   C) better physical condition of potential mothers.
   D) increased exposure to new sources of radiation.
   E) a rise in the quality of prenatal care.

Answer: B
Topic: Opening Essay
Skill: Factual Recall

2) Which of the following statements best characterizes asexual reproduction?
   A) It allows animals that do not move around to produce offspring without finding mates.
   B) It allows an animal to produce many offspring quickly.
   C) It saves the time and energy required to produce gametes.
   D) It produces genetically uniform populations.
   E) It allows a population to expand quickly to exploit available resources.

Answer: D
Topic: 27.1
Skill: Conceptual Understanding

3) Fission is an asexual process
   A) that allows regeneration of lost body parts.
   B) that occurs in individuals that live in isolated areas.
   C) in which a parent separates into two or more individuals.
   D) in which a parent fragments into several pieces.
   E) that is advantageous to individuals that produce gametes.

Answer: C
Topic: 27.1
Skill: Conceptual Understanding

4) Which of the following statements regarding sexual reproduction is *true*?
   A) Sexual reproduction creates an individual that is a genetic copy of one parent.
   B) Sexual reproduction generates greater genetic variation than asexual reproduction.
   C) Sexual reproduction allows animals to expand their populations faster than asexual reproduction.
   D) Populations of organisms that reproduce through sexual reproduction generally have difficulty adapting to changing environments.
   E) Sexual reproduction produces $2n$ gametes.

Answer: B
Topic: 27.2
Skill: Conceptual Understanding

5) Hermaphrodites are animals that
   A) possess both male and female reproductive systems.
   B) have the gonads of one sex but the external appearance of the other.
   C) develop from unfertilized eggs.
   D) must fertilize themselves.
   E) have abnormal reproductive systems.

Answer: A
Topic: 27.2
Skill: Factual Recall

6) Reproductive systems with external fertilization are most common in
   A) terrestrial animals.
   B) populations with many more males than females.
   C) animals that are widely dispersed.
   D) aquatic animals.
   E) populations with many more females than males.

Answer: D
Topic: 27.2
Skill: Factual Recall

7) Which of the following statements about the reproductive system of human females is *true*?
   A) In human females, eggs develop within the uterus.
   B) The corpus luteum secretes progesterone, which helps maintain the uterine lining during pregnancy.
   C) After 9 months of development, an embryo is called a fetus.
   D) The cervix is an important structure of sexual arousal.
   E) The labia minora are a pair of thick, fatty ridges that protect the entire genital region.

Answer: B
Topic: 27.3
Skill: Factual Recall

8) The human egg is swept through the oviduct toward the uterus by
   A) the beating of the egg's cilia.
   B) the beating of the egg's flagella.
   C) rhythmic contractions of the oviduct.
   D) rhythmic contractions of the uterus.
   E) the beating of cilia in the oviduct.

Answer: E
Topic: 27.3
Skill: Factual Recall

9) Fertilization in the female reproductive tract most often takes place in the
    A) ovary.
    B) upper third of the oviduct.
    C) lower third of the oviduct.
    D) uterus.
    E) vagina.

Answer: B
Topic: 27.3
Skill: Factual Recall

10) The embryo implants in the _____ of the uterus.
    A) exometrium
    B) myometrium
    C) perimetrium
    D) epimetrium
    E) endometrium

Answer: E
Topic: 27.3
Skill: Factual Recall

11) Human testes are positioned in an external sac rather than in the abdominal cavity
    A) to shorten the distance that semen must travel during ejaculation.
    B) to shorten the distance that sperm must swim during insemination.
    C) so the testes can be kept away from the urinary bladder.
    D) so the testes can be kept cooler than the body's interior.
    E) so the testes can enlarge during sexual maturation.

Answer: D
Topic: 27.4
Skill: Conceptual Understanding

12) Men who take very long, hot baths are likely to
    A) produce more sperm.
    B) produce healthier sperm.
    C) produce more sperm and ones that are healthier.
    D) produce fewer sperm.
    E) produce nonfunctional sperm.

Answer: D
Topic: 27.4
Skill: Conceptual Understanding

13) After being produced in the testes, sperm mature further in a structure called the
    A) vas deferens.
    B) epididymis.
    C) prostate.
    D) seminal vesicle.
    E) bulbourethral gland.

Answer: B
Topic: 27.4
Skill: Factual Recall

14) Which of the following produces a thick fluid containing fructose, which is used for energy by sperm?
    A) prostate gland
    B) bulbourethral gland
    C) seminal vesicles
    D) vas deferens
    E) epididymis

Answer: C
Topic: 27.4
Skill: Factual Recall

15) Which of the following statements regarding spermatogenesis and oogenesis is *true*?
    A) Meiosis in spermatogenesis produces two cells from one primary spermatocyte.
    B) Meiosis in oogenesis produces one mature egg from one primary oocyte.
    C) Oogenesis begins at puberty.
    D) Spermatogenesis begins at birth.
    E) Oogenesis is not completed without stimulation by estrogen.

Answer: B
Topic: 27.5
Skill: Conceptual Understanding

16) Which of the following statements comparing spermatogenesis and oogenesis is *true*?
    A) During oogenesis, four cells are produced with each sharing equally the cytoplasm from the parent cell.
    B) During oogenesis, there is a resting period that lasts for about 30 days.
    C) Men, but not women, can produce gametes throughout their lives.
    D) Spermatogenesis and oogenesis rely upon mitosis to produce gametes.
    E) Spermatogenesis, but not oogenesis, is an example of gametogenesis.

Answer: C
Topic: 27.5
Skill: Factual Recall

17) Menstruation
    A) is triggered by an LH surge.
    B) is triggered by HCG.
    C) is triggered by an increase in the levels of estrogen and progesterone.
    D) coincides with the postovulatory phase of the ovarian cycle.
    E) coincides with the beginning of the pre–ovulatory phase of the ovarian cycle.

Answer: E
Topic: 27.6
Skill: Conceptual Understanding

18) In human females, the ovarian cycle begins when
    A) the levels of estrogen reach their maximum.
    B) the hypothalamus increases its release of FSH and LH.
    C) the hypothalamus stimulates the anterior pituitary to increase its output of FSH and LH.
    D) the level of progesterone drops precipitously.
    E) the levels of FSH and LH drop precipitously.

Answer: C
Topic: 27.6
Skill: Factual Recall

19) Which of the following hormones stimulates the growth of an ovarian follicle?
    A) LH
    B) FSH
    C) estrogen
    D) progesterone
    E) releasing hormone

Answer: B
Topic: 27.6
Skill: Factual Recall

20) A decrease in _____ is followed by the gradual degradation of the corpus luteum.
    A) LH
    B) FSH
    C) estrogen
    D) progesterone
    E) releasing hormone

Answer: A
Topic: 27.6
Skill: Factual Recall

21) Which of the following agents can cause an infection that can ultimately develop into pelvic inflammatory disease in women?
    A) *Treponema pallidum*
    B) papilloma virus
    C) *Trichomonas vaginalis*
    D) *Candida albicans*
    E) *Chlamydia trachomatis*

Answer: E
Topic: 27.7
Skill: Factual Recall

22) Which of the following types of pathogens cause sexually transmitted diseases that cannot be treated with antibiotics?
    A) bacteria
    B) spirochetes
    C) viruses
    D) fungi
    E) syndromes

Answer: C
Topic: 27.7
Skill: Conceptual Understanding

23) Which of the following STDs is caused by a virus that can also cause cancer?
    A) genital warts
    B) syphilis
    C) gonorrhea
    D) trichomoniasis
    E) candidiasis

Answer: A
Topic: 27.7
Skill: Factual Recall

24) The only totally effective way to prevent the spread of STDs is through
    A) using condoms.
    B) abstaining from sexual intercourse.
    C) using condoms and spermicides.
    D) using birth control pills.
    E) using a diaphragm and spermicide.

Answer: B
Topic: 27.8
Skill: Factual Recall

25) Sterilization, in which the sperm is surgically prevented from reaching the egg, is accomplished by
    A) MAPs.
    B) the rhythm method.
    C) tubal ligation or vasectomy.
    D) cervical capping.
    E) mifepristone.

Answer: C
Topic: 27.8
Skill: Factual Recall

26) Which of the following statements regarding birth control is *true*?
   A) The most widely used birth control pills contain a combination of FSH and LH.
   B) Natural family planning is generally reliable.
   C) Morning–after pills taken within three days of unprotected intercourse prevent
      fertilization or implantation about 75% of the time.
   D) Spermicides used alone are generally reliable.
   E) Birth control pills work primarily by preventing fertilization and implantation.

Answer: C
Topic: 27.8
Skill: Factual Recall

27) The function of a sperm cell's acrosome is to
   A) carry the sperm's nucleus.
   B) fuse with the jelly coat of the egg cell.
   C) carry enzymes that are released to form a hole in the egg's jelly coat when the sperm
      encounters an egg.
   D) contain the fuel that powers the sperm.
   E) carry the sperm's helical mitochondria.

Answer: C
Topic: 27.9
Skill: Factual Recall

28) Which of the following generates the ATP that is required for movement of the sperm's
   tail?
   A) mitochondria in the neck and middle piece
   B) mitochondria in the sperm head
   C) mitochondria in the sperm tail
   D) the sperm plasma membrane
   E) the acrosome

Answer: A
Topic: 27.9
Skill: Factual Recall

29) Fertilization
   A) joins two diploid sets of chromosomes.
   B) activates development in the egg.
   C) joins two haploid sets of chromosomes.
   D) joins two haploid sets of chromosomes and activates development in the egg.
   E) joins two diploid sets of chromosomes and activates development in the egg.

Answer: D
Topic: 27.9
Skill: Conceptual Understanding

30) Which of the following serves as an impenetrable barrier that prevents more than one sperm from fertilizing an egg?
    A) the acrosome
    B) the jelly coat of the egg
    C) the sperm's plasma membrane
    D) the fertilization envelope
    E) the zygote's cytoplasm

Answer: D
Topic: 27.9
Skill: Conceptual Understanding

31) Which of the following events occurs first during embryonic development?
    A) gastrulation
    B) neurulation
    C) cleavage
    D) implantation
    E) aggregation

Answer: C
Topic: 27.10
Skill: Factual Recall

32) Which of the following results from cleavage?
    A) formation of the nervous system
    B) formation of the digestive system
    C) formation of the notochord
    D) formation of more cells
    E) segmentation

Answer: D
Topic: 27.10
Skill: Factual Recall

33) Which of the following processes is most similar to the process of cleavage?
    A) slicing up a pie into eight pieces
    B) stringing beads onto a string
    C) inflating a balloon
    D) stretching a rubber band
    E) melting a stick of butter in a hot pan

Answer: A
Topic: 27.10
Skill: Conceptual Understanding

34) Two important contributions that cleavage makes to development are to
    A) establish the basic tissues of the body and define the future digestive tract.
    B) establish the basic tissues of the body and define the future nervous system.
    C) create a multicellular embryo and partition the embryo into developmental regions.
    D) create a multicellular embryo and establish the basic tissues of the body.
    E) establish the basic body plan and determine the location of the mouth and anus.

Answer: C
Topic: 27.10
Skill: Conceptual Understanding

35) The ectoderm is one of the embryonic tissue layers produced during gastrulation that forms the
    A) embryonic digestive tract.
    B) embryonic nervous system.
    C) outer layer of the gastrula.
    D) brain.
    E) space between the ectoderm and endoderm.

Answer: C
Topic: 27.11
Skill: Factual Recall

36) What occurs during gastrulation?
    A) A solid embryo is changed into a hollow morula.
    B) A solid blastula is changed into a hollow embryo that has four tissue layers.
    C) A hollow blastula is changed into a hollow embryo that has three tissue layers.
    D) A neural tube is created by invagination of the ectoderm.
    E) A notochord is created by invagination of the ectoderm.

Answer: C
Topic: 27.11
Skill: Conceptual Understanding

37) Which of the following structures develops from mesodermal tissue?
    A) notochord
    B) lining of the digestive tract
    C) skin
    D) cornea and lens of the eye
    E) nervous system

Answer: A
Topic: 27.11
Skill: Factual Recall

38) Which of the following statements regarding gastrulation is *true*?
    A) The notochord provides support for the mesoderm.
    B) The neural tube lies directly below the notochord.
    C) The neural tube develops from the mesodermal layer.
    D) The notochord is composed of paired blocks of mesoderm that will give rise to structures including vertebrae and associated muscles.
    E) The notochord in the embryo is in the position of the future backbone.

Answer: E
Topic: 27.12
Skill: Factual Recall

39) Which of the following options correctly represents the sequence in which most animals develop?
   A) zygote, cleavage, blastula, gastrula, organ formation
   B) cleavage, zygote, gastrula, blastula, organ formation
   C) zygote, cleavage, gastrula, blastula, organ formation
   D) zygote, cleavage, organ formation, blastula, gastrula
   E) blastula, cleavage, zygote, organ formation, gastrula

Answer: A
Topic: 27.12
Skill: Conceptual Understanding

40) When a chemical signal from a group of embryonic cells causes a different, nearby group of cells to embark on a particular developmental course (say, differentiating into a leg), the interaction between the two groups of cells is called
   A) induction.
   B) coordinated differentiation.
   C) codifferentiation.
   D) entrainment.
   E) potentiation.

Answer: A
Topic: 27.13
Skill: Factual Recall

41) Cells migrate from one place to another during gastrulation by
   A) means of cilia.
   B) cellular protrusions.
   C) means of flagella.
   D) peristalsis.
   E) being pushed by new cells generated by mitosis.

Answer: B
Topic: 27.13
Skill: Factual Recall

42) Which of the following occurs during cellular migration and development into specialized tissue?
   A) Cells are transferred to the appropriate region of the embryo via the bloodstream.
   B) Membrane lipids enable the migrating cells to recognize similar cells.
   C) Cells fuse to produce multinucleated giant cells.
   D) Similar cells glue themselves in place by secreting glycoproteins.
   E) Most cells of the developing tissue undergo the process of apoptosis.

Answer: D
Topic: 27.13
Skill: Conceptual Understanding

43) Which of the following defines apoptosis?
   A) cellular suicide
   B) gastrulation
   C) cleavage
   D) phagocytosis
   E) neural tube formation

Answer: A
Topic: 27.13
Skill: Factual Recall

44) The way cells behave during pattern formation is most like
   A) the blending together of different paints to form a new paint color.
   B) mixing together ingredients to bake cookies.
   C) a person finding his or her way home by noticing familiar sights and sounds.
   D) washing clothes to remove the dirt and stains that are not wanted.
   E) mowing the grass in a yard to trim back the growth and keep a regular grass thickness.

Answer: C
Topic: 27.14–Evolution Connection
Skill: Conceptual Understanding

45) Research indicates that _____ respond(s) to _____ signals that inform a cell about its position relative to other cells in the embryo.
   A) nervous tissue . . . hormonal
   B) master control genes . . . chemical
   C) organs . . . radio
   D) organelles . . . chemical
   E) embryos . . . environmental

Answer: B
Topic: 27.14–Evolution Connection
Skill: Conceptual Understanding

46) The discovery of _____ explains embryonic pattern formation in a wide variety of organisms.
   A) the three-dimensional forms of animals
   B) induction
   C) homeotic genes
   D) somites
   E) programmed cell death

Answer: C
Topic: 27.14–Evolution Connection
Skill: Factual Recall

47) A major goal of developmental research is to understand
    A) how DNA directs formation of a three-dimensional animal.
    B) evolutionary similarities between species.
    C) DNA transcription.
    D) hormone interactions.
    E) how cellular signals stimulate mitosis.

Answer: A
Topic: 27.14–Evolution Connection
Skill: Conceptual Understanding

48) Another term for gestation is
    A) conception.
    B) fertilization.
    C) ovulation.
    D) development.
    E) pregnancy.

Answer: E
Topic: 27.15
Skill: Factual Recall

49) When does the human blastocyst implant in the wall of the uterus?
    A) within a few hours of fertilization
    B) about a day after conception
    C) about a week after conception
    D) about an hour after organ formation
    E) only after all four extraembryonic membranes become established.

Answer: C
Topic: 27.15
Skill: Factual Recall

50) The yolk sac of humans
    A) stores nutrients to support the developing embryo.
    B) is evidence of human's relationships to egg-laying vertebrates.
    C) secretes HCG.
    D) absorbs nutrients from, and releases waste to, the mother's blood.
    E) envelops the developing fetus.

Answer: B
Topic: 27.15
Skill: Conceptual Understanding

51) The human embryo's first blood cells arise in the
    A) developing liver.
    B) developing bone marrow.
    C) amnion.
    D) yolk sac.
    E) allantois.

Answer: D
Topic: 27.15
Skill: Factual Recall

52) What would happen if the trophoblast of an implanting embryo, and later the chorion, failed to secrete human chorionic gonadotropin?
   A) The maternal elements of the placenta would fail to develop.
   B) The fetal elements of the placenta would fail to develop.
   C) Neural tube formation would not occur, and the embryo would have no central nervous system.
   D) Blood and blood vessel formation would fail to develop.
   E) The embryo would be aborted.

Answer: E
Topic: 27.15
Skill: Application

53) Which of the following structures contributes to the structure of the placenta as well as completely surrounding the embryo?
   A) corpus luteum
   B) chorion
   C) amnion
   D) yolk sac
   E) allantois

Answer: B
Topic: 27.15
Skill: Factual Recall

54) At which gestational age does a developing human fetus first look obviously human and not like other vertebrate embryos?
   A) 2 weeks
   B) 4 weeks
   C) 9 weeks
   D) 4 months
   E) 7 months

Answer: C
Topic: 27.16
Skill: Factual Recall

55) At about what point in gestation does the fetal heartbeat become audible using a stethoscope?
   A) 5 weeks
   B) 12 weeks
   C) 25 weeks
   D) 30 weeks
   E) 40 weeks

Answer: B
Topic: 27.16
Skill: Factual Recall

56) Which of the following processes dominates the third trimester of human development?
  A) formation of internal organs
  B) formation of external features such as arms and legs
  C) formation of hair and fingernails
  D) rapid growth
  E) organ formation

Answer: D
Topic: 27.16
Skill: Factual Recall

57) The induction and maintenance of labor represent an example of which type of control?
  A) control of uterine events by anterior pituitary hormones
  B) control of uterine events by posterior pituitary hormones
  C) positive feedback involving pituitary, uterine, and placental hormones and prostaglandins
  D) positive feedback involving uterine substances only
  E) negative feedback involving pituitary hormones and uterine prostaglandins

Answer: C
Topic: 27.17
Skill: Conceptual Understanding

58) Contractions in uterine smooth muscle during labor are initiated by
  A) progesterone.
  B) epinephrine.
  C) estrogen.
  D) oxytocin.
  E) prolactin.

Answer: D
Topic: 27.17
Skill: Conceptual Understanding

59) Which of the following options correctly lists the three stages of labor in the order in which they occur?
  A) dilation, expulsion, delivery of the placenta
  B) dilation, crowning, expulsion
  C) contractions, dilation, expulsion
  D) contractions, dilation, crowning
  E) dilation, crowning, delivery of the placenta

Answer: A
Topic: 27.18
Skill: Factual Recall

60) Which of the following statements regarding infertility and fertilization procedures is *true?*
    A) The most common cause of human infertility is female infertility problems.
    B) Embryos fertilized through assisted reproductive technologies cannot be frozen for later use, as they degrade rapidly.
    C) In GIFT, sperm are injected into an embryo *in vitro,* and the embryo is placed into the oviducts.
    D) In IVF, fertilization occurs in a dish. The embryo is allowed to develop for several days, then the embryo is placed into the uterus.
    E) Children conceived using reproductive technologies such as IVF and ICSI display a high rate of abnormalities resulting from these procedures.

Answer: D
Topic: 27.19
Skill: Factual Recall

Art Questions

1)

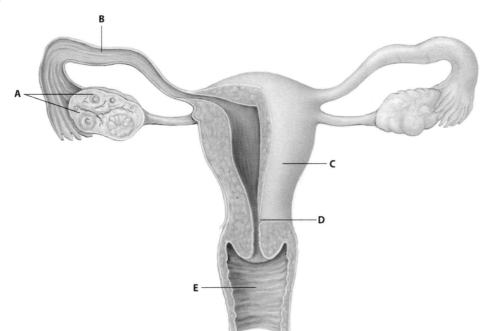

In which part of the human female reproductive system does fertilization normally take place?
    A) part A
    B) part B
    C) part C
    D) part D
    E) part E

Answer: B
Topic: 27.3
Skill: Application

2)

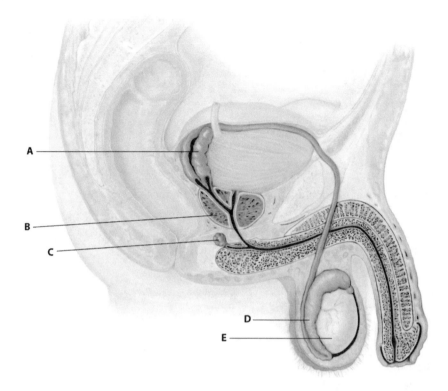

Which part of this figure depicting the human male reproductive system is the epididymis?
   A) part A
   B) part B
   C) part C
   D) part D
   E) part E

Answer: D
Topic: 27.4
Skill: Factual Recall

3)

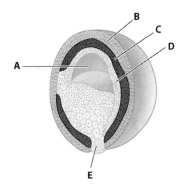

Which part of this figuring depicting a gastrula is the mesoderm?
A) part A
B) part B
C) part C
D) part D
E) part E

Answer: C
Topic: 27.11
Skill: Factual Recall

Scenario Questions

After reading the following paragraph, answer the question(s) below.

Brittany's family includes several individuals with a genetic disorder that affects primarily males. Her husband Tony has no history of the disease to pass on to their children. They've decided that their best chance to have a healthy family is to have only daughters. Through a new type of assisted reproductive technology, it's possible to separate sperm that will produce sons from those that will produce daughters. Brittany's eggs will be fertilized by in vitro fertilization (IVF) with sperm that can produce only daughters. The developing female embryos can be implanted into her uterus to complete development normally.

1) The daughter–producing sperm used to fertilize Brittany's eggs should be
A) diploid with one sex chromosome.
B) haploid with two sex chromosomes.
C) haploid with one sex chromosome.
D) diploid with two sex chromosomes.
E) haploid with no sex chromosomes.

Answer: C
Topic: 27.2, 27.5
Skill: Factual Recall

2) For IVF to be completed successfully, several _____ should be removed from Brittany's ovaries.
    A) primary oocytes
    B) secondary oocytes
    C) follicles
    D) endometrial fragments
    E) trophoblasts

Answer: B
Topic: 27.2, 27.5, 27.18
Skill: Conceptual Understanding

Chapter 28 Nervous Systems

Multiple-Choice Questions

1) The central communication conduit between the brain and the rest of the body is the
   A) brain stem.
   B) nerve bundle.
   C) spinal cord.
   D) nervous system.
   E) neuron.

   Answer: C
   Topic: Opening Essay
   Skill: Factual Recall

2) The two major anatomical divisions of the nervous system are the
   A) ANS and SNS.
   B) sympathetic nervous system and parasympathetic nervous system.
   C) central nervous system and peripheral nervous system.
   D) sensory nervous system and motor nervous system.
   E) voluntary nervous system and involuntary nervous system.

   Answer: C
   Topic: 28.1
   Skill: Factual Recall

3) Nervous system effector cells
   A) are white cells found in the circulatory system.
   B) consist of sensory cells.
   C) perform responses to signals from integration centers.
   D) are fibrous.
   E) provide automatic responses to stimuli.

   Answer: C
   Topic: 28.1
   Skill: Conceptual Understanding

4) Which of the following statements regarding the nervous system is *true*?
   A) Sensory neurons convey signals from the CNS to sensory receptors.
   B) Motor neurons convey signals from the CNS to effector cells.
   C) Interneurons integrate data and relay appropriate signals to receptors.
   D) The PNS is composed entirely of nerves.
   E) The CNS and the brain are the same thing.

   Answer: B
   Topic: 28.1
   Skill: Factual Recall

5) Sensory input is one of the nervous system's interconnected functions that
   A) interprets sensory signals and formulates responses.
   B) conducts signals from integration centers.
   C) involves conveying signals from the CNS to effector cells.
   D) conducts signals from sensory receptors to integration centers.
   E) performs body functions.

Answer: D
Topic: 28.1
Skill: Conceptual Understanding

6) The functional unit of the nervous system is the
   A) dendrite.
   B) cell body.
   C) neuron.
   D) axon.
   E) synapse.

Answer: C
Topic: 28.2
Skill: Conceptual Understanding

7) What part of a nerve cell carries signals toward the part of the cell that houses the nucleus?
   A) node of Ranvier
   B) axon
   C) cell body
   D) dendrite
   E) neuron

Answer: D
Topic: 28.2
Skill: Conceptual Understanding

8) The speed of impulse conduction along an axon may be increased by
   A) the nodes of Ranvier.
   B) a graded potential.
   C) IPSPs.
   D) neurotransmitters.
   E) EPSPs.

Answer: A
Topic: 28.2
Skill: Factual Recall

9) Multiple sclerosis results from an immune system disorder that primarily involves
   A) destruction of the hippocampus.
   B) deterioration of the corpus callosum.
   C) destruction of the myelin sheath.
   D) destruction of regions of the motor cortex.
   E) deterioration of parts of the spinal cord.

Answer: C
Topic: 28.2
Skill: Factual Recall

10) Which of the following statements about resting potential is *true*?
   A) A resting membrane allows much more sodium than potassium to diffuse across.
   B) The concentration of sodium is much higher inside the cell than outside.
   C) The resting potential exists because of differences in glucose concentration inside and outside the cell.
   D) The sodium–potassium pump contributes to the resting membrane potential.
   E) The sodium–potassium pump actually transports K^+ out of the cell and Na^+ into the cell.

Answer: D
Topic: 28.3
Skill: Conceptual Understanding

11) Once an action potential is triggered, the first major chemical change is
   A) a reversal of the membrane polarity, with the interior of the cell becoming positively charged.
   B) a reversal of the membrane polarity, with the interior of the cell becoming negatively charged.
   C) an increase in the negative charges inside the neuron.
   D) a sudden rush of potassium into the neuron.
   E) a sudden impermeability of the membrane to the transport of ions.

Answer: A
Topic: 28.4
Skill: Conceptual Understanding

12) Once the threshold potential is reached,
   A) the membrane potential is positive.
   B) K^+ channels open.
   C) Na^+ channels close.
   D) an action potential is inevitable.
   E) the interior of the cell becomes negative with respect to the outside.

Answer: D
Topic: 28.4
Skill: Conceptual Understanding

13) Action potentials normally travel along an axon
   A) toward the cell body.
   B) away from the cell body.
   C) in either direction, depending on the needs of the animal.
   D) away from the synapse.
   E) into dendrites.

Answer: B
Topic: 28.5
Skill: Conceptual Understanding

14) Action potentials relay different intensities of information due to the
   A) amplitude of action potentials relative to the strength of the stimulus.
   B) frequency of action potentials relative to the strength of the stimulus.
   C) speed of travel of action potentials relative to the strength of the stimulus.
   D) duration of action potentials relative to the strength of the stimulus.
   E) shape of action potentials relative to the strength of the stimulus.

Answer: B
Topic: 28.5
Skill: Conceptual Understanding

15) Which of the following is most like a shiver that raises goose bumps as it spreads all over your body?
   A) an action potential traveling over a neuron
   B) the functions of nodes of Ranvier
   C) the functions of myelin sheaths
   D) the chemical reactions at a synapse
   E) a rise in body temperature

Answer: A
Topic: 28.5
Skill: Conceptual Understanding

16) The gap between the transmitting and receiving neurons in a chemical synapse is known as the
   A) synaptic node.
   B) synaptic knob.
   C) gap junction.
   D) synaptic cleft.
   E) gap myelin.

Answer: D
Topic: 28.6
Skill: Factual Recall

17) During transmission across a typical chemical synapse,
   A) neurotransmitter molecules are stored in the synaptic knob.
   B) action potentials trigger chemical changes that make the synaptic vesicles fuse with each other.
   C) vesicles containing neurotransmitter diffuse to the receiving cell's plasma membrane.
   D) neurotransmitter molecules bind to receptors in the receiving cell's plasma membrane.
   E) the binding of neurotransmitters to receptors initiates exocytosis.

Answer: D
Topic: 28.6
Skill: Conceptual Understanding

18) The signal that crosses a synapse is stopped when
  A) a second action potential traveling down the signaling cell sounds a "retreat," and the ions reverse direction.
  B) the responding cell runs out of sodium and is no longer able to respond to the stimulus.
  C) the responding cell runs out of potassium and is no longer able to respond to the stimulus.
  D) the chemically gated ion channels of the receiving cell's membrane release neurotransmitters.
  E) the neurotransmitter is enzymatically broken down or transported back to the signaling cell.

Answer: E
Topic: 28.6
Skill: Factual Recall

19) Neurotransmitters that open Na$^+$ channels and trigger action potentials in receiving cells are called
  A) inhibitory.
  B) cross-linked.
  C) excitatory.
  D) blocked.
  E) obligatory.

Answer: C
Topic: 28.7
Skill: Factual Recall

20) The strength of a neurotransmitter's signal is increased by
  A) more neurotransmitters binding to the receiving neuron.
  B) fewer neurotransmitters binding to the receiving neuron.
  C) a synapse located closer to the base of the receiving neuron's axon.
  D) a synapse located farther away from the base of the receiving neuron's axon.
  E) more neurotransmitters binding closer to the base of the receiving neuron's axon.

Answer: E
Topic: 28.7
Skill: Factual Recall

21) Botulism toxin produced by certain bacteria will
  A) prevent enzymatic breakdown of neurotransmitters.
  B) cause continual contraction of smooth muscle.
  C) initiate an increase in the strength of a transmitted signal.
  D) inhibit the release of acetylcholine.
  E) inhibit the action of biogenic amines.

Answer: D
Topic: 28.8
Skill: Factual Recall

22) The neurotransmitter associated with sleep, mood, attention, and learning is
    A) acetylcholine.
    B) GABA.
    C) epinephrine.
    D) serotonin.
    E) endorphins.

Answer: D
Topic: 28.8
Skill: Factual Recall

23) Parkinson's disease is associated with a deficiency in
    A) dopamine.
    B) epinephrine.
    C) serotonin.
    D) acetylcholine.
    E) endorphins.

Answer: A
Topic: 28.8
Skill: Factual Recall

24) Valium, a prescription drug used to treat depression, works by
    A) binding and activating acetylcholine receptors.
    B) initiating inhibitory signals.
    C) increasing the inhibitory effect of GABA.
    D) increasing the release and availability of norepinephrine and dopamine at synapses.
    E) activating neurotransmitter receptors for GABA.

Answer: E
Topic: 28.9
Skill: Factual Recall

25) Morphine, codeine, and heroin are all opiates that function by
    A) binding to acetylcholine receptors.
    B) blocking the removal of serotonin from synapses.
    C) binding to GABA receptors.
    D) binding to endorphin receptors.
    E) blocking the reuptake of dopamine and norepinephrine.

Answer: D
Topic: 28.9
Skill: Factual Recall

26) The uniformity in the way nerve cells function within the animal kingdom
    A) indicates that the PNS evolved before the CNS.
    B) is evidence that the neuron was an early evolutionary adaptation.
    C) is proof of neurotransmitter efficiency.
    D) must have prevented the development of diversity.
    E) is considered by many to be a consequence of overexposure to ultraviolet rays in sunlight.

Answer: B
Topic: 28.10–Evolution Connection
Skill: Conceptual Understanding

27) The simplest animals to display cephalization and centralization of the nervous system are
   A) sponges.
   B) flatworms.
   C) cnidarians.
   D) mollusks.
   E) echinoderms.

Answer: B
Topic: 28.10–Evolution Connection
Skill: Factual Recall

28) One of the most important branch points in the evolution of animals and their nervous systems was the appearance of
   A) radical symmetry.
   B) centralized nervous systems.
   C) bilateral symmetry.
   D) the spinal column.
   E) specialized cells for transmitting signals.

Answer: C
Topic: 28.10–Evolution Connection
Skill: Factual Recall

29) The brain and sensory system of a bilaterally symmetric organism function most like
   A) the engine of a motorboat.
   B) the pilot of an airplane.
   C) the passengers on a train.
   D) a cook baking bread.
   E) a member of a marching band.

Answer: B
Topic: 28.10–Evolution Connection
Skill: Conceptual Understanding

30) Which of the following statements regarding the peripheral nervous system is *true*?
   A) The brain is part of the peripheral nervous system.
   B) The spinal cord is part of the peripheral nervous system.
   C) Nerves are part of the peripheral nervous system.
   D) Ganglia are part of the peripheral nervous system.
   E) Spinal nerves contain either sensory or motor axons, but not both.

Answer: C
Topic: 28.10–Evolution Connection
Skill: Factual Recall

31) Natural selection tends to correlate the structures of a nervous system with an animal's interaction with the environment. A good example are mollusks, which
   A) have little or no cephalization and simple sense organs.
   B) hibernate most of their adult life.
   C) use chemical synapses to process complex information.
   D) have a brain that functions as a master control center.
   E) use their circulatory system as a mechanism for distributing nerve impulses.

Answer: A
Topic: 28.10–Evolution Connection
Skill: Factual Recall

32) Which of the following statements regarding the brain is *true?*
   A) Ventricles in the brain are filled with interstitial fluid.
   B) The blood–brain barrier maintains a stable chemical environment for the brain.
   C) Layers of tissue, called epithelium, surround and protect the brain and spinal cord.
   D) White matter is mainly dendrites.
   E) Cranial nerves carry signals from the spinal cord.

Answer: B
Topic: 28.11
Skill: Factual Recall

33) The relationship between spinal nerves and the spinal cord is most like the relationship between
   A) the hairs on a person's head.
   B) the vertical and horizontal threads woven together to form a piece of cloth..
   C) the teeth on a comb.
   D) an interstate highway and the many roads that intersect with it via on– and off–ramps.
   E) a bowl of spaghetti and the sauce that is poured onto it.

Answer: D
Topic: 28.11
Skill: Conceptual Understanding

34) Which division of the human nervous system carries signals to skeletal muscles?
   A) autonomic nervous system
   B) parasympathetic nervous system
   C) sympathetic nervous system
   D) sensory nervous system
   E) somatic nervous system

Answer: E
Topic: 28.12
Skill: Factual Recall

35) The autonomic nervous system
    A) integrates sensory inputs to the brain.
    B) carries signals to and from skeletal muscles.
    C) regulates the internal environment of the body.
    D) is mostly voluntary.
    E) is part of the central nervous system.

Answer: C
Topic: 28.12
Skill: Factual Recall

36) Which of the following results from stimulation by the parasympathetic nervous system?
    A) increased heart rate
    B) expanded bronchi
    C) inhibition of the digestive organs
    D) inhibition of urination
    E) stimulation of saliva production

Answer: E
Topic: 28.13
Skill: Conceptual Understanding

37) Which of the following results from stimulation by the sympathetic nervous system?
    A) release of glucose from the liver
    B) decreased heart rate
    C) stimulation of the digestive organs
    D) constriction of the bronchi
    E) decreased rate of breathing

Answer: A
Topic: 28.13
Skill: Conceptual Understanding

38) The enteric division of the autonomic nervous system consists of neurons in the digestive tract, the gallbladder, and the
    A) heart.
    B) lymphatic system.
    C) pancreas.
    D) thyroid gland.
    E) endocrine system.

Answer: C
Topic: 28.13
Skill: Factual Recall

39) When you are very nervous, perhaps before you must speak in front of your college class, you notice that your mouth is dry and your heart is racing. This is most likely due to stimulation by the
   A) enteric division of your autonomic nervous system.
   B) sympathetic division of your autonomic nervous system.
   C) parasympathetic division of your autonomic nervous system.
   D) neurasthenic division of your sympathetic nervous system.
   E) somatic division of your parasympathetic nervous system.

Answer: B
Topic: 28.13
Skill: Application

40) In all vertebrates, the brain consists of the
   A) cerebrum, forebrain, and hindbrain.
   B) cerebrum, midbrain, and hindbrain.
   C) forebrain, midbrain, and hindbrain.
   D) cerebrum, cerebellum, and hindbrain.
   E) cerebrum, cerebellum, and medulla.

Answer: C
Topic: 28.14
Skill: Factual Recall

41) The sophisticated behavior of mammals and birds is directly related to
   A) their relatively large cerebrum.
   B) the presence of a hindbrain.
   C) the presence of a midbrain.
   D) the presence of a forebrain.
   E) the presence of a notochord.

Answer: A
Topic: 28.14
Skill: Conceptual Understanding

42) The brain of humans is strongly oriented toward the interpretation of
   A) smell.
   B) vision.
   C) hearing.
   D) taste.
   E) touch.

Answer: B
Topic: 28.14
Skill: Factual Recall

43) A physician friend of yours is telling you about a patient with a head injury who suddenly stopped breathing. Your friend explains that the bony rim was pressing against the breathing center. You guess that the "bony rim" (whatever that is) must have been exerting pressure in the region of the
   A) basal ganglia and hippocampus.
   B) cerebellum and cerebrum.
   C) thalamus and hypothalamus.
   D) medulla oblongata and pons.
   E) spinal column of the upper back.

Answer: D
Topic: 28.15
Skill: Application

44) You start to fall but then catch yourself, regaining your balance. Which of the following brain regions is responsible for the rapid coordination of muscle activity that kept you from falling?
   A) motor cortex
   B) thalamus
   C) hypothalamus
   D) cerebellum
   E) pons

Answer: D
Topic: 28.15
Skill: Application

45) What part of the brain sorts incoming information, such as touch signals from your hand, into categories before relaying it to the cerebral cortex?
   A) thalamus
   B) hypothalamus
   C) pons
   D) corpus callosum
   E) hippocampus

Answer: A
Topic: 28.15
Skill: Factual Recall

46) Which of the following brain regions controls the secretion of pituitary hormones and exerts direct control over many other aspects of homeostasis?
   A) thalamus
   B) hypothalamus
   C) medulla oblongata
   D) hippocampus
   E) cerebellum

Answer: B
Topic: 28.15
Skill: Factual Recall

47) Our biological clock, which regulates the sleep–wake cycle, is housed within the
    A) cerebrum.
    B) hypothalamus.
    C) cerebellum.
    D) midbrain.
    E) brain stem.

Answer: B
Topic: 28.15
Skill: Factual Recall

48) The human cerebral cortex accounts for what percentage of the total mass of the brain?
    A) 10%
    B) 20%
    C) 40%
    D) 60%
    E) 80%

Answer: E
Topic: 28.16
Skill: Factual Recall

49) Which of the following statements correctly represents a structure/function correlation?
    A) Cognitive regions are the sites of higher mental activities.
    B) The motor cortex sends commands to cardiac and smooth muscle.
    C) The somatosensory cortex receives and integrates signals about touch, pain, temperature, and pressure.
    D) Language results from complex interactions among neurons on the left side of the brain.
    E) The left brain is more often associated with spatial relations.

Answer: C
Topic: 28.16
Skill: Factual Recall

50) Which of the following statements regarding brain activity is *true*?
    A) Recent research has revealed that the 1848 accident involving Phineas Gage caused damage to his hindbrain.
    B) People usually die following a hemispherectomy.
    C) People cannot function when the communication channels between the hemispheres are cut.
    D) The cerebral cortex has cells that can detect pain.
    E) New techniques, such as PET scans and fMRIs, allow researchers to study brain activities.

Answer: E
Topic: 28.17
Skill: Factual Recall

51) fMRI technology can provide significant insights into brain function by
    A) measuring areas of electronegativity.
    B) detecting damaged areas of the brain.
    C) measuring changes in blood oxygen usage at sites of brain activity.
    D) stimulating oxygen–depleted areas.
    E) measuring the pathway of nerve impulses.

Answer: C
Topic: 28.18
Skill: Conceptual Understanding

52) The network of neurons that extends through the core of the brainstem and selects information that reaches the cerebral cortex during sleep is the
    A) medulla.
    B) serotonin storage area.
    C) limbic system.
    D) reticular formation.
    E) brainstem core.

Answer: D
Topic: 28.19
Skill: Factual Recall

53) During REM sleep, an EEG shows
    A) a flat trace with very few waves.
    B) mainly alpha waves.
    C) sleep waves.
    D) mainly delta waves.
    E) an irregular, rapidly changing pattern.

Answer: E
Topic: 28.19
Skill: Factual Recall

54) Our emotions, learning, and memory depend upon the
    A) RAS.
    B) limbic system.
    C) parietal lobes.
    D) frontal lobes.
    E) occipital lobes.

Answer: B
Topic: 28.20
Skill: Factual Recall

55) What part of the brain seems to be a memory filter?
    A) hippocampus
    B) amygdala
    C) prefrontal cortex
    D) associational cortex
    E) corpus callosum

Answer: B
Topic: 28.20
Skill: Factual Recall

56) Which of the following statements is *true?*
    A) The limbic system plays a key role in recognizing facial expressions.
    B) The amygdala helps form and recall memories.
    C) Laughing and crying are mediated by the corpus callosum.
    D) The transfer of information from short-term to long-term memory is enhanced by rehearsal.
    E) Skill memories usually involve the cortex.

Answer: D
Topic: 28.20
Skill: Factual Recall

57) Schizophrenia
    A) can best be described as feeling a sense of worthlessness.
    B) is a state where the patient loses the ability to distinguish what is real.
    C) is best treated with antidepressant drugs.
    D) causes changes in body weight and sleeping patterns.
    E) is best defined as a mental deterioration or dementia.

Answer: B
Topic: 28.21
Skill: Factual Recall

58) Treatments for depression often include drugs that help correct imbalances in the levels of
    A) serotonin.
    B) dopamine.
    C) acetylcholine.
    D) nitric oxide.
    E) epinephrine.

Answer: A
Topic: 28.21
Skill: Factual Recall

59) Which of the following statements about Alzheimer's disease is *true?*
    A) Alzheimer's disease is suspected if a patient cannot retain his or her balance.
    B) Alzheimer's disease is age-related, increasing in frequency as people age.
    C) Alzheimer's disease often reverses or improves with time.
    D) Alzheimer's disease frequently involves positive changes in personality.
    E) Alzheimer's disease is frequently reversed by injections of beta-amyloid.

Answer: B
Topic: 28.21
Skill: Factual Recall

60) Which of the following statements about Parkinson's disease is *true?*
    A) Parkinson's disease can be cured with injections of serotonin.
    B) Parkinson's disease results from environmental factors.
    C) Parkinson's disease results from the death of neurons in the cerebellum.
    D) Parkinson's disease is a motor disorder, affecting physical movements of the body.
    E) Parkinson's disease is age-related, decreasing in frequency as people age.

Answer: D
Topic: 28.21
Skill: Factual Recall

Art Questions

1)

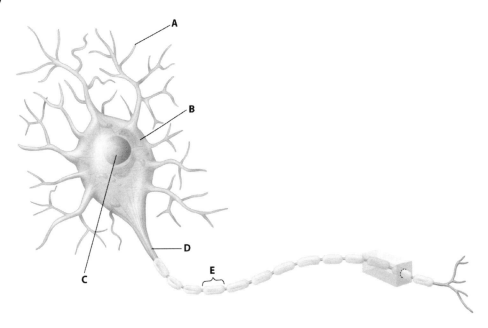

Which part of this diagram of a neuron depicts the axon?
  A) part A
  B) part B
  C) part C
  D) part D
  E) part E

Answer: D
Topic: 28.2
Skill: Factual Recall

2)

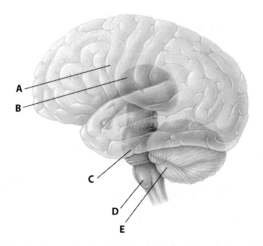

Which part of this diagram of the human brain depicts the cerebellum?
   A) part A
   B) part B
   C) part C
   D) part D
   E) part E

Answer: E
Topic: 28.15
Skill: Factual Recall

Scenario Questions

After reading the following paragraph, answer the question(s) below.

You recently sprayed your apartment with insecticide to remove an infestation of cockroaches. In your kitchen, you noticed some roaches lying on their backs twitching furiously before they died. This aroused your curiosity, so you decided to investigate exactly how the insecticide works on the nervous system.

In your research, you discover that the insecticide you used contains a permanent acetylcholinesterase inhibitor. Acetylcholine is a neurotransmitter that stimulates skeletal muscle to contract. Acetylcholinesterase removes acetylcholine from the synapse after the signal is received. Exposure to high pesticide concentrations has a similar effect on humans and can also be caused by exposure to the nerve gas Sarin and other chemical agents.

1) Why did the insecticide cause uncontrollable twitching in the roaches?
   A) Acetylcholine was released, but the insecticide prevented it from diffusing across the synapse.
   B) Acetylcholine was released, but the insecticide prevented it from binding to the receptor sites of the postsynaptic neurons.
   C) The insecticide caused continuous stimulation of the postsynaptic neurons.
   D) The insecticide prevented the release of acetylcholine from the presynaptic neuron.
   E) The insecticide prevented acetylcholinesterase from being removed from the synapse.

Answer: C
Topic: 28.6, 28.7, 28.8, 28.9
Skill: Conceptual Understanding

2) Since pesticides affect humans in a manner similar to that of roaches, it would be valid to conclude that
   A) acetylcholinesterase affects the DNA of all animals.
   B) the mechanism of nerve transmission must be similar in humans and roaches.
   C) pesticides are more harmful to roaches than humans.
   D) pesticides block sensory neurons to the brain in both roaches and humans.
   E) the terminal end of the axon releases acetylcholine in roaches, but not in humans.

Answer: B
Topic: 28.6, 28.7, 28.8, 28.9
Skill: Application

Chapter 29 The Senses

Multiple-Choice Questions

1) The special sensing mechanism sharks use to detect hidden prey is known as
   A) photoreception.
   B) magnetic resonance.
   C) ultrasound.
   D) electroreception.
   E) magentoreception.

   Answer: D
   Topic: Opening Essay
   Skill: Factual Recall

2) _____ is the awareness of a stimulus.
   A) Transduction
   B) Perception
   C) Reception
   D) Adaptation
   E) Sensation

   Answer: E
   Topic: 29.1
   Skill: Factual Recall

3) Perceptions are constructed in
   A) a neuron.
   B) the brain.
   C) the space between neurons.
   D) the spinal cord.
   E) sensory organs.

   Answer: B
   Topic: 29.1
   Skill: Factual Recall

4) Sensory transduction occurs in the
   A) cerebral cortex.
   B) thalamus.
   C) spinal cord.
   D) cell body of sensory cells.
   E) plasma membrane of sensory cells.

   Answer: E
   Topic: 29.2
   Skill: Factual Recall

5) Sensory receptor cells convert a stimulus
    A) from a physical to a chemical form.
    B) from an action potential to a synaptic potential.
    C) into potential energy stored by the membrane.
    D) into a sensation by integrating incoming action potentials.
    E) into different forms to be sent to the brain.

Answer: C
Topic: 29.2
Skill: Conceptual Understanding

6) The receptor potential is the
    A) membrane potential produced when a neurotransmitter molecule binds to its
        receptor.
    B) membrane potential produced in the receptor cell by sensory transduction.
    C) membrane potential produced by sensation.
    D) electrical signal produced by perception.
    E) membrane potential produced at a muscle cell.

Answer: B
Topic: 29.2
Skill: Conceptual Understanding

7) Which of the following is an example of sensory adaptation of receptors?
    A) going into deep sleep
    B) distinguishing between different colors
    C) ignoring the shoes on your feet
    D) thinking about what you would do with a million dollars
    E) detecting sound and light simultaneously

Answer: C
Topic: 29.2
Skill: Conceptual Understanding

8) Which of the following statements best describes the basis of sensory adaptation?
    A) A continuously stimulated sensory receptor gradually ceases to release
        neurotransmitters.
    B) A continuously stimulated sensory receptor gradually returns to its unstimulated
        rate of neurotransmitter release.
    C) The nerve fiber synapsed with a sensory receptor gradually returns to its baseline
        level of firing despite continued neurotransmitter stimulation.
    D) The spinal cord interneurons that receive a prolonged stimulus gradually come to
        ignore it.
    E) The thalamic centers that receive a prolonged stimulus gradually come to ignore it.

Answer: B
Topic: 29.2
Skill: Conceptual Understanding

9) Which of the following classes of sensory receptors is the most diverse?
    A) thermoreceptors
    B) mechanoreceptors
    C) electromagnetic receptors
    D) pain receptors
    E) chemoreceptors

Answer: B
Topic: 29.3
Skill: Conceptual Understanding

10) Receptors with naked, branched nerve fiber endings are
    A) tendon stretch receptors.
    B) deep pressure receptors.
    C) utricle hair cells.
    D) pain receptors.
    E) temperature receptors.

Answer: D
Topic: 29.3
Skill: Factual Recall

11) Receptors that transduce when the plasma membrane becomes more permeable to positive ions as it changes shape are called
    A) pain receptors.
    B) thermoreceptors.
    C) mechanoreceptors.
    D) chemoreceptors.
    E) electromagnetic receptors.

Answer: C
Topic: 29.3
Skill: Factual Recall

12) You exercised to the point that you were breathing heavily. Your heavy breathing was the result of _____ relaying information about the amount of O_2 in your blood to the medulla, which ultimately resulted in your increased rate of breathing.
    A) mechanoreceptors
    B) electromagnetic receptors
    C) chemoreceptors
    D) nocioceptors
    E) thermoreceptors

Answer: C
Topic: 29.3
Skill: Conceptual Understanding

13) Fish that quickly and accurately sense the location of a nearby motionless fish in cloudy water are probably using
    A) lateral line system mechanoreceptors.
    B) electromagnetic receptors.
    C) infrared detectors.
    D) chemoreceptors.
    E) nocioceptors.

Answer: B
Topic: 29.3
Skill: Application

14) Which of the following options *incorrectly* pairs a class of sensory receptor with one of the stimuli it detects?
    A) electromagnetic receptors = light
    B) chemoreceptors = molecular structure
    C) photoreceptors = infrared radiation
    D) mechanoreceptors = sound
    E) thermoreceptors = touch

Answer: E
Topic: 29.3
Skill: Conceptual Understanding

15) The cochlea is
    A) a coiled structure found in the inner ear.
    B) a fluid–filled canal.
    C) part of the organ of Corti.
    D) involved in the maintenance of body temperature.
    E) associated with the outer ear.

Answer: A
Topic: 29.4
Skill: Factual Recall

16) Where is the organ of Corti?
    A) in the pinna
    B) in the outer ear
    C) in the inner ear
    D) in the middle ear
    E) in the Eustachian tube

Answer: C
Topic: 29.4
Skill: Conceptual Understanding

17) Which of the following options correctly lists the order in which structures within the ear transfer a sound wave during hearing?
A) eardrum, auditory canal, hammer, anvil, stirrup, oval window
B) eardrum, hammer, anvil, stirrup, oval window, auditory canal
C) eardrum, stirrup, hammer, anvil, oval window, auditory canal
D) auditory canal, eardrum, hammer, anvil, stirrup, oval window
E) auditory canal, eardrum, stirrup, hammer, anvil, oval window

Answer: D
Topic: 29.4
Skill: Factual Recall

18) The nervous system determines the pitch of a tone by
A) sites along the basilar membrane where vibrations are most vigorous.
B) peak amplitude of basilar membrane displacement.
C) frequency of basilar membrane vibration.
D) sites along the basilar membrane where vibrations are longest.
E) the frequency of oval window vibration.

Answer: A
Topic: 29.4
Skill: Conceptual Understanding

19) Which of the following choices lists structures involved *only* in the sense of hearing?
A) middle ear bones, semicircular canals, basilar membrane
B) eardrum, utricle, organ of Corti
C) oval window, cochlea, aqueous humor
D) middle ear bones, saccule, basilar membrane
E) oval window, basilar membrane, organ of Corti

Answer: E
Topic: 29.5
Skill: Conceptual Understanding

20) The semicircular canals
A) are arranged in three perpendicular planes.
B) contain a thin basilar membrane.
C) are lined by long rows of hair cells along their entire length.
D) drain directly into the middle ear to prevent fluid buildup and infections.
E) transmit vibrations from the oval window to the saccule.

Answer: A
Topic: 29.5
Skill: Factual Recall

21) The hair cells in the utricle detect
   A) subsonic sound vibrations.
   B) rotation of the head in an anteroposterior plane (a plane that cuts through you from front to back).
   C) rotation of the head in a horizontal plane (assuming you are standing).
   D) rotation of the head in a coronal plane (a plane that cuts through you from side to side).
   E) the position of the head with respect to gravity.

Answer: E
Topic: 29.5
Skill: Factual Recall

22) Which of the following structures is involved in the human sense of balance?
   A) the outer ear
   B) the oral window
   C) the auditory canal
   D) the utricle
   E) the basilar membrane

Answer: D
Topic: 29.5
Skill: Factual Recall

23) If you are in an airplane encountering turbulence and you start feeling sick to your stomach, would closing your eyes help? Why?
   A) Yes. It will calm you by allowing the sensory information from your chemoreceptors to properly readjust.
   B) Yes. It will eliminate the disturbing information that you are falling.
   C) Yes. It will eliminate the conflict between information from your inner ears and information from your eyes.
   D) No. It will intensify the feeling of falling by eliminating the sight of the cabin.
   E) No. It will focus your attention on the nausea.

Answer: C
Topic: 29.6
Skill: Application

24) The eyes of a planarian provide
   A) a three-dimensional image, but in black and white.
   B) a three-dimensional image in color.
   C) a two-dimensional image.
   D) a higher degree of resolution than human eyes.
   E) information about light intensity and direction.

Answer: E
Topic: 29.7-Evolution Connection
Skill: Factual Recall

25) Which of the following statements regarding compound eyes is *true?*
   A) Compound eyes have one light–focusing lens.
   B) Compound eyes are poor motion detectors.
   C) The ommatidia form an image that is transferred to the brain.
   D) Most insect compound eyes provide excellent color vision.
   E) Compound eyes can perceive only visible light.

Answer: D
Topic: 29.7–Evolution Connection
Skill: Factual Recall

26) The evolutionary event that allowed some species, such as the honeybee, to discriminate between different flowers was development of
   A) color vision.
   B) chemoreceptors.
   C) a single lens.
   D) eye cups.
   E) basilar membranes.

Answer: A
Topic: 29.7–Evolution Connection
Skill: Conceptual Understanding

27) One of the evolutionary advantages of having two eyes is that
   A) two lenses provide greater magnification.
   B) overlapping fields of view provide uninterrupted images.
   C) there are more sensory neurons for greater action potentials.
   D) formation of mosaic images is possible.
   E) the blind spot is eliminated.

Answer: B
Topic: 29.7–Evolution Connection
Skill: Conceptual Understanding

28) Which of the following components of the human eye forms the iris?
   A) sclera
   B) choroid
   C) retina
   D) pupil
   E) vitreous humor

Answer: B
Topic: 29.8
Skill: Factual Recall

29) If the aqueous humor circulates but does not drain properly, the likely result will be the development of
   A) glaucoma.
   B) myopia.
   C) astigmatism.
   D) hyperopia.
   E) strabismus.

Answer: A
Topic: 29.8
Skill: Conceptual Understanding

30) Which of the following statements about the humors of the eye is *true?*
    A) The vitreous humor fills the chamber behind the lens.
    B) The aqueous humor is a liquid similar to blood.
    C) The vitreous humor circulates.
    D) The vitreous humor carries off wastes.
    E) The humors help keep the outside of the eye moist.

Answer: A
Topic: 29.8
Skill: Conceptual Understanding

31) Which of the following options correctly lists the order of structures through which light must pass on its way to the retina of the human eye?
    A) pupil, cornea, aqueous humor, lens
    B) lens, aqueous humor, pupil, cornea
    C) cornea, aqueous humor, pupil, lens
    D) cornea, pupil, aqueous humor, lens
    E) pupil, cornea, lens, aqueous humor

Answer: C
Topic: 29.8
Skill: Factual Recall

32) Which of the following statements about the focusing of light by the eyes is *true?*
    A) Squid and many fish have stable lenses.
    B) In humans, the thicker the lens, the less sharply light is bent.
    C) Mammals focus by changing the shape of their lenses.
    D) Mammals focus on distant objects by contracting muscles.
    E) Mammalian lenses thicken when focused on distant objects.

Answer: C
Topic: 29.8
Skill: Factual Recall

33) A person who cannot focus on distant objects has
    A) hyperopia.
    B) myopia.
    C) an astigmatism.
    D) presbyopia.
    E) excellent visual acuity.

Answer: B
Topic: 29.9
Skill: Factual Recall

34) When farsightedness develops in a person's forties, the cause may be a(n)
    A) stiffening lens.
    B) lengthening eyeball.
    C) misshapen lens.
    D) reduction in the density of rods.
    E) increase in the refractive index of the vitreous humor.

Answer: A
Topic: 29.9
Skill: Factual Recall

35) A person whose eyeball is shorter than normal suffers from
    A) hyperopia.
    B) myopia.
    C) astigmatism.
    D) presbyopia.
    E) glaucoma

Answer: A
Topic: 29.9
Skill: Factual Recall

36) A person who has blurred vision caused by a misshapen lens or cornea has
    A) hyperopia.
    B) myopia.
    C) astigmatism.
    D) presbyopia.
    E) night blindness.

Answer: C
Topic: 29.9
Skill: Factual Recall

37) Which of the following statements regarding rods and cones is *true?*
    A) Rods are more sensitive to light than cones.
    B) Cones are responsible for night vision.
    C) Rods are found at the greatest density at the fovea, the retina's center of focus.
    D) The increased ability of some birds to see additional detail results from a greater density of rods in their fovea.
    E) Rods contain the visual pigment called photopsin.

Answer: A
Topic: 29.10
Skill: Factual Recall

38) Where does the information from the light receptors undergo its first level of neural processing?
    A) in the retina
    B) in the optic nerve
    C) in the lateral geniculate body of the thalamus
    D) in the primary visual cortex
    E) in the hippocampus

Answer: A
Topic: 29.10
Skill: Conceptual Understanding

39) The optic nerve is formed by
　　　A) axons from neurons that help integrate signals from rods and cones.
　　　B) axons from the rods and cones that are surrounded by glial cells from the interneuron region.
　　　C) extensions of the choroid layer that is squeezed between the rods and cones in the retina.
　　　D) an extension of the photoreceptors.
　　　E) junctions of synaptic knobs.

Answer: A
Topic: 29.10
Skill: Conceptual Understanding

40) You are driving at night and decide to pass a slow-moving car. As you look at the car as you pass, it dawns on you that although you can see the car, you can't tell what color it is. The reason is
　　　A) the poor ability of cones to function in low light.
　　　B) the poor ability of rods to function in low light.
　　　C) a reduced ability to focus in low light situations.
　　　D) the constriction of your pupil in low light situations, which reduces color vision.
　　　E) that the retina is not sensitive to dim light.

Answer: A
Topic: 29.10
Skill: Application

41) The olfactory receptor cells are located in the
　　　A) forebrain.
　　　B) semicircular canals.
　　　C) saccule.
　　　D) nasal cavity.
　　　E) vitreous chamber.

Answer: D
Topic: 29.11
Skill: Factual Recall

42) Our sense of taste results from receptors organized into taste buds
　　　A) in the upper portions of nasal passages.
　　　B) on the tongue.
　　　C) in sensory neurons.
　　　D) that are also responsible for smell.
　　　E) with long cilia that are constantly in motion.

Answer: B
Topic: 29.11
Skill: Factual Recall

43) A molecule that is detected by our sense of smell first binds to
    A) specific receptor proteins on the cilia of receptor cells located in the epithelium of the upper nasal cavity.
    B) hairs that extend beyond the mucus layer and line the upper and lower nasal cavities.
    C) special mechanoreceptor cells located in the epithelium of the lower nasal cavity.
    D) special receptor proteins located at the surface of thermoreceptor cells lining the upper nasal cavity.
    E) sensory neurons located throughout the nasal cavity.

Answer: A
Topic: 29.11
Skill: Factual Recall

44) "Supertasters" are individuals who
    A) prefer foods that are somewhat bitter, such as vegetables.
    B) cannot detect propylthiouracil.
    C) typically have more food dislikes.
    D) have fewer fungiform papillae on their tongue.
    E) tend to eat healthier and have fewer diseases.

Answer: C
Topic: 29.12
Skill: Factual Recall

45) Integration of sensory stimuli occurs
    A) in highly specialized receptors such as the organ of Corti.
    B) in all receptors.
    C) at synapses in the peripheral nervous system.
    D) in the brain.
    E) in the central and peripheral nervous systems.

Answer: D
Topic: 29.13
Skill: Conceptual Understanding

Art Questions

1)

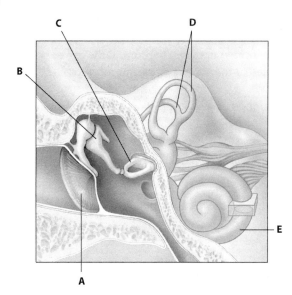

Which part of this figure depicting an ear is the cochlea?
   A) part A
   B) part B
   C) part C
   D) part D
   E) part E
Answer: E
Topic: 29.4
Skill: Factual Recall

2)

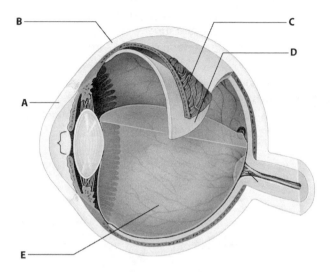

Which part of this figure depicting an eye is the retina?
  A) part A
  B) part B
  C) part C
  D) part D
  E) part E

Answer: D
Topic: 29.7
Skill: Factual Recall

Scenario Questions

After reading the following paragraph, answer the question(s) below.

Bats and marine mammals are well-known examples of animals that produce high-frequency sound waves beyond the range of human hearing. The high-frequency waves are used for echolocation. Research has shown that bats can send and receive sounds as high as 100,000 Hertz (Hz).

On the other hand, several mammals, such as elephants and whales, produce extremely low-frequency sounds. Elephant calls range from 5 to 50 Hz. Low-frequency sounds have long wavelengths, which means they're less likely to be distorted or interrupted by features in the environment. In favorable weather conditions, low-frequency sound waves can be transmitted over several kilometers.

1) What advantage does the extended hearing range of elephants provide?
  A) ability to communicate with other species with extended hearing ranges
  B) ability to locate obstacles in their migration routes
  C) ability to communicate with other elephants long distances away
  D) advance warning to take shelter when storms are coming
  E) ability to detect food resources with electroreception

Answer: C
Topic: Opening Essay, 29.4
Skill: Conceptual Understanding

2) If you were observing two elephants separated by a distance of four miles, could the sensory receptors of your ear receive any signals passing between them?
   A) Yes, because in humans both the middle and inner ears magnify sound.
   B) Yes, because human ears have sound reception over the same range of frequencies as elephants.
   C) Yes, because the organ of Corti in humans is more highly evolved than the comparable organ in elephants.
   D) No, because elephants have a much wider range of high–frequency hearing.
   E) No, because human ears can't hear sounds lower than 20 Hz.

Answer: E
Topic: 29.4
Skill: Factual Recall

Chapter 30 How Animals Move

Multiple-Choice Questions

1) A major difference between movement in humans and horses is
   A) that humans generate more ATP.
   B) that humans can run faster over longer distances.
   C) differences in degree of joint flexibility.
   D) the size of the heart in relation to the rest of the body.
   E) the length of limbs.

   Answer: C
   Topic: Opening Essay
   Skill: Conceptual Understanding

2) Which of the following statements about locomotion is *true*?
   A) Locomotion requires animals to overcome friction and gravity.
   B) Gravity is a greater locomotion problem for animals in water than those on land.
   C) A snake can overcome the effects of friction on movement by moving in an S pattern.
   D) Overcoming friction is a greater locomotion problem for land animals than for those that live in water.
   E) Bone strength is more important than body shape in the locomotion of land animals.

   Answer: A
   Topic: 30.1
   Skill: Factual Recall

3) If you inflate a balloon and then let it go, the air rushing out moves the balloon in a way that is similar to the way that a _____ moves.
   A) snake
   B) kangaroo
   C) squid
   D) shark
   E) hawk

   Answer: C
   Topic: 30.1
   Skill: Application

4) The way the tendons in the legs of a kangaroo aid in locomotion is most like
   A) stepping in mud and the mud spreading out as your foot sinks in.
   B) stretching and contracting a rubber band.
   C) the circular movements of the wheels of an automobile.
   D) smashing an apple to make applesauce.
   E) converting electrical energy into mechanical energy in an electric motor.

   Answer: B
   Topic: 30.1
   Skill: Application

5) A racehorse cannot stand on one leg, but when it runs it rarely has more than one leg on the ground. Why is a running horse more stable than a standing one?
    A) Its legs tilt so the hooves fall in line with its center of gravity.
    B) Its momentum gives it stability.
    C) Its brain has neural circuits that balance its muscles when it runs.
    D) Its internal organs act like a gyroscope.
    E) It uses its neck for balance the way a tightrope walker uses a pole.

Answer: B
Topic: 30.1
Skill: Application

6) Earthworms crawl by
    A) undulating from side to side.
    B) peristalsis.
    C) the leg–like action of their belly scales.
    D) pushing themselves forward from the tail.
    E) lateral undulations.

Answer: B
Topic: 30.1
Skill: Factual Recall

7) An airfoil provides lift because air moving over a wing must travel
    A) a *greater* distance than air moving under the wing, creating a *lower* pressure system above the wing.
    B) a *greater* distance than air moving under the wing, creating a *higher* pressure system above the wing.
    C) a *lesser* distance than air moving under the wing, creating a *lower* pressure system above the wing.
    D) a *lesser* distance than air moving under the wing, creating a *higher* pressure system above the wing.
    E) in a cyclical direction, looping back beneath the wing to provide lift.

Answer: A
Topic: 30.1
Skill: Factual Recall

8) All eukaryotic cellular movement is based upon contractile systems involving
    A) cilia and flagella.
    B) pseudopodia and jet propulsion.
    C) cilia and microtubules.
    D) microtubules and microfilaments.
    E) swimming and jet propulsion.

Answer: D
Topic: 30.1
Skill: Factual Recall

9) An important function of the bones in the skeleton is to
   A) provide a source of calcium.
   B) generate hormones.
   C) add to movement via peristaltic activity.
   D) add weight.
   E) maintain body shape.

Answer: E
Topic: 30.2
Skill: Conceptual Understanding

10) Earthworms have
    A) an exoskeleton.
    B) an endoskeleton.
    C) a hydrostatic skeleton.
    D) an appendicular skeleton.
    E) a peristaltic skeleton.

Answer: C
Topic: 30.2
Skill: Factual Recall

11) Which of the following statements about hydrostatic skeletons is *true*?
    A) Hydrostatic skeletons make the animal round.
    B) Hydrostatic skeletons are nonflexible.
    C) Hydrostatic skeletons provide little support for muscle action.
    D) Hydrostatic skeletons produce rigid animals that maintain one shape.
    E) Hydrostatic skeletons can protect internal organs.

Answer: E
Topic: 30.2
Skill: Factual Recall

12) Which of the following objects is most like a hydrostatic skeleton?
    A) a water balloon
    B) a hot air balloon
    C) a piece of M & M candy
    D) a baseball
    E) a bowling ball

Answer: A
Topic: 30.2
Skill: Application

13) Which of the following animals has an exoskeleton?
    A) human
    B) trout
    C) shark
    D) clam
    E) sea urchin

Answer: D
Topic: 30.2
Skill: Factual Recall

14) Why is a newly molted crab unusually slow and clumsy?
    A) Its new exoskeleton tends to bend and crumple under the force of its muscles.
    B) It temporarily lacks an exoskeleton.
    C) Its muscles are still forming their connections with the new exoskeleton.
    D) Its neurons are still forming their connections with the new muscles.
    E) It is still semitorpid.

Answer: A
Topic: 30.2
Skill: Conceptual Understanding

15) Which of the following structures is most like an exoskeleton?
    A) the wood frame of a house
    B) a water balloon
    C) a suit of armor
    D) the hair covering the surface of a bear
    E) ice covering the surface of a pond

Answer: C
Topic: 30.2
Skill: Application

16) Which of the following animals has an endoskeleton made entirely of cartilage?
    A) bullfrog
    B) bull snake
    C) mackerel
    D) nurse shark
    E) robin

Answer: D
Topic: 30.2
Skill: Factual Recall

17) The evolution of the vertebrate skeleton system
    A) originated with a snake–like animal whose descendents gradually developed limbs.
    B) enabled tetrapods to colonize land.
    C) originated in an earlier exoskeleton.
    D) made animals significantly taller.
    E) originated in an earlier appendicular skeleton.

Answer: B
Topic: 30.3–Evolution Connection
Skill: Conceptual Understanding

18) Which of the following structures constitutes part of the axial skeleton?
    A) skull
    B) pelvic girdle
    C) shoulder girdle
    D) leg bones
    E) hand and foot bones

Answer: A
Topic: 30.3–Evolution Connection
Skill: Factual Recall

19) Which of the following attaches the forelimbs to the axial skeleton in a human?
    A) shoulder girdle
    B) pelvic girdle
    C) vertebra
    D) pelvis
    E) appendicular skeleton

Answer: A
Topic: 30.3–Evolution Connection
Skill: Conceptual Understanding

20) Evolution has provided enormous diversity in the number of vertebrae among vertebrate species. Vertebrae are differentiated during embryonic development by
    A) hormone induction.
    B) the length of the backbone.
    C) the degree of structural support needed.
    D) the pattern of master control genes expressed.
    E) mitochondrial DNA expression.

Answer: D
Topic: 30.3–Evolution Connection
Skill: Factual Recall

21) The contacting surfaces of a moving joint, such as your hip joint, consist of
    A) collagen.
    B) fibrous connective tissue.
    C) cartilage.
    D) spongy bone.
    E) compact bone.

Answer: C
Topic: 30.4
Skill: Factual Recall

22) Which part of a bone contains mostly stored fat?
    A) red bone marrow
    B) fibrous connective tissue
    C) cartilage
    D) spongy bone
    E) yellow bone marrow

Answer: E
Topic: 30.4
Skill: Factual Recall

23) Which part of a bone contains the cells that produce blood cells?
    A) compact bone
    B) fibrous connective tissue
    C) cartilage
    D) spongy bone
    E) yellow bone marrow

Answer: D
Topic: 30.4
Skill: Conceptual Understanding

24) Bone is composed of
    A) living cells.
    B) a hard composite of phosphate and sodium ions.
    C) compartments for transporting nutrients.
    D) channels containing lymphoid tissue.
    E) hardened cartilage.

Answer: A
Topic: 30.4
Skill: Factual Recall

25) To repair and heal a broken bone, physicians will
    A) graft new bone to the region.
    B) exercise the area of the broken bone.
    C) inject calcium into the region of the broken bone.
    D) prescribe a regime of bed rest and calcium supplements.
    E) return the broken bone parts to their natural position and then immobilize them.

Answer: E
Topic: 30.5
Skill: Factual Recall

26) Osteoporosis is characterized by
    A) hairline cracks in long bones, such as the femur.
    B) structural deterioration of bone tissue.
    C) low phosphate levels in bone.
    D) good bone health.
    E) lack of vitamin E in bone tissue.

Answer: B
Topic: 30.5
Skill: Factual Recall

27) Osteoporosis is emerging as a health concern for
    A) women in their 20s and 30s.
    B) teenage men.
    C) postmenopausal women.
    D) men over the age of 65.
    E) men and younger people in general.

Answer: E
Topic: 30.5
Skill: Factual Recall

28) The shoulder joint where the humerus meets the shoulder girdle is an example of
    A) a hinge joint.
    B) a sliding joint.
    C) a pivot joint.
    D) a fixed joint.
    E) a ball-and-socket joint.

Answer: E
Topic: 30.6
Skill: Factual Recall

29) If you lay your forearm along the table, you can rotate it so that your hand changes from a palm-down to a palm-up position. This is possible because your radius and ulna join at a
A) ball-and-socket joint.
B) suture joint.
C) hinge joint.
D) pivot joint.
E) twist joint.

Answer: D
Topic: 30.6
Skill: Factual Recall

30) Muscles are connected to bones by
A) Sharpey's fibers.
B) ligaments.
C) tendons.
D) other muscles.
E) myofibrils.

Answer: C
Topic: 30.7
Skill: Factual Recall

31) If we think of the human skeleton as a lever system, the joint plays the same role as the
A) weight.
B) force.
C) fulcrum.
D) lever.
E) resistance.

Answer: C
Topic: 30.7
Skill: Conceptual Understanding

32) Skeletal muscles
A) are found in and around internal organs.
B) get longer when they contract.
C) contain deposits of calcium phosphate.
D) work in antagonistic pairs.
E) push on bones to make them move.

Answer: D
Topic: 30.7
Skill: Conceptual Understanding

33) Which of the following statements about skeletal muscle fibers is *true*?
A) Each muscle fiber is composed of multinucleated cells.
B) Each muscle fiber is composed of globular proteins.
C) Each muscle fiber is a bundle of sarcomeres.
D) Each muscle fiber contains one sarcomere.
E) Each muscle fiber contains actin and myosin.

Answer: E
Topic: 30.8
Skill: Factual Recall

34) Functionally, the muscle fiber's fundamental unit of contraction is the
    A) thick filament.
    B) thin filament.
    C) myofibril.
    D) sarcomere.
    E) Z line.

Answer: D
Topic: 30.8
Skill: Conceptual Understanding

35) Structurally, a sarcomere is
    A) an array of myofibrils.
    B) the region between two thick filaments.
    C) the region between two Z lines.
    D) an array of Z units.
    E) the region between a thick filament and the next thin filament.

Answer: C
Topic: 30.8
Skill: Factual Recall

36) A thick filament consists of
    A) actin.
    B) actin and regulatory proteins.
    C) myosin.
    D) myosin and regulatory filaments.
    E) actin and myosin.

Answer: C
Topic: 30.8
Skill: Factual Recall

37) Which of the following options lists muscle components in the correct order from smallest to largest?
    A) muscle, sarcomeres, myofibrils, muscle fibers
    B) sarcomeres, myofibrils, muscle fibers, muscle
    C) sarcomeres, myofibrils, muscle, muscle fibers
    D) myofibrils, muscle, sarcomeres, muscle fibers
    E) muscle, sarcomeres, muscle fibers, myofibrils

Answer: B
Topic: 30.8
Skill: Factual Recall

38) According to the sliding filament model of muscle contraction, a sarcomere contracts when its
    A) thick filaments slide across its Z lines.
    B) thin filaments slide across its Z lines.
    C) thick filaments slide toward each other across its thin filaments.
    D) thin filaments slide toward each other across its thick filaments.
    E) thick filaments shorten, pulling the opposed sets of thin filaments past each other.

Answer: D
Topic: 30.9
Skill: Conceptual Understanding

39) Changes occur within a sarcomere during muscle contraction. One change is that the
   A) thin filaments get thicker.
   B) thick filaments move closer together.
   C) Z lines move closer together.
   D) thick filaments get thicker.
   E) Z lines move closer to the plasma membrane.

Answer: C
Topic: 30.9
Skill: Conceptual Understanding

40) During muscle contraction,
   A) only the thin filaments shorten.
   B) only the sarcomere shortens.
   C) only the thick filaments shorten.
   D) both the thick and thin filaments shorten.
   E) both the thick filaments and the sarcomere shorten.

Answer: B
Topic: 30.9
Skill: Conceptual Understanding

41) Which of the following statements best describes the molecular basis of muscle shortening?
   A) Individual filamentous proteins contract.
   B) Individual filamentous proteins shorten by coiling.
   C) Rod–shaped protein polymers shorten by losing subunits from their ends.
   D) Rod–shaped, gel–like proteins contract by dehydrating.
   E) Protein filaments crawl along other protein filaments.

Answer: E
Topic: 30.9
Skill: Conceptual Understanding

42) Which of the following statements best describes the power stroke of muscle contraction?
   A) The myosin head bends, pulling the thick filament toward the center of the sarcomere.
   B) The myosin head bends, pulling the thin filament toward the center of the sarcomere.
   C) The actin head bends, pulling the thin filament toward the center of the sarcomere.
   D) The actin head bends, pulling the thick filament toward the center of the sarcomere.
   E) The myosin head bends, pushing the thick filament toward the center of the sarcomere.

Answer: B
Topic: 30.9
Skill: Factual Recall

43) The sequence of events that cause a muscle to contract can be summed up in the correct order as
   A) detach, extend, contract, attach.
   B) detach, pull, extend, contract.
   C) detach, extend, attach, pull.
   D) pull, contract, detach, recoil.
   E) recoil, detach, extend, pull.

Answer: C
Topic: 30.9
Skill: Factual Recall

44) The neurotransmitter found at the synapse between nerves and human skeletal muscle cells is
   A) acetylcholine.
   B) glutamate.
   C) epinephrine.
   D) dopamine.
   E) serotonin.

Answer: A
Topic: 30.10
Skill: Factual Recall

45) The cell bodies and dendrites of motor neurons are located in the
   A) motor units.
   B) peripheral nervous system.
   C) sympathetic nervous system.
   D) central nervous system.
   E) neuromuscular junction.

Answer: D
Topic: 30.10
Skill: Conceptual Understanding

46) The synapses between neurons and muscle fibers are called
   A) muscle synapses.
   B) muscle junctions.
   C) musculoneural junctions.
   D) neuromuscular junctions.
   E) neuromotor junctions.

Answer: D
Topic: 30.10
Skill: Conceptual Understanding

47) The calcium that triggers muscle contraction is stored in
   A) the motor neuron.
   B) the interstitial fluid.
   C) synaptic vesicles.
   D) the endoplasmic reticulum.
   E) the mitochondria.

Answer: D
Topic: 30.10
Skill: Factual Recall

48) A motor unit is
    A) the bundle of axons that goes from the spinal cord to a muscle.
    B) one of the connective tissue–wrapped bundles of muscle fibers in a muscle.
    C) a motor neuron and all of the muscle fibers it controls.
    D) a bundle of axons and all of the muscle fibers they control.
    E) the muscle or group of muscles that accomplishes a specific movement.

Answer: C
Topic: 30.10
Skill: Factual Recall

49) Which of the following would have the greatest number of muscle cells per motor unit?
    A) muscles controlling the movement of our hands
    B) facial muscles
    C) a thigh muscle
    D) muscles controlling the movement of an eyeball
    E) muscles in our tongue

Answer: C
Topic: 30.10
Skill: Application

50) The role of calcium in muscle contraction is to
    A) release ADP and phosphate from myosin.
    B) make it possible for ATP to bind to actin.
    C) make it possible for ADP to bind to actin.
    D) make it possible for myosin to bind to actin.
    E) make it possible for ATP to bind to myosin.

Answer: D
Topic: 30.10
Skill: Factual Recall

51) Which of the following statements regarding exercise is *true*?
    A) Anaerobic exercise supplies only a fraction of the ATP obtainable through aerobic exercise.
    B) Aerobic exercise decreases the efficiency and fatigue resistance of muscles.
    C) Aerobic exercise decreases the size and number of muscle mitochondria.
    D) World–class athletes usually focus on aerobic and not anaerobic exercise.
    E) Muscles are strengthened when their supply of ATP does not keep up with demand.

Answer: A
Topic: 30.11
Skill: Factual Recall

52) Muscles that are constantly active, such as those maintaining our body posture, have a high proportion of
   A) fast, fatigue–resistant fibers.
   B) fast, fatigue–susceptible fibers.
   C) slow, fatigue–resistant fibers.
   D) slow, fatigue–susceptible fibers.
   E) both slow and fast fatigue–resistant fibers.

Answer: C
Topic: 30.12
Skill: Conceptual Understanding

53) A tennis player serving the ball uses fast muscle fibers and fatigue–resistant intermediate muscle fibers. The ATP needed to accomplish this would come from
   A) anaerobic glycolysis.
   B) aerobic respiration.
   C) conversion of lactic acid to ATP.
   D) microaerophilic respiration.
   E) the Krebs cycle.

Answer: A
Topic: 30.12
Skill: Application

Art Questions

1)

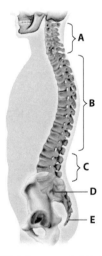

Which part of this figure depicts the thoracic vertebrae?
   A) part A
   B) part B
   C) part C
   D) part D
   E) part E

Answer: B
Topic: 30.3
Skill: Factual Recall

2)

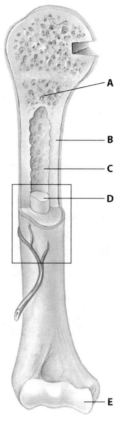

Which part of this figure depicting a bone shows spongy bone tissue?
   A) part A
   B) part B
   C) part C
   D) part D
   E) part E

Answer: A
Topic: 30.4
Skill: Factual Recall

Scenario Questions

After reading the following paragraph, answer the question(s) below.

Rickets is a softening of the bones that can lead to frequent fractures and skeletal deformities. The legs of a person with rickets tend to bow outward under the force exerted by body weight and movement. British scientists recently found a serious increase in the incidence of rickets and other bone deficiencies among women in Middle Eastern countries who cover their bodies completely to express a form of Muslim religious belief, as well as among their breast–fed children.

Most of the body's vitamin D, which is necessary for calcium absorption by bone tissue, is obtained through sunlight acting on the skin. Doctors warn that women who completely cover their skin don't get enough sunlight to produce the vitamin D necessary for bone health. This lack of sun exposure also lowers the level of vitamin D in their breast milk, which means that their children may develop the same vitamin D deficiencies. Lack of calcium and phosphorous, which are needed for bone repair and replacement, can also lead to rickets. Rickets caused by a dietary lack of these minerals is more common in developing countries because dairy products and green vegetables, the best sources of calcium, are not commonly eaten.

1) As a physician caring for a nursing Muslim woman who has chosen to cover her skin but is concerned about rickets developing in her baby, you might advise her to
   A) exercise more.
   B) move to a country near the equator.
   C) eats lots of meat and potatoes.
   D) take vitamin D and calcium supplements.
   E) give up smoking.

Answer: D
Topic: 30.4, 30.5
Skill: Conceptual Understanding

2) In rickets, lack of calcium decreases the strength of the mineral matrix of compact bone so that it is unable to
   A) resist compression.
   B) complete extension.
   C) complement muscle contraction.
   D) bend at the joints.
   E) form cross–bridges with thin filaments.

Answer: A
Topic: 30.4, 30.5, 30.8
Skill: Conceptual Understanding

Chapter 31   Plant Structure, Reproduction, and Development

Multiple–Choice Questions

1) Why can a single redwood tree be thought of as an entire ecosystem?
   A) because a single redwood is bigger than some ecosystems
   B) because a single redwood can support many other species of organisms
   C) because redwoods are autotrophic producers in ecosystems
   D) because many redwoods have been lost to lumbering
   E) because redwoods are found in some of the world's densest forests

   Answer: B
   Topic: Opening Essay
   Skill: Conceptual Understanding

2) The tallest plant on Earth is
   A) a 500-foot kelp living off the coast of California.
   B) a three-mile-square sheet of red algae growing along the coastline of Alaska.
   C) a 379-foot redwood tree in California.
   D) a 740-foot white oak tree in Illinois.
   E) a giant seed fern in southern Peru.

   Answer: C
   Topic: Opening Essay
   Skill: Factual Recall

3) What event that occurred around 10,000 years ago led to genetic changes in many of the plants we are most familiar with?
   A) the beginning of agriculture
   B) the domestication of animals
   C) the invention of genetic engineering
   D) increased volcanic activity
   E) the mass extinction of herbivores

   Answer: A
   Topic: 31.1
   Skill: Factual Recall

4) Most angiosperms are dicots and most dicots are
   A) cycads.
   B) gymnosperms.
   C) eudicots.
   D) monocots.
   E) mosses.

   Answer: C
   Topic: 31.2
   Skill: Factual Recall

5) Monocot floral parts usually occur in multiples of
    A) five.
    B) four.
    C) seven.
    D) two.
    E) three.

Answer: E
Topic: 31.2
Skill: Factual Recall

6) Which of the following is a characteristic of eudicots?
    A) parallel leaf venation
    B) vascular bundles scattered throughout the stem
    C) lack of secondary growth
    D) a flower with six petals
    E) a taproot system

Answer: E
Topic: 31.2
Skill: Factual Recall

7) Which of the following statements is *false*?
    A) Stems and leaves depend on the water and minerals absorbed by the roots.
    B) Roots depend upon sugars produced in photosynthetic organs such as leaves.
    C) Plant roots absorb carbon dioxide needed for photosynthesis from the soil.
    D) The terminal bud in many plants produces hormones that inhibit growth in the axillary buds.
    E) The shoot system of a plant consists of the stems, leaves, and adaptations for reproduction.

Answer: C
Topic: 31.3
Skill: Factual Recall

8) What is the node of a plant stem?
    A) the point of leaf attachment
    B) the point of apical dominance
    C) the area between the shoots and the roots
    D) a small pore where gases are exchanged
    E) the main photosynthetic organ of the stem

Answer: A
Topic: 31.3
Skill: Factual Recall

9) Removing the terminal bud of a plant that shows apical dominance will cause
    A) an increase in the growth of the root system.
    B) an increase in the size of the leaves.
    C) increased growth of the terminal bud.
    D) increased growth of the axillary buds.
    E) an immediate flowering of the plant.

Answer: D
Topic: 31.3
Skill: Conceptual Understanding

10) The chief function of root hairs is to
    A) decrease the anchoring power of roots.
    B) increase the surface area for absorption of water and minerals.
    C) provide a direct passageway from the soil to the vascular cylinder.
    D) provide a home for symbiotic bacteria.
    E) protect roots from freezing temperatures.

Answer: B
Topic: 31.3
Skill: Factual Recall

11) A plant stem modified for storage of food such as starch is called a
    A) bulb.
    B) tuber.
    C) taproot.
    D) rhizome.
    E) runner.

Answer: B
Topic: 31.4
Skill: Factual Recall

12) Which of the following statements is *false*?
    A) Stalks of celery are the petioles of the plant.
    B) The main body of a barrel cactus is its stem.
    C) White potatoes are modified plant roots.
    D) A carrot is an example of a taproot.
    E) The layers of an onion are actually modified leaves.

Answer: C
Topic: 31.4
Skill: Factual Recall

13) Which of the following types of plant cells help regulate the movement of carbon dioxide into and out of a leaf?
    A) guard cells
    B) root hairs
    C) sieve tubes
    D) xylem
    E) companion cells

Answer: A
Topic: 31.5
Skill: Factual Recall

14) The cells that store starch in dicot roots are located between the
    A) xylem rays within the vascular cylinder.
    B) xylem and the phloem.
    C) epidermis and the root hairs.
    D) epidermis and the vascular cylinder.
    E) epidermis and the cortex.

Answer: D
Topic: 31.5
Skill: Factual Recall

15) In general, plant dermal tissues are found
    A) at the surface of plant organs.
    B) near the center of the plant stems and roots.
    C) lining the vascular tissue.
    D) throughout the plant body.
    E) only in plants that have secondary growth.

Answer: A
Topic: 31.5
Skill: Factual Recall

16) Which of the following statements is *false*?
    A) The ground tissue system of a leaf is called the mesophyll.
    B) Each vein in a leaf is composed of either xylem or phloem, but not both.
    C) The veins in a leaf are continuous with the veins of a stem.
    D) The pith of a stem is often important in food storage.
    E) Tissues that are neither dermal nor vascular are known as the ground tissue system.

Answer: B
Topic: 31.5
Skill: Factual Recall

17) Which of the following structures is found in both plant and animal cells?
    A) chloroplasts
    B) mitochondria
    C) a large central vacuole containing fluid
    D) cell wall surrounding the plasma membrane
    E) middle lamella

Answer: B
Topic: 31.6
Skill: Conceptual Understanding

18) The type of plant vascular tissue specialized to conduct foods such as sugars is known as
    A) xylem.
    B) collenchyma.
    C) phloem.
    D) sclerenchyma.
    E) parenchyma.

Answer: C
Topic: 31.6
Skill: Factual Recall

19) Which type of vascular tissue cell in a plant is dead at maturity?
    A) vessel elements
    B) companion cells
    C) sieve-tube cells
    D) collenchyma cells
    E) parenchyma cells

Answer: A
Topic: 31.6
Skill: Factual Recall

20) Which of the following substances, by providing strength, allows some of a plant's vascular tissue to provide support and play a role analogous to that of an animal's skeleton?
   A) lignin
   B) sucrose
   C) glucose
   D) starch
   E) chlorophyll

Answer: A
Topic: 31.6
Skill: Factual Recall

21) Photosynthesis occurs in which type of plant tissue?
   A) parenchyma
   B) vascular cambium
   C) epidermal tissue
   D) sclerenchyma
   E) collenchyma

Answer: A
Topic: 31.6
Skill: Factual Recall

22) Which of the following is a function of sclerenchyma cells?
   A) food storage
   B) photosynthesis
   C) production of sex cells
   D) regeneration of injured parts
   E) long-distance water conduction

Answer: E
Topic: 31.6
Skill: Factual Recall

23) Which of the following cells provide flexible support to the growing parts of plants?
   A) tracheids
   B) collenchyma cells
   C) sieve-tube members
   D) sclerenchyma cells
   E) parenchyma cells

Answer: B
Topic: 31.6
Skill: Factual Recall

24) New growth that increases stem length on a plant arises mainly from
   A) the base of the stem.
   B) apical meristems.
   C) the tips of leaves.
   D) the vascular cambium.
   E) cotyledons.

Answer: B
Topic: 31.7
Skill: Conceptual Understanding

25) The growth that pushes a root down through the soil takes place through
    A) cell elongation at the tip of the root cap.
    B) cell division in the apical meristem.
    C) cell elongation behind the apical meristem.
    D) differentiation of xylem cells in the apical meristem.
    E) branch root formation.

Answer: C
Topic: 31.7
Skill: Conceptual Understanding

26) If you carve your initials in the trunk of a tree, will they move up as the tree grows?
    A) Yes, because a tree elongates from the ground up.
    B) Yes, because secondary growth will cause them to move up.
    C) No, because trees stop growing if they are damaged.
    D) No, because elongation occurs in the tips of growing stems in the apical meristems.
    E) Yes, because growth continues in all parts of a plant throughout its life.

Answer: D
Topic: 31.7
Skill: Conceptual Understanding

27) The three tissue systems of a mature plant complete their development in the root zone of
    A) maturation.
    B) elongation.
    C) cell division.
    D) differentiation.
    E) vascularization.

Answer: A
Topic: 31.7
Skill: Factual Recall

28) Most trees and shrubs continue to grow year after year. Such plants are known as
    A) transannuals.
    B) biennials.
    C) perennials.
    D) annuals.
    E) superannuals.

Answer: C
Topic: 31.7
Skill: Factual Recall

29) The increase in girth associated with production of wood and bark in trees occurs as a consequence of
    A) primary growth.
    B) secondary growth.
    C) sexual reproduction.
    D) growth in apical meristems.
    E) indeterminate growth.

Answer: B
Topic: 31.8
Skill: Factual Recall

30) Bark consists of
   A) functioning xylem, secondary phloem, cork cambium, and cork.
   B) vascular cambium, secondary phloem, cork cambium, and cork.
   C) secondary phloem, cork cambium, and cork.
   D) cork cambium and cork.
   E) cork only.

Answer: C
Topic: 31.8
Skill: Factual Recall

31) A vascular cambium cell divides to produce an inner and an outer daughter cell. Which of the following represents the probable fate of these cells?
   A) Both cells continue to divide to produce wood.
   B) The inner cell will differentiate into xylem, and the outer cell will divide again.
   C) The inner cell will differentiate into phloem, and the outer cell will differentiate into xylem.
   D) The inner cell will differentiate into phloem and the outer cell will differentiate into cork.
   E) Both cells will continue to divide without differentiating into specialized cells.

Answer: B
Topic: 31.8
Skill: Conceptual Understanding

32) A woody plant lives through five years of drought, followed by five years of good growing conditions. The xylem cells formed during the five good years will
   A) be larger in diameter than those formed during the drought years.
   B) be living, whereas those formed during the drought years will be dead.
   C) form smaller growth rings than those formed during the drought years.
   D) conduct a higher ratio of sugar to water than those formed during the drought years.
   E) form heartwood, as compared to the sapwood formed during the drought years.

Answer: A
Topic: 31.8
Skill: Conceptual Understanding

33) How many layers of vascular cambium will there be in the trunk of a ten-year-old tree?
   A) one
   B) two
   C) ten
   D) one hundred
   E) thousands

Answer: A
Topic: 31.8
Skill: Conceptual Understanding

34) What is the difference between the heartwood and sapwood of a tree?
  A) Heartwood contains xylem and sapwood contains phloem.
  B) Sapwood contains xylem and heartwood contains phloem.
  C) Heartwood no longer transports water and minerals, while sapwood still conducts
     xylem sap.
  D) Sapwood no longer transports water and minerals, while heartwood still conducts
     xylem sap.
  E) Heartwood contains old phloem that no longer functions, and sapwood contains
     functioning phloem.

Answer: C
Topic: 31.8
Skill: Factual Recall

35) The male organ of a flower is the
  A) style.
  B) stigma.
  C) stamen.
  D) sepal.
  E) carpel.

Answer: C
Topic: 31.9
Skill: Factual Recall

36) In a showy flower such as a magnolia or rose, the flower parts that play the main role in
attracting the notice of animal pollinators are the
  A) petals.
  B) stamens.
  C) sepals.
  D) fruits.
  E) stigmas.

Answer: A
Topic: 31.9
Skill: Factual Recall

37) Before it opens up into full blossom, the outer green layer of a rosebud consists of the
leaflike
  A) sepals.
  B) stamen.
  C) ovary.
  D) stigma.
  E) petals.

Answer: A
Topic: 31.9
Skill: Application

38) Flowers bear seeds that develop from ovules housed in protective chambers called
   A) cones.
   B) stamens.
   C) sepals.
   D) ovaries.
   E) antheridia.

Answer: D
Topic: 31.9
Skill: Factual Recall

39) How many chromosomes are there in a maize egg cell nucleus as compared to a maize pollen cell nucleus?
   A) half as many
   B) twice as many
   C) the same number
   D) half as many or the same number, depending on whether the pollen cell has divided to produce sperm or not
   E) twice as many or the same number, depending on which of the egg nuclei is considered

Answer: C
Topic: 31.10
Skill: Factual Recall

40) In a flowering plant, sperm are produced by meiosis in the
   A) petals.
   B) ovaries.
   C) sepals.
   D) anthers.
   E) stigma.

Answer: D
Topic: 31.10
Skill: Factual Recall

41) Which of the following flower parts produces female gametophytes?
   A) anthers
   B) petals
   C) ovules
   D) stigmas
   E) sepals

Answer: C
Topic: 31.10
Skill: Factual Recall

42) How does the sperm of an angiosperm reach the egg?
   A) via the pollen tube that grows from the pollen grain through the carpel tissues to the ovule
   B) via the pollen tube that grows from the ovule to reach the pollen grain on the stigma
   C) usually via an insect, which places sperm in the ovary while probing for nectar
   D) by actively swimming down through the style to the egg
   E) via raindrops or a dew film that allows the sperm to swim from the male plant to the female plant

Answer: A
Topic: 31.10
Skill: Factual Recall

43) In angiosperms, the process of _____ ensures that the endosperm will develop only in ovules containing a fertilized egg.
   A) cytogenesis
   B) meiosis
   C) mitosis
   D) double fertilization
   E) cytokinesis

Answer: D
Topic: 31.10
Skill: Conceptual Understanding

44) A seed develops from a(n)
   A) pollen grain.
   B) fruit.
   C) ovary.
   D) ovule.
   E) sporophyte.

Answer: D
Topic: 31.11
Skill: Conceptual Understanding

45) The "halves" of an individual peanut, which represent its cotyledons, develop from the fertilized zygote and are composed of
   A) triploid endosperm cells.
   B) haploid endosperm cells.
   C) diploid embryo sporophyte cells.
   D) diploid maternal sporophyte cells.
   E) diploid gametophyte cells.

Answer: C
Topic: 31.11
Skill: Conceptual Understanding

46) How many chromosomes are there in a maize embryo cell nucleus as compared to a maize endosperm cell nucleus?
   A) half as many
   B) two-thirds as many
   C) the same number
   D) a third again as many
   E) twice as many

Answer: B
Topic: 31.11
Skill: Conceptual Understanding

47) While cleaning out the attic, you find a packet of seeds that your grandmother gathered from her garden. You plant them outside, and some of them sprout. What was the condition of these germinating seeds while they were in the attic?
   A) The endosperm cells were dead; the embryo cells were alive but inactive.
   B) They were dead, but the embryo cells revived in response to water.
   C) They were alive and very metabolically active.
   D) They were turgid because of lack of water.
   E) They were alive but dormant.

Answer: E
Topic: 31.11
Skill: Conceptual Understanding

48) Which of the following is a function of fruits?
   A) production of food for the developing embryo
   B) pollen dispersal
   C) seed dispersal
   D) attracting pollinators
   E) production of ovules

Answer: C
Topic: 31.12
Skill: Factual Recall

49) A mature ovary, specialized as a vessel that houses and protects seeds, is a
   A) fruit.
   B) seed.
   C) ovule.
   D) cotyledon.
   E) seed coat.

Answer: A
Topic: 31.12
Skill: Factual Recall

50) Which of the following statements is *false*?
    A) A pea pod is a kind of fruit.
    B) Individual peas each develop from separate ovules.
    C) An entire pea pod represents many fruits fused together.
    D) A pea pod is the mature form of the ovary of the pea flower.
    E) Each ovary in a pea plant contains multiple ovules.

Answer: C
Topic: 31.12
Skill: Conceptual Understanding

51) Which of the following structures is the first to emerge from a germinating dicot seed?
    A) the embryonic shoot hook
    B) cotyledons
    C) the embryonic root
    D) the shoot sheath
    E) root hairs

Answer: C
Topic: 31.13
Skill: Factual Recall

52) Which of the following statements about germination is *false*?
    A) The germination of a seed represents the beginning of life.
    B) Germination usually begins when a seed takes up water.
    C) A hydrated seed expands, rupturing its seed coat.
    D) Germination usually takes place after a period of dormancy.
    E) The embryonic root of a germinating seed extends down into the soil.

Answer: A
Topic: 31.13
Skill: Factual Recall

53) What happens to the cotyledons of pea and maize seeds?
    A) They remain in the soil and decompose.
    B) They form a protective sheath around the developing root system.
    C) They surround the base of the shoot to provide additional strength.
    D) They form the ovule of the next generation of plants.
    E) They immediately begin to use the sun's energy in photosynthesis.

Answer: A
Topic: 31.13
Skill: Factual Recall

54) Which of the following plant parts commonly contributes to asexual reproduction?
    A) seeds
    B) roots
    C) flowers
    D) fruits
    E) ovules

Answer: B
Topic: 31.14
Skill: Conceptual Understanding

55) The genetically identical organisms that result from asexual reproduction are called
    A) clones.
    B) seeds.
    C) seedlings.
    D) rootlets.
    E) gametophytes.

Answer: A
Topic: 31.14
Skill: Factual Recall

56) Which of the following is an advantage of cloning horticultural crops over sexual propagation?
    A) Cloned plants are healthier and less susceptible to disease.
    B) Plants produced by cloning grow more uniformly.
    C) Cloned plants grow more slowly, but have stronger stems.
    D) Cloning requires special training. while sexual propagation is cheap and easy.
    E) Cloning provides more variation in flower color and size.

Answer: B
Topic: 31.14
Skill: Conceptual Understanding

57) Which of the following is a disadvantage of cloning as a propagation technique?
    A) Cloning produces monocultures that can potentially be wiped out by a single disease.
    B) Cloning is more expensive and more difficult than growing from seeds.
    C) Cloning is time-consuming, with slow results.
    D) Cloning requires more space than traditional seed propagation.
    E) Cloned organisms are dangerous and unpredictable.

Answer: A
Topic: 31. 14
Skill: Conceptual Understanding

58) Foreign genes can be inserted into a single plant cell that is then cultured to produce
    A) a genetically modified plant.
    B) genetically modified seeds.
    C) new plant species.
    D) clones of the original plant cell's genes.
    E) clones of the organisms from which the genes were taken.

Answer: A
Topic: 31.14
Skill: Conceptual Understanding

59) What is the evolutionary advantage of the very long life span of some plants?
    A) the ability to adapt to changing environments
    B) the ability to develop resistance to many diseases
    C) the ability to produce many offspring over many years
    D) the ability to attract many mates during a lifetime
    E) the ability to grow back after being damaged.

Answer: C
Topic: 31.15–Evolution Connection
Skill: Conceptual Understanding

Art Questions

1)

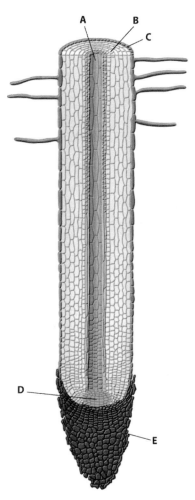

Which part of this root tip is the apical meristem?
   A) part A
   B) part B
   C) part C
   D) part D
   E) part E

Answer: D
Topic: 31.7
Skill: Factual Recall

2)

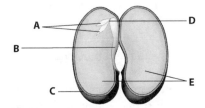

Which part of this seed contains stored food to allow the seed to grow until it can perform photosynthesis?

   A) part A
   B) part B
   C) part C
   D) part D
   E) part E

Answer: E
Topic: 31.11
Skill: Application

Scenario Questions

After reading the following paragraph, answer the question(s) below.

The redwood groves in Northern California are one of America's greatest natural resources. Redwoods can live more than 2,000 years and grow taller than 350 feet. When tourism became popular in the late 1800s, large tunnels were cut through the center of several of these giant trees to allow wagons to pass through (and to attract tourists to the location). Even today, visitors wait in line to be photographed driving their cars through a tunnel. When the groves were converted into national parks, the tunneling was discontinued, but several tunneled trees are still alive.

1) Which of the following choices correctly states the sequence of tissues a tunnel would pass through (starting from the outer surface of the tree and passing through the central core)?
   A) cork, cork cambium, secondary phloem, vascular cambium, sapwood, heartwood
   B) epidermis, cortex, primary phloem, primary xylem, heartwood, sapwood
   C) heartwood, wood rays, cork cambium, secondary xylem, secondary phloem, vascular cambium
   D) bark, periderm, growth rings, cork cambium, sapwood, heartwood
   E) bark, wood rays, growth rings, lateral meristems, primary phloem, secondary, phloem

Answer: A
Topic: 31.8
Skill: Factual Recall

2) When the redwood tunnels were first constructed, not much consideration was given to the long-term effects of a tunnel on a tree's health. Nevertheless, many trees have survived more than 100 years after the tunnel was cut through their trunks. This is possible because
    A) the wood rays run laterally through the trunk, so water and nutrients can still travel to all the tree's tissues.
    B) the remaining heartwood is able to transport water and nutrients through the trunk.
    C) the secondary xylem and phloem run vertically on either side of the vascular cambium and aren't disrupted by the tunnel.
    D) the leaves, trunk, and roots each have independent transportation systems for water and nutrients.
    E) mature cork cells are dead, so their loss doesn't disrupt nutrient and water transport.

Answer: C
Topic: 31.8
Skill: Conceptual Understanding

Chapter 32 Plant Nutrition and Transport

Multiple-Choice Questions

1) What is phytoremediation?
   A) The use of native plants to restore habitat for wildlife after disasters such as Hurricane Katrina.
   B) The use of plants to clean up polluted soil and groundwater.
   C) Treatment of soils and groundwater with chemicals to prevent plant death.
   D) The use of plants to remove carbon dioxide from the atmosphere.
   E) The use of plants to improve the appearance of devastated areas after disasters.

   Answer: B
   Topic: Opening Essay
   Skill: Factual Recall

2) In an attempt to find out where a growing plant gets its mass, van Helmont planted a willow seedling in a pot of soil. After five years, the willow weighed 76.8 kg, and the soil had lost 0.06 kg of weight. Only water had been added to the pot. Which of the following conclusions *should* van Helmont have drawn?
   A) Plants get their mass from water.
   B) Plants get their mass from water and air.
   C) Plants get their mass from water and atmospheric CO_2.
   D) Plants make carbon compounds using carbon, hydrogen, and oxygen.
   E) Plants get all or almost all of their mass from a source other than soil.

   Answer: E
   Topic: 32.1
   Skill: Conceptual Understanding

3) Where do plants get most of their mass?
   A) from chemical elements in the soil
   B) from nitrogen in the atmosphere
   C) from carbon dioxide in the atmosphere
   D) from water, as van Helmont predicted
   E) from organic molecules taken up from the soil

   Answer: C
   Topic: 32.1
   Skill: Factual Recall

4) What is the physical barrier in the root that regulates the flow of water to xylem via cell walls?
   A) phloem
   B) epidermis
   C) Casparian strip
   D) cortex
   E) plasmodesmata

   Answer: C
   Topic: 32.2
   Skill: Factual Recall

5) _____ increase the surface area of roots.
    A) Plasmodesmata
    B) Cell walls and endoplasmic reticulum
    C) Mycorrhizae
    D) Root hairs
    E) Root hairs and mycorrhizae

Answer: E
Topic: 32.2
Skill: Factual Recall

6) Which of the following options correctly lists the sequence of structures through which water passes into a root?
    A) guard cell, endodermis, cortex, xylem
    B) root hair, cortex, xylem, endodermis
    C) epidermis, endodermis, guard cell, xylem
    D) epidermis, cortex, endodermis, xylem
    E) root hair, xylem, endodermis, phloem

Answer: D
Topic: 32.2
Skill: Factual Recall

7) How do mineral ions get into the xylem cells of a plant root by way of the intracellular route?
    A) They percolate between root cells to the xylem and then enter a xylem vessel.
    B) They are taken directly up from the soil by xylem cells.
    C) They are actively taken in to the xylem of root hairs.
    D) They are taken up by root hair cells and transferred from cell to cell via plasmodesmata.
    E) They move in solution through cell walls of the endodermis.

Answer: D
Topic: 32.2
Skill: Factual Recall

8) Which of the following produces the greatest amount of transpiration–cohesion–tension force?
    A) the push of water from the soil
    B) pumping by xylem cells
    C) the pull on water from dry air
    D) the cohesive force of water
    E) the osmotic pull of solutes on water from the soil

Answer: C
Topic: 32.3
Skill: Factual Recall

9) In the water relations of vascular plants, the cohesive property of water is most important in the
   A) epidermis.
   B) endodermis.
   C) xylem.
   D) internal air spaces.
   E) stomata.

Answer: C
Topic: 32.3
Skill: Conceptual Understanding

10) What force is responsible for the cohesiveness of water?
    A) osmosis
    B) hydrogen bonding between water molecules
    C) negative pressure created by evaporation
    D) diffusion of ions
    E) ionic bonding

Answer: B
Topic: 32.3
Skill: Factual Recall

11) The two main forces that move water through a plant are
    A) transpiration and root pressure.
    B) root pressure and photosynthesis.
    C) transpiration and pressure flow.
    D) active transport and cohesion.
    E) transpiration and translocation.

Answer: A
Topic: 32.3
Skill: Factual Recall

12) A hot, dry summer will reduce crop yields in part because
    A) the stomata of the plants stay open to help cool the leaves.
    B) too much carbon dioxide enters the plants when stomata are wide open.
    C) carbon dioxide uptake is reduced by the stomata closing to prevent excessive water loss.
    D) oxygen uptake is reduced by the stomata closing to prevent excessive water loss.
    E) carbon dioxide release is reduced by the stomata closing to prevent excessive water loss.

Answer: C
Topic: 32.4
Skill: Conceptual Understanding

13) Under which of the following weather conditions would transpiration be most rapid?
   A) rainy weather
   B) hot, humid weather
   C) cold, humid weather
   D) hot, dry weather
   E) windy, wet weather

Answer: D
Topic: 32.4
Skill: Conceptual Understanding

14) Which of the following options best describes the mechanism that causes a stoma to open?
   A) K^+ enters the guard cells and water follows passively, making the cells turgid.
   B) K^+ activates water pumps in the guard cell membrane that make them turgid.
   C) K^+ leaves the guard cells and water follows passively, making the cells flaccid.
   D) Loss of K^+ from guard cells creates positive pressure and expands the guard cells.
   E) Loss of K^+ causes actin filaments in the guard cells to contract, deforming the cells.

Answer: A
Topic: 32.4
Skill: Factual Recall

15) The pores that facilitate gas exchange in plant leaves are called
   A) cuticles.
   B) stomata.
   C) guard cells.
   D) lenticels.
   E) plasmodesmata.

Answer: B
Topic: 32.4
Skill: Factual Recall

16) Which of the following causes stomata to open?
   A) Water molecules entering the stomatal pore.
   B) Water loss from the stomatal pore.
   C) Hot, dry weather, and strong winds.
   D) Sunrise on a clear morning.
   E) A cool night is setting in.

Answer: D
Topic: 32.4
Skill: Factual Recall

17) Dew, fog, high humidity, and rainfall mostly affect vascular plants by
   A) being absorbed through the leaves.
   B) reducing the transpiration rate.
   C) keeping herbivorous animals inactive.
   D) stopping lumbering activity in old–growth forests.
   E) decreasing the plant's metabolic rate by lowering the temperature.

Answer: B
Topic: 32.4
Skill: Conceptual Understanding

18) If a plant is kept in the dark,
   A) the stomata continue their daily rhythm of opening and closing.
   B) the stomata will remain closed the entire time that the plant is in the dark.
   C) the stomata will remain open the entire time that the plant is in the dark.
   D) the guard cells will open as water is added.
   E) the transpiration rate will increase.

Answer: A
Topic: 32.4
Skill: Factual Recall

19) Generally speaking, fluids in plants are
   A) pushed through phloem and pulled through xylem.
   B) pushed through xylem and pulled through phloem.
   C) pushed through both xylem and phloem.
   D) pulled through both xylem and phloem.
   E) actively pumped throughout the plant.

Answer: A
Topic: 32.3, 32.5
Skill: Conceptual Understanding

20) Which of the following would be the best way to determine whether aphids must actively draw phloem sap into their digestive tract or if hydrostatic pressure in the phloem tube could force the sap into them?
   A) Cut a phloem tube off an aphid and see if it can still feed.
   B) Cut a phloem tube from a plant and see if an aphid can still take up sap from it.
   C) Measure relative rates of sugar manufacture in leaves with and without aphids.
   D) Measure relative sap uptake in aphids of different sizes.
   E) Insert mouth parts removed from an aphid, without including the digestive tract, and see if phloem sap keeps flowing through them.

Answer: E
Topic: 32.5
Skill: Conceptual Understanding

21) The sugar "sink" in roots is created by the
   A) active transport of mineral ions into xylem cells.
   B) osmosis of water into xylem cells.
   C) absorption of water from the soil through epidermal cells.
   D) active transport of sugars from phloem to root cells.
   E) pull of gravity on sugar molecules.

Answer: D
Topic: 32.5
Skill: Factual Recall

22) The existence of a hydrostatic pressure gradient in phloem tubes can be accounted for by
    A) the fact that the leaves are higher than the roots, which means that gravity creates pressure.
    B) the diffusion of water from one sieve-tube cell to the next.
    C) the diffusion of solutes from sieve-tube cells to companion cells.
    D) the loading of sugars into phloem at sources and removal of sugars at sinks.
    E) the active transport of water from sugar sources to sugar sinks.

Answer: D
Topic: 32.5
Skill: Conceptual Understanding

23) How do sugars move from one sieve-tube cell to the next?
    A) by osmotic diffusion through the sieve plate
    B) by flowing along with water through perforations in the sieve plate
    C) by active transport across cell membranes at the sieve plate
    D) by active transport through a companion cell that spans the sieve plate
    E) by diffusion through a companion cell that spans the sieve plate

Answer: B
Topic: 32.5
Skill: Factual Recall

24) Which of the following essential macronutrient for plants is obtained directly from the air?
    A) manganese
    B) nitrogen
    C) magnesium
    D) hydrogen
    E) carbon

Answer: E
Topic: 32.1, 32.6
Skill: Conceptual Understanding

25) Micronutrients function in plants mainly as
    A) joining elements in organic molecule carbon skeletons.
    B) regulators of membrane transport.
    C) cofactors in chemical reactions.
    D) components of microtubules.
    E) food reserves for pollen grains.

Answer: C
Topic: 32.6
Skill: Factual Recall

26) Which of the following options lists the set of plant macronutrients that make up about 98% of a plant's dry weight?
   A) carbon, oxygen, hydrogen, potassium, zinc, and copper
   B) carbon, oxygen, nitrogen, potassium, zinc, and copper
   C) carbon, nitrogen, potassium, manganese, sulfur, and phosphorus
   D) nitrogen, potassium, manganese, sulfur, copper, and phosphorus
   E) carbon, oxygen, hydrogen, nitrogen, sulfur, and phosphorus

Answer: E
Topic: 32.6
Skill: Factual Recall

27) What are the macronutrients present in most commercial fertilizers?
   A) C, H, and N
   B) N, P and K
   C) C, N, and P
   D) C, H, and O
   E) N, C and K

Answer: B
Topic: 32.7
Skill: Factual Recall

28) A fertilizer with which of the following nitrogen–phosphorous–potassium ratios would most likely solve the problem of yellowed leaves and stunted growth?
   A) 20:0:0
   B) 0:20:0
   C) 0:0:20
   D) 0:20:20
   E) 0:0:0

Answer: A
Topic: 32.7
Skill: Factual Recall

29) Which of the following are important in breaking down organic material in fertile topsoil?
   A) abrasive granite particles
   B) humus and cations
   C) bacteria, protozoans, and fungi
   D) plant roots
   E) sands and clay

Answer: C
Topic: 32.8
Skill: Conceptual Understanding

30) If you examine the soil profile revealed by a fresh road cut through a grassy rise, which of the following features will you probably find in the B horizon?
   A) an abundance of worms and burrowing insects
   B) an abundance of decomposing organic material
   C) an abundance of fine clay but not much organic material
   D) a predominance of slightly weathered rock and gravel
   E) the solid parent material of the soil

Answer: C
Topic: 32.8
Skill: Factual Recall

31) Which of the following essential nutrients is most likely to leach from the soil?
   A) Ca^{2+}
   B) Mg^{2+}
   C) K^+
   D) H^+
   E) NO_3-

Answer: E
Topic: 32.8
Skill: Application

32) Why has drip irrigation been developed?
   A) Drip irrigation uses less water than traditional methods.
   B) Drip irrigation increases soil erosion.
   C) Drip irrigation increases soil salinity.
   D) Drip irrigation increases evaporation and drainage.
   E) Drip irrigation allows more water to be applied to plants more quickly.

Answer: A
Topic: 32.9
Skill: Factual Recall

33) Commercial inorganic fertilizers have greatly increased agricultural productivity. Which of the following is an advantage of using inorganic rather than organic fertilizers?
   A) It is easier for plants to absorb nutrients in an inorganic form.
   B) Nutrients are released faster from inorganic fertilizers.
   C) Inorganic nutrients bind more tightly to soil particles.
   D) Inorganic fertilizers increase the water–holding capacity of the soil.
   E) Soil becomes less compacted with inorganic nutrients.

Answer: B
Topic: 32.9
Skill: Factual Recall

34) Smart plants can reduce overuse of fertilizers by
  A) using photosynthesis and fungal relationships to generate their own fertilizer.
  B) informing the grower of a nutrient deficiency before damage occurs.
  C) slowing the process of minerals washing out of the soils.
  D) binding specifically to certain fertilizers before they are needed and storing them in their root systems.
  E) requiring significantly less fertilizer than comparable organisms throughout their lifespan.

Answer: B
Topic: 32.9
Skill: Conceptual Understanding

35) Compared to conventional agriculture, organic farming
  A) uses fewer synthetic chemicals.
  B) exposes farm workers to greater health risks.
  C) increases crop yields.
  D) guarantees the safety and extra health benefits of food.
  E) requires much less hands-on work.

Answer: A
Topic: 32.10
Skill: Conceptual Understanding

36) Which of the following is a potential problem associated with genetically engineered plants?
  A) Genetically engineered plants will not be able to reproduce on their own.
  B) Disease-resistant genes from genetically engineered plants may escape into the wild.
  C) Genetically engineered plants are typically adapted to a far narrower range of conditions than naturally arising species.
  D) Genetically engineered plants will be less nutritious.
  E) Genetically engineered plants will be more susceptible to viral and bacterial diseases.

Answer: B
Topic: 32.11
Skill: Application

37) Why don't the countries that most need high-protein crops raise them?
  A) High-protein crops usually require fertilizers, which may not be affordable to these countries.
  B) High-protein crops require extensive irrigation, which may not be affordable to these countries.
  C) High-protein crops are more difficult to process, making the foods they produce too expensive.
  D) High-protein crops are typically low in most other vital nutrients.
  E) High-protein crops are labor-intensive and poor countries can't afford the labor.

Answer: A
Topic: 32.11
Skill: Conceptual Understanding

38) On a trip to the Southwest, you and a friend collect some seeds from a piñon, which is a type of pine tree. Your friend also gathers a small bagful of soil from under the piñon tree. Back home, both of you plant your seeds in commercial sterilized potting soil, but your friend adds a spoonful of the collected dirt to each of her pots. Her seedlings do better than yours. Which of the following is the likeliest reason?
 A) Pine seedlings are better adapted to the sandy soil of the Southwest than to commercial potting mix.
 B) The soil from the Southwest probably contained macronutrients missing from the potting mix.
 C) The soil from the Southwest probably contained nitrogen-fixing bacteria that colonized the seedlings' root nodules.
 D) The soil from the Southwest probably contained fungi able to establish a mycorrhizal association with the seedlings' roots.
 E) The soil from the Southwest probably contained the eggs of worms and other soil animals.

Answer: D
Topic: 32.12
Skill: Application

39) The relationship between a plant and mycorrhizal fungi is best described as
 A) parasitic.
 B) competitive.
 C) mutualistic.
 D) commensal.
 E) neutral.

Answer: C
Topic: 32.12
Skill: Factual Recall

40) What is the role of the fungus in a mycorrhizal association?
 A) photosynthesis
 B) production of sugars
 C) absorption of phosphate
 D) secretion of growth factors
 E) release of water

Answer: C
Topic: 32.12
Skill: Factual Recall

41) Most plants can absorb and use which of the following forms of nitrogen directly?
 A) nitrite and nitrate
 B) nitrate only
 C) ammonium and nitrogen gas
 D) nitrate and ammonium
 E) ammonium only

Answer: D
Topic: 32.12
Skill: Factual Recall

42) Nitrogen fixation consists of
   A) the conversion of ammonia to nitrate.
   B) the conversion of nitrate to ammonia.
   C) the production of ammonium from decomposing organic matter.
   D) the conversion of N_2 to ammonia.
   E) the conversion of N_2 to ammonia or nitrate.

Answer: D
Topic: 32.12
Skill: Factual Recall

43) Legumes, such as beans or peas,
   A) form mutualistic associations with nitrogen-fixing bacteria.
   B) form mycorrhizal associations to increase nitrogen fixation in the soil.
   C) form parasitic relationships with other photosynthetic plants.
   D) are poor sources of nitrogen because they are unable to fix N_2 on their own.
   E) fix N_2 from the atmosphere in their leaves.

Answer: A
Topic: 32.13–Evolution Connection
Skill: Factual Recall

44) Legumes are frequently grown in rotation with primary field crops. What is the benefit in this?
   A) A greater amount of the primary crop can be harvested each year.
   B) Nitrogen is added to the soil by nitrogen-fixing bacteria.
   C) Soil erosion is reduced by frequent plowing.
   D) Aeration of the soil is decreased.
   E) Legumes decrease the amount of organic material in the soil.

Answer: B
Topic: 32.13–Evolution Connection
Skill: Conceptual Understanding

45) Much research is being done to increase the nitrogen-fixing ability of plants with root nodules. Why is this an important goal for agricultural researchers?
   A) Decreasing the size of nodules will allow plants to fix more nitrogen into their own molecules.
   B) Nitrogen is an essential component of the amino acids used to form protein.
   C) Increasing the nitrogen-fixing ability of plants will allow them to make better use of nitrogen fertilizers.
   D) By removing the bacteria from the root nodules, more fixed nitrogen will be available to the plants.
   E) Bacteria with improved nitrogen fixation will be able to make more efficient use of expensive fertilizers.

Answer: B
Topic: 32.13–Evolution Connection
Skill: Conceptual Understanding

46) Why might mutualistic relationships between plants and other organisms be expected to evolve?
   A) because the plants and organisms occupy the same environment
   B) because they benefit both organisms and increase their fitness
   C) because they tend to decrease mutation rate
   D) because they decrease competition in plant populations
   E) because the plants and organisms have existed for millions of years

Answer: B
Topic: 32.13–Evolution Connection
Skill: Conceptual Understanding

47) Under what conditions would you expect a mycorrhizal relationship to evolve?
   A) low atmospheric carbon dioxide levels
   B) low soil nitrogen levels
   C) low soil phosphorus levels
   D) very hot and wet conditions
   E) high atmospheric carbon dioxide levels

Answer: C
Topic: 32.13–Evolution Connection
Skill: Application

48) Carnivorous plants are more likely to grow in acid bogs because
   A) organic matter decays so slowly there.
   B) acid soil inhibits growth of plant roots.
   C) acid rain damages leaves and stems.
   D) the acid soils kill most bacteria and fungi.
   E) mycorrhizal growth is inhibited.

Answer: A
Topic: 32.14
Skill: Conceptual Understanding

49) Carnivorousness in plants is primarily an adaptation for
   A) growing in soil poor in organic material.
   B) growing in soil poor in usable nitrogen.
   C) obtaining supplemental carbon for photosynthesis.
   D) discouraging herbivorous insects.
   E) providing extra nutrients for mycorrhizal fungi.

Answer: B
Topic: 32.14
Skill: Factual Recall

50) An example of an organism that parasitizes a host plant is
   A) a mycorrhizal fungus.
   B) nitrogen-fixing bacteria in root nodules.
   C) a Venus flytrap.
   D) mistletoe.
   E) a legume.

Answer: D
Topic: 32.14
Skill: Factual Recall

51) Which of the following is most likely to be an epiphyte?
   A) a plant growing on the branches of another plant
   B) a plant that captures insects
   C) a plant with a very deep root system
   D) a plant that parasitizes another plant
   E) a plant with fungal and bacterial symbionts

Answer: A
Topic: 32.14
Skill: Factual Recall

Art Questions

1)

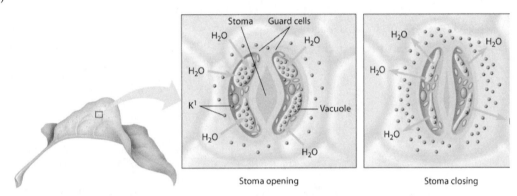

What is true of the guard cells shown in the right-hand panel of this figure?
   A) Their turgor pressure is increasing.
   B) Water is entering these cells.
   C) These cells are undergoing crenation.
   D) These cells are hypertonic to their immediate surrounding.
   E) These cells are hypotonic to their immediate surrounding.

Answer: E
Topic: 32.4
Skill: Application

2)

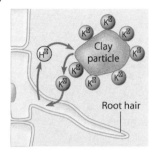

What is implied by this figure?

    A) The clay particle has a negative charge at its surface.

    B) The clay particle has a positive charge at its surface.

    C) The root hair has a negative charge at its surface.

    D) The plant does not need K^+.

    E) H^+ and K^+ have opposite charges.

Answer: A
Topic: 32.8
Skill: Application

3)

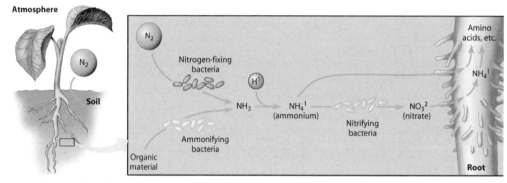

According to this figure, which of the following can directly use atmospheric N_2?

    A) plant leaves

    B) plant roots

    C) nitrogen–fixing bacteria

    D) ammonifying bacteria

    E) nitrifying bacteria

Answer: C
Topic: 32.13
Skill: Conceptual Understanding

Scenario Questions

After reading the following paragraph, answer the question(s) below.

Over the next several decades, world population growth will necessitate as much as a 60% increase in food production, primarily in developing countries. These countries are often the most seriously affected by drought and salinity. Even if irrigation water is available, flooding fields with irrigation water leads to the gradual accumulation of sodium ions and other salts in the soil.

To respond to this growing problem, scientists at the University of Connecticut have genetically engineered a plant that can survive in salty soil and withstand extended drought conditions. The new transgenic plant contains a gene for an ion pump. Salt ions are transported from the soil and stored in vacuoles in the cytoplasm. The enhanced uptake of ions into their vacuoles in turn improves water retention in the transgenic plants and their resistance to drought. The concentration of solutes inside and outside plant cells affects the direction of water movement through osmosis.

The researchers found that the salt concentration in the cells of the new transgenic plants was significantly higher than in wild plants used as a control. In addition, the transgenic plants survived longer when deprived of water.

1) The experimental plants were more drought resistant because
   A) their vacuoles pumped water directly into the cytoplasm.
   B) salt stored in their vacuoles enabled the cytoplasm to retain water better.
   C) salt stored in their vacuoles was equal in amount to the salt in the soil.
   D) water was stored in their vacuoles until the next rainfall.
   E) they were genetically engineered to convert salty water into pure water.

Answer: B
Topic: 32.2, 32.9
Skill: Application

2) In addition to drought resistance, planting these transgenic crops periodically would be beneficial to the environment because
   A) the plants would help clean accumulated salts deposited in the soil by irrigation.
   B) the transgenic plants would also fix nitrogen and improve soil fertility.
   C) the plants would remove carbon dioxide and decrease global warming.
   D) the plants would resist diseases and decrease herbicide use.
   E) the plants would release toxic ions to the soil and decrease insect pest populations.

Answer: A
Topic: 32.10
Skill: Application

Chapter 33 Control Systems in Plants

Multiple-Choice Questions

1) Which of the following is a health benefit associated with increasing the amount of soybeans in the human diet?
    A) decreased LDL levels
    B) removal of antioxidants fromo the body
    C) decreased amount of fiber in the diet
    D) increased levels of triglycerides
    E) decreased HDL levels

    Answer: A
    Topic: Opening Essay
    Skill: Factual Recall

2) Plants grow toward light through the action of
    A) enzymes.
    B) hormones.
    C) nerves.
    D) solar energy.
    E) chloroplasts.

    Answer: B
    Topic: 33.1
    Skill: Factual Recall

3) Grass shoots bend toward the light because, on the shadowed side, a(n)
    A) reduction in auxin levels promotes cell elongation.
    B) reduction in gibberellin levels promotes cell elongation.
    C) reduction in auxin levels prevents cell elongation.
    D) increase in auxin levels promotes cell elongation.
    E) increase in auxin levels promotes cell division.

    Answer: D
    Topic: 33.1
    Skill: Factual Recall

4) One of the experiments in phototropism involved cutting off the tips of grass seedlings before exposing them to light from one side. The decapitated seedlings did not bend toward light. A valid conclusion from this experiment would be that
    A) plants cannot engage in photosynthesis without the tip of the plant.
    B) light is perceived by the tip of grass plants.
    C) a foil cover over the tip of the seedlings would cause them to bend.
    D) hormones are produced in all parts of the plant.
    E) cell elongation causes plants to bend toward light.

    Answer: B
    Topic: 33.1
    Skill: Conceptual Understanding

5) Plant hormones
   A) must be produced in large quantities to be effective.
   B) act on all cells they encounter.
   C) usually work independently of each other.
   D) are chemical signals that influence growth and development.
   E) are rare and produced only in response to stress.

Answer: D
Topic: 33.2
Skill: Factual Recall

6) Which of the following statements about plant hormones is *true*?
   A) Plant hormones are produced in very small concentrations.
   B) Plant hormones mainly affect reproductive processes.
   C) Individual hormones typically have single, specific effects.
   D) Plant hormones have little or no effect on plant growth.
   E) Plant hormones play a vital role in photosynthesis.

Answer: A
Topic: 33.2
Skill: Factual Recall

7) What is the main effect of auxins on plant growth?
   A) They reduce growth by inhibiting cell division.
   B) They increase growth by promoting cell division and elongation.
   C) They increase growth by increasing the rate of photosynthesis.
   D) They reduce growth by preventing cell elongation.
   E) Auxins have no effect on plant growth.

Answer: B
Topic: 33.3
Skill: Factual Recall

8) If the auxin that is produced by an apical meristem is transported in equal amounts down all sides of a twig, the twig will probably
   A) elongate evenly.
   B) branch near its tip.
   C) flower.
   D) develop fruit.
   E) bend away from the apical meristem.

Answer: A
Topic: 33.3
Skill: Conceptual Understanding

9) When a nursery worker pinches off the terminal buds on a young chrysanthemum plant to make it grow bushy, which of the following plant hormones is mainly responsible for growth of side branches?
    A) an auxin
    B) a gibberellin
    C) a cytokinin
    D) abscisic acid
    E) ethylene

Answer: C
Topic: 33.4
Skill: Factual Recall

10) Which class of hormones produced in the roots of plants promotes cell division and growth, and retards the aging of flowers and leaves?
    A) gibberellins
    B) phytochromes
    C) cytokinins
    D) ethylene
    E) abscisic acid

Answer: C
Topic: 33.4
Skill: Factual Recall

11) The most reliable way to stimulate branching in a plant is to
    A) apply auxin to the axillary buds.
    B) remove the terminal buds.
    C) give short–day light treatments.
    D) apply ethylene.
    E) add extra fertilizer.

Answer: B
Topic: 33.4
Skill: Factual Recall

12) Shoot branching is controlled mainly by the interaction of
    A) auxins and gibberellins.
    B) auxins and cytokinins.
    C) gibberellins and cytokinins.
    D) gibberellins and abscisic acid.
    E) cytokinins and abscisic acid.

Answer: B
Topic: 33.4
Skill: Factual Recall

13) The event that triggers fruit formation is the growth of a pollen tube through the carpel of a flower. Which of the following would be a reasonable hypothesis about the basis of this effect?

A) Pollen tubes grow in response to a cytokinin produced by the carpel.
B) Pollen tubes grow in response to abscisic acid.
C) The growing pollen tube produces ethylene.
D) The growing pollen tube produces auxins and/or gibberellins.
E) The growing pollen tube produces phytochrome.

Answer: D
Topic: 33.5
Skill: Conceptual Understanding

14) Which of the following hormones might induce seeds treated with it to break dormancy?

A) an auxin
B) a cytokinin
C) a gibberellin
D) abscisic acid
E) ethylene

Answer: C
Topic: 33.5
Skill: Factual Recall

15) Fruit that forms on an unpollinated plant in response to a hormone will lack

A) flavor.
B) seeds.
C) carpels.
D) rind.
E) naturally occurring hormones.

Answer: B
Topic: 33.5
Skill: Conceptual Understanding

16) Bush beans grow as small bushes rather than as vines because their internodes are short and they branch close to the apical meristem. Which of the following substances, if applied to a bush bean, might cause it to revert to a vine habit?

A) a cytokinin
B) a gibberellin
C) abscisic acid
D) ethylene
E) phytochrome

Answer: B
Topic: 33.5
Skill: Conceptual Understanding

17) Which of the following substances induces "bolting," the rapid elongation of a plant stem?
    A) a cytokinin
    B) a gibberellin
    C) abscisic acid
    D) ethylene
    E) phytochrome

Answer: B
Topic: 33.5
Skill: Conceptual Understanding

18) About how many gibberellins have been identified in plants?
    A) one
    B) five
    C) twenty
    D) over one hundred
    E) thousands

Answer: D
Topic: 33.5
Skill: Factual Recall

19) Which type of plant hormone generally acts as a growth inhibitor?
    A) auxins
    B) gibberellins
    C) cytokinins
    D) abscisic acid
    E) ethylene

Answer: D
Topic: 33.6
Skill: Factual Recall

20) Under what conditions would you expect a plant to have the highest concentration of abscisic acid?
    A) in a wet tropical rain forest
    B) in a very cold environment such as the Arctic
    C) in a cool environment after a heavy rain
    D) in a houseplant growing in low light conditions
    E) in a desert after a long drought

Answer: E
Topic: 33.6
Skill: Conceptual Understanding

21) Which hormone prevents a seed released in the fall from germinating immediately?
    A) auxins
    B) abscisic acid
    C) gibberellins
    D) ethylene
    E) cytokinins

Answer: B
Topic: 33.6
Skill: Factual Recall

22) What stimulates germination of desert plant seeds after a hard rain?
   A) production of auxins
   B) removal of abscisic acid
   C) cooler temperatures
   D) activation of cytokinins
   E) removal of ethylene

Answer: B
Topic: 33.6
Skill: Factual Recall

23) In leaf abscission, the abscission layer forms where the
   A) leaf stalk joins the root.
   B) leaf stalk joins the stem.
   C) axillary bud joins the stem.
   D) root joins the stem.
   E) leaf stalk joins the leaf.

Answer: B
Topic: 33.7
Skill: Factual Recall

24) Which of the following would be a good way to ripen a green tomato?
   A) putting it in a darkened area such as a drawer or box
   B) wrapping it in foil and putting it in the refrigerator
   C) placing it in a sealed plastic bag with an overripe banana
   D) placing it in a microwave, on low power, for 5 minutes
   E) placing it under a bright light for 24 hours

Answer: C
Topic: 33.7
Skill: Conceptual Understanding

25) Which of the following is one adaptive advantage for deciduous plants that lose their
leaves during the winter?
   A) It prevents water loss from leaves when soil water is unavailable due to freezing.
   B) Production of new leaves each spring is more efficient than supporting old leaves
      all winter.
   C) It improves reproductive success in insect–pollinated plants.
   D) If leaves are damaged by frost, the tree will die.
   E) A layer of leaves on the ground helps keep plant roots warm.

Answer: A
Topic: 33.7
Skill: Factual Recall

26) Ethylene is a gaseous hormone produced by plants, often in response to stress. What is another way to produce ethylene?
   A) as a natural by-product of animal respiration
   B) through the evaporation of alcohol
   C) through the combustion of kerosene
   D) through extraction from the cell walls of algae
   E) through the fermentation of soybeans

Answer: C
Topic: 33.7
Skill: Factual Recall

27) In many grocery stores, fresh fruits are sold prebagged in plastic bags dotted with holes so that they will not overripen. The main function of the holes is to
   A) permit the fruit to drain after being washed.
   B) facilitate diffusion of ethylene away from the fruit.
   C) prevent anaerobic conditions within the bag.
   D) prevent buildup of CO_2.
   E) facilitate diffusion of O_2 to the fruit.

Answer: B
Topic: 33.7
Skill: Application

28) Which of the following options lists the events leading to leaf fall in deciduous trees in the correct order?
   A) formation of abscission layer, increase in ethylene levels, decrease in auxin levels
   B) cooler temperatures, increase in ethylene production, formation of abscission layer
   C) shortening days, formation of abscission layer, decrease in ethylene levels
   D) shortening days, decrease in ethylene levels, formation of the abscission layer
   E) decrease in ethylene levels, shortening days, formation of abscission layer

Answer: B
Topic: 33.7
Skill: Factual Recall

29) Synthetic auxins are used commercially
   A) to promote fruit ripening.
   B) to promote seed germination.
   C) to promote flowering in ornamental crops.
   D) to promote side branching to produce bushier crops.
   E) as a broadleaf week killer.

Answer: E
Topic: 33.8
Skill: Factual Recall

30) There is concern over the use of dioxin, a synthetic plant hormone, as a weed killer because
    A) it can cause irreversible mutations in crop plants.
    B) it causes massive fish kills when it gets into lakes and streams.
    C) it kills just as many crop plants as weeds.
    D) it can cause birth defects and leukemia in humans.
    E) it weakens the shells of the eggs of predatory birds, resulting in the death of their offspring.

Answer: D
Topic: 33.8
Skill: Factual Recall

31) Which of the following growth responses causes the shoots of a plant grown in the dark to grow upward?
    A) phototropism
    B) thigmotropism
    C) photoperiodism
    D) gravitropism
    E) heterotropism

Answer: D
Topic: 33.9
Skill: Conceptual Understanding

32) The plant growth response to touch is known as
    A) gravitropism.
    B) geotropism.
    C) bolting.
    D) thigmotropism.
    E) phototropism.

Answer: D
Topic: 33.9
Skill: Factual Recall

33) What dense storage granules in plant cells are thought to contribute to gravitropism?
    A) starch
    B) lipids
    C) cellulose
    D) proteins
    E) chlorophyll

Answer: A
Topic: 33.9
Skill: Factual Recall

34) Which of the following processes underlies the thigmotropic behavior of a green bean tendril?
    A) rotation of the tendril in response to photoperiod
    B) rotation of the tendril in response to a biological clock
    C) extra proliferation of cells on the shaded side of the tendril
    D) extra growth of cells on the lower side of the tendril
    E) extra growth of cells on the side opposite of an object that is touching the tendril

Answer: E
Topic: 33.9
Skill: Factual Recall

35) *Mimosa* plants spread their leaflets during the day and fold them at night. You decide to design an experiment to test whether *mimosa*'s leaf movements are controlled by a biological clock. Which of the following experiments would test your hypothesis?
    A) Growing the plant indoors and turning the lights on in the middle of the night. If a biological clock is controlling leaf movement, the leaves will open.
    B) Putting the plant in a dark closet in the middle of the day. If the leaves close, a biological clock mechanism is ruled out.
    C) Subjecting the plant to a flash of red light in the middle of the night. If the leaves open at the usual time the next morning, a biological clock mechanism is ruled out.
    D) Putting the plant in a dark closet at nightfall. Check on the plant in the morning about 10 hours later, while the plant is still in the closet. If the leaves are open, a biological clock is indicated.
    E) Putting the plant in a dark closet at nightfall and leaving it there for 36 hours. If the leaves open on only one of the two mornings while it is in the closet, a biological clock is indicated.

Answer: D
Topic: 33.10
Skill: Conceptual Understanding

36) Which of the following statements concerning biological clocks is *false*?
    A) Innate circadian rhythms generally differ slightly from a 24–hour period.
    B) Circadian rhythms occur with or without external stimuli.
    C) Researchers have identified a protein that may contribute to the mechanisms of a biological clock.
    D) Biological clocks are strongly influenced by external temperatures.
    E) Movement of plants long distances very quickly induces a kind of plant "jet lag."

Answer: D
Topic: 33.10
Skill: Factual Recall

37) Which of the following plant responses is affected by photoperiod?
    A) fertilization of eggs
    B) gravitropism
    C) apical dominance
    D) onset of dormancy
    E) cell division

Answer: D
Topic: 33.11
Skill: Factual Recall

38) What is the specific term that refers to seasonal changes in the relative lengths of night and day?
A) photoperiod
B) circadian rhythm
C) chemotaxis
D) gravitropism
E) phototaxis

Answer: A
Topic: 33.11
Skill: Factual Recall

39) A plant with a critical minimum day length of 14 hours that flowers in summer is a
A) long–day plant.
B) short–night plant.
C) short–day plant.
D) neutral–day plant.
E) neutral–night plant.

Answer: A
Topic: 33.11
Skill: Factual Recall

40) A biologist interested in determining which plant organs (stems, buds, leaves, etc.) are responsible for sensing photoperiod might perform which of the following experiments?
A) remove the apical meristems from different parts of the plant
B) measure auxin levels in different parts of the plant before and after exposure to light
C) spray cytokinins on different plant organs
D) cover different plant organs with a foil covering to prevent light exposure
E) expose the plants to different wavelengths of light

Answer: D
Topic: 33.11
Skill: Application

41) Which of the following is the factor that initiates flowering in long–day plants?
A) nights shorter than a critical length
B) nights longer than a critical length
C) days longer than the intervening nights
D) days shorter than a critical length
E) days longer than a critical length

Answer: A
Topic: 33.11
Skill: Factual Recall

42) Christmas cactus is a short-day plant that usually blooms in the winter. Which of the following strategies might induce it to bloom for the 4th of July?
   A) putting it in the cold basement every night during the early summer
   B) putting it in a cool, well-lighted place from time to time during June
   C) leaving it in a dark closet all night and part of each morning during June
   D) putting it in a dark closet for a short time every afternoon during June
   E) exposing it to light several times during each night in June

Answer: C
Topic: 33.11
Skill: Conceptual Understanding

43) Iris is a long-day plant that normally flowers in the spring. Which of the following regimens would be the most effective in making an iris bloom in late fall?
   A) interrupting the plants' nights at 2:00 A.M. with a flash of far-red light
   B) interrupting the plants' nights at 2:00 A.M. with a flash of red light followed by a flash of far-red light
   C) interrupting the plants' nights at 2:00 A.M. with a red flash, then a far-red flash, then a red flash
   D) interrupting the plants' days at 2:00 P.M. by putting them in the dark
   E) interrupting the plants' days at 2:00 P.M. with a flash of red light

Answer: C
Topic: 33.12
Skill: Conceptual Understanding

44) How does phytochrome control flowering?
   A) by determining whether day length exceeds a critical minimum
   B) by determining whether day length is shorter than a critical maximum
   C) by sensing sunrise and sunset
   D) by inducing cell division in apical meristems
   E) by inducing differentiation of cells in the apical meristem

Answer: C
Topic: 33.12
Skill: Factual Recall

45) Joanne Chory's studies of *Arabidopsis* have increased our understanding of
   A) photosynthesis.
   B) signal transduction pathways.
   C) hormone structure.
   D) asexual reproduction.
   E) plant immune responses.

Answer: B
Topic: 33.13
Skill: Factual Recall

46) A plant's first line of defense against infection is
    A) *Avr* genes.
    B) its epidermis.
    C) systemic acquired resistance.
    D) *R* genes.
    E) salicylic acid.

Answer: B
Topic: 33.14–Evolution Connection
Skill: Factual Recall

47) Which of the following is a way that plants use animals as a defense against herbivores?
    A) production of an amino acid that harms herbivores
    B) attraction of wasps that kill herbivorous caterpillars
    C) release of microbe–killing chemicals in response to infection
    D) coevolution between plants and predators
    E) production of hormones to induce acquired resistance to herbivores

Answer: B
Topic: 33.14–Evolution Connection
Skill: Conceptual Understanding

48) Salicylic acid, the main component of aspirin, may be an example of a(n)
    A) substance that attracts wasps to a plant being eaten by caterpillars.
    B) phytochrome.
    C) substance encoded for by *Avr* genes.
    D) amino acid that, when consumed by an insect, will kill that insect.
    E) alarm hormone.

Answer: E
Topic: 33.14–Evolution Connection
Skill: Factual Recall

49) The study of how animals use plants to medicate themselves is called
    A) zoopharmacognosy.
    B) pharmacology.
    C) ethnobotany.
    D) phytoremedication.
    E) bioremediation.

Answer: A
Topic: 33.15
Skill: Factual Recall

50) Humans probably first started using plants as medicines as a result of
    A) experiments by chemists in the 1800s.
    B) trial-and-error studies in the 1700s.
    C) watching what plants were eaten by wild animals.
    D) chemical analysis of commonly grown plants.
    E) bioengineering of agricultural plants.

Answer: C
Topic: 33.15
Skill: Conceptual Understanding

Art Questions

1)

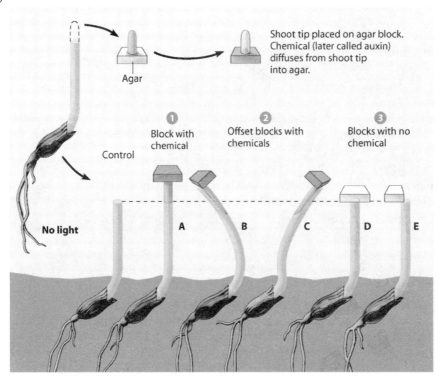

Which plant in Went's experiment shows auxin stimulating elongation in the left side of the plant only?
 A) plant A
 B) plant B
 C) plant C
 D) plant D
 E) plant E

Answer: C
Topic: 33.1
Skill: Application

2)

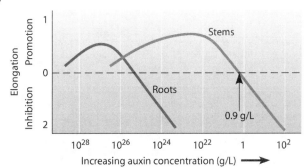

Which of the following statements is supported by this figure?

    A) The greater the concentration of auxin, the more promotion of root elongation occurs.

    B) The greater the concentration of auxin, the more promotion of stem elongation occurs.

    C) Auxin concentrations below 10^{-8} g/L promote both root and stem elongation.

    D) Auxin concentrations around 10^{-4} g/L promote stem elongation but inhibit root elongation.

    E) Auxin concentrations above 0.9 g/L are best for promoting stem elongation.

Answer: D
Topic: 33.3
Skill: Conceptual Understanding

Scenario Questions

After reading the following paragraph, answer the question(s) below.

A student taking a plant physiology class is interested in investigating what will happen if the apical bud is removed from a growing plant and supplementary hormones are introduced.

He set up his experiment with two groups of plants of the same species. In groups A and B, the apical buds were removed and the cut apical ends were wrapped with hormone–impregnated cotton. The plants were observed over a five–week period for growth and development. In group A, many axillary buds and leaves appeared along the sides of the stem, but the plants had minimal root growth. In group B, minimal growth occurred in the shoot and roots and no axillary buds formed.

    1) What hormone was in the cotton used to wrap the apical ends of the group A plants?

        A) cytokinin

        B) giberellin

        C) ethylene

        D) abscisic acid

        E) auxin

Answer: A
Topic: 33.3, 33.4
Skill: Conceptual Understanding

2) What hormone was in the cotton used to wrap the apical ends of the group B plants?
A) cytokinin
B) giberellin
C) ethylene
D) abscisic acid
E) auxin

Answer: D
Topic: 33.2, 33.6
Skill: Conceptual Understanding

Chapter 34 The Biosphere: An Introduction to Earth's Diverse Environments

Multiple-Choice Questions

1) The sum of all Earth's ecosystems is called the
   A) stratosphere.
   B) lithosphere.
   C) biosphere.
   D) hydrosphere.
   E) troposphere.

   Answer: C
   Topic: Opening Essay
   Skill: Factual Recall

2) The primary source of energy for hydrothermal vent communities is
   A) the heat of the water emerging from the vents.
   B) oxidation of petroleum compounds in the vent water.
   C) oxidation of hydrogen sulfide in the vent water.
   D) reduction of sulfates in the vent water.
   E) reduction of carbon dioxide in the vent water.

   Answer: C
   Topic: Opening Essay
   Skill: Factual Recall

3) While on a walk through a forest, you notice birds in trees, earthworms in the soil, and fungi on plant litter on the forest floor. Based on your observations, you conclude that each of these organisms occupies a different
   A) habitat.
   B) biome.
   C) ecosystem.
   D) biosphere.
   E) abiome.

   Answer: A
   Topic: 34.1
   Skill: Application

4) The level of ecologic organization that incorporates abiotic factors is the
   A) community.
   B) ecosystem.
   C) population.
   D) species.
   E) symbioses

   Answer: B
   Topic: 34.1
   Skill: Factual Recall

5) Which of the following could be a topic for a community-level study of a hydrothermal vent ecosystem?
   A) the populations of species occupying the water column above the vent
   B) the relationships between crabs at the vent and other areas of the ocean
   C) evolution of bacteria in response to the changing composition of the water emitted by the hydrothermal vents
   D) the composition of the water emitted by hydrothermal vents
   E) the interactions between Yeti crabs near hydrothermal vents

Answer: E
Topic: 34.1
Skill: Conceptual Understanding

6) Rachel Carson's book, *Silent Spring,* deals with the
   A) destruction of polar habitats caused by global warming.
   B) environmental effects of pesticides.
   C) effects of lynx predation on snow hare populations.
   D) hydrological cycle.
   E) fate of tropical rain forests.

Answer: B
Topic: 34.2
Skill: Factual Recall

7) The immediate results of the widespread use of pesticides and fertilizers included _____, but long-term results included _____.
   A) dramatic increases in crop yields . . . the evolution of pest resistance
   B) the increased spread of malaria . . . delayed resistance to pesticides
   C) terrible declines in agricultural productivity . . . worldwide distribution of DDT
   D) global declines in undesirable pests, such as mice, rats, crows, and sharks . . . increases in these pests
   E) dramatic declines in crop pests . . . localized distribution of DDT

Answer: A
Topic: 34.2
Skill: Conceptual Understanding

8) In many dense forests, plants living near the ground level engage in intense competition for
   A) oxygen.
   B) water.
   C) carbon dioxide.
   D) sunlight.
   E) nitrogen.

Answer: D
Topic: 34.3
Skill: Factual Recall

9) Which of the following environmental factors usually has the greatest direct effect on an organism's rate of water loss by evaporation?
   A) soil type
   B) wind
   C) fires, hurricanes, and tornadoes
   D) moisture
   E) barometric pressure

Answer: B
Topic: 34.3
Skill: Factual Recall

10) What is the primary reason that a hot spring will kill a fish placed in it, but encourage the growth of certain bacteria?
   A) The high temperatures denature most of the fish's enzymes, but the bacteria have enzymes adapted to these temperatures.
   B) Fish cannot feed directly on bacteria, but the bacteria can feed on dead fish.
   C) At hot spring temperatures, the metabolic activity of the fish's cells is so rapid that it runs out of food reserves and dies; the bacteria feed on the dead fish.
   D) Bacterial growth at high temperatures is so rapid that it deoxygenates the water and kills the fish.
   E) The bacteria in hot springs are poisonous to fish.

Answer: A
Topic: 34.3
Skill: Conceptual Understanding

11) The pronghorn antelope of the United States and the saiga antelope of the central Asian steppes live in similar habitats and have similar adaptations. Which of the following features would you be surprised to find in a saiga antelope?
   A) camouflaging coloration
   B) teeth adapted to grinding tough forage
   C) the ability to obtain most or all of the water needed for life from the vegetation in the diet
   D) a warmly insulating winter coat
   E) a digestive tract that separates nutrients from cellulose and rapidly excretes cellulose

Answer: E
Topic: 34.4–Evolution Connection
Skill: Conceptual Understanding

12) The reason that the pronghorn antelope is not found outside North America is most likely that
   A) it is a relatively new species in evolutionary terms.
   B) it has never dispersed beyond this region.
   C) its nutritional requirements cannot be met outside this region.
   D) there are too many pronghorn predators outside North America.
   E) its temperature requirements are stringent and not met outside North America.

Answer: B
Topic: 34.4–Evolution Connection
Skill: Factual Recall

13) The adaptations of pronghorns
   A) to open country can be a disadvantage in a densely forested environment.
   B) include a reflective coat, an ability to find small pools of water, and chemical defenses against most predators.
   C) to the open plains and shrub deserts of North America have helped them spread to nearly every continent.
   D) demonstrate that meeting the demands of local environmental conditions helps organisms extend their ranges to other types of environments.
   E) allow them to survive in forests, since they are herbivores.

Answer: A
Topic: 34.4–Evolution Connection
Skill: Factual Recall

14) In terms of global air circulation, the tropics are a region where air
   A) descends and warms, dropping rain.
   B) descends and warms, creating an arid belt.
   C) rises and warms, creating an arid belt.
   D) rises and cools, creating an arid belt.
   E) rises and cools, dropping rain.

Answer: E
Topic: 34.5
Skill: Conceptual Understanding

15) The greatest annual input and least seasonal variation in solar radiation occurs in the
   A) Northern Hemisphere.
   B) Southern Hemisphere.
   C) temperate zones.
   D) tropics.
   E) polar regions.

Answer: D
Topic: 34.5
Skill: Factual Recall

16) If you travel from west to east through Ecuador, you will pass through tundra, taiga, temperate forest, and tropical forest. Which of the following climatic factors remains constant on such a trip?
   A) maximum temperature
   B) average rainfall
   C) soil type
   D) day length
   E) wind

Answer: D
Topic: 34.5
Skill: Conceptual Understanding

17) Most of the world's deserts are located at latitudes where
    A) hot, dry air moving toward the equator rises.
    B) hot, dry air moving toward the poles rises.
    C) hot, dry air moving toward the poles descends.
    D) cold, dry air moving toward the poles descends.
    E) cold, dry air moving toward the equator descends.

Answer: D
Topic: 34.5
Skill: Conceptual Understanding

18) When people speak of the "rain shadow" of the California Coast Range, they are referring to the
    A) shadow cast by the mist and clouds that hover above the crest of the range.
    B) forested condition of the eastern flank of the range compared to the western flank.
    C) scarcity of rain on the eastern flank and adjacent lowlands compared to the western flank.
    D) dark–colored chaparral vegetation that grows on the eastern flank.
    E) fact that the vegetation of the eastern flank stays green further into the summer than the vegetation of the western flank or adjacent lowlands.

Answer: C
Topic: 34.5
Skill: Application

19) A sperm whale in the middle of the Atlantic Ocean is in which oceanic zone?
    A) intertidal
    B) benthic
    C) neritic
    D) pelagic
    E) estuarine

Answer: D
Topic: 34.6
Skill: Factual Recall

20) Except near hydrothermal vents, the communities of the oceanic aphotic zone get their energy mainly from
    A) photosynthesis by local phytoplankton.
    B) photosynthesis by local zooplankton.
    C) oxidation of sulfur by sulfur bacteria.
    D) oxidation of silicates by silicate bacteria.
    E) organic matter sinking from the photic zone.

Answer: E
Topic: 34.6
Skill: Factual Recall

21) Which ocean zone is the most productive biologically and the most demanding physically?
   A) intertidal
   B) pelagic
   C) abyssal
   D) upwelling
   E) bathypelagic

Answer: A
Topic: 34.6
Skill: Factual Recall

22) Fresh water and seawater mix in a(n)
   A) pelagic zone.
   B) estuary.
   C) benthic zone.
   D) limnetic zone.
   E) littoral zone.

Answer: B
Topic: 34.6
Skill: Factual Recall

23) Under the conditions known as El Niño, the mineral nutrient content of the seawater off the coast of Peru declines to very low levels. What effect will this likely have on marine life in the area?
   A) The lower the levels of minerals, the less polluted the water; hence, most populations will increase.
   B) It will result in toxic red tides, which will reduce the populations of many species.
   C) It will reduce the abundance of phytoplankton and, consequently, the abundance of other organisms.
   D) It will increase the productivity of phytoplankton and, therefore, the productivity of other organisms by decreasing salinity.
   E) It will increase the productivity of phytoplankton and, therefore, the productivity of other organisms by allowing sunlight to penetrate deeper into the ocean.

Answer: C
Topic: 34.7
Skill: Application

24) Usually, a river _____ at its source compared to farther downstream.
   A) has less phytoplankton
   B) is warmer
   C) is murkier
   D) is wider
   E) flows more slowly

Answer: A
Topic: 34.7
Skill: Conceptual Understanding

25) Why is the runoff from fertilized agricultural fields, even if free of pesticides, often harmful to the ecosystems of temperate lakes?
   A) Fertilizer compounds are toxic to fish.
   B) The runoff causes a surface algal bloom, which reduces the lake's oxygen by cutting off the sunlight and fouling the water with dead organic matter.
   C) The runoff raises the levels of inorganic nutrients in the surface waters to levels that are toxic for algae and other lake organisms.
   D) Runoff water pools at the lake's bottom, where the fertilizer compounds react with materials in the sediment to form toxic substances.
   E) The runoff is acid, and acidification kills key lake organisms.

Answer: B
Topic: 34.7
Skill: Factual Recall

26) Species in widely separated biomes often appear display similar characteristics because of
   A) convergence.
   B) coevolution.
   C) mutations.
   D) evolutionary drift.
   E) dominance.

Answer: A
Topic: 34.8
Skill: Factual Recall

27) Which of the following statements about biomes, the major terrestrial ecosystems covering the Earth, is *true*?
   A) Each of the nine major biomes is restricted to just one or two continents.
   B) The major factors affecting the distribution of biomes are wind and sunlight.
   C) Most biomes are characterized by a particular group of species.
   D) Most natural biomes are unaffected by human activity.
   E) Fire is very important in some biomes.

Answer: E
Topic: 34.8
Skill: Conceptual Understanding

28) Which of the following statements about tropical forests is *true*?
   A) Tropical forests occur in equatorial regions with 6- to 8-hour days.
   B) In tropical regions with distinct wet and dry seasons, tropical deciduous trees and shrubs are common.
   C) Once stripped, tropical rain forests regrow quickly, although with slightly less diversity.
   D) Horizontal stratification provides many different habitats in tropical rain forests.
   E) The soils of tropical rain forests are typically rich in nutrients.

Answer: B
Topic: 34.9
Skill: Factual Recall

29) The kind of vegetation in a tropical rain forest is generally determined by the amount of
  A) rainfall.
  B) nitrogen in the soil.
  C) carbon dioxide in the air.
  D) minerals in the soil.
  E) light.

Answer: A
Topic: 34.9
Skill: Factual Recall

30) The major reason for tropical deforestation is
  A) hurricane destruction of large regions.
  B) governments of developing countries selling off land to earn cash.
  C) people clearing forests to open up land for agriculture.
  D) governments clearing forests to build cities.
  E) natural succession as global warming occurs.

Answer: C
Topic: 34.9
Skill: Factual Recall

31) A photograph of a Victorian trophy room shows the heads of 15 species of hoofed mammals, all shot within a day's walk of a single hunting camp in Africa. This camp was probably located in
  A) tropical rain forest.
  B) tropical deciduous forest.
  C) chaparral.
  D) savanna.
  E) desert.

Answer: D
Topic: 34.10
Skill: Conceptual Understanding

32) The dominant herbivores in savannas are
  A) gophers.
  B) insects.
  C) antelope.
  D) giraffes.
  E) worms.

Answer: B
Topic: 34.10
Skill: Factual Recall

33) Which of the following options correctly pairs a biome and its characteristics?
   A) temperate broadleaf forest=mild winters, moderate rainfall, predominantly dicot vegetation
   B) temperate grassland=cool to cold winters, wet summers
   C) chaparral=mild, rainy winters; long, hot, but wet summers
   D) savanna=long, cold winters, vegetation dominated by conifers
   E) tundra=very cold winters; only the upper layer of the soil thaws during summer

Answer: E
Topic: 34.10, 34.12, 34.13, 34.16,
Skill: Factual Recall

34) Which of the following statements about deserts and the organisms that live there is *true*?
   A) Air temperatures in cold deserts, such as those west of the Rocky Mountains, may never fall below 30 degrees C.
   B) Growth and reproduction occur year–round in deserts.
   C) Deserts typically occur at the equator.
   D) Desert plants typically produce very few seeds.
   E) Many desert animals are nocturnal.

Answer: E
Topic: 34.11
Skill: Factual Recall

35) You are reading the journal of an amateur naturalist who visited the Sonoran Desert in the last century. Which of his descriptions of desert plants would you question?
   A) a plant whose seeds will not germinate unless soaked
   B) a perennial that flowers only after years of vegetative growth and produces a large number of seeds
   C) a late winter hillside covered with wildflowers
   D) a common annual that produces one large seed per plant
   E) a moth–pollinated perennial

Answer: D
Topic: 34.11
Skill: Application

36) Chaparral vegetation occurs around much of the central valley of central and southern California. This biome is very similar to that found
   A) along the coast of Great Britain.
   B) in the Australian interior.
   C) in the Mediterranean region.
   D) on the southeast coast of the United States.
   E) in central Asia.

Answer: C
Topic: 34.12
Skill: Factual Recall

37) Which of the following is characteristic of the chaparral biome?
   A) dense, broadleaf shrubs
   B) low amounts of rainfall at unpredictable periods throughout the year
   C) vegetation that is particularly susceptible to periodic fires
   D) many plants with seeds that need fire to germinate
   E) animals species limited to lizards and snakes

Answer: D
Topic: 34.12
Skill: Factual Recall

38) Most of the best agricultural soils in the United States are found in areas that were formerly
   A) temperate grasslands.
   B) savanna.
   C) taiga forest.
   D) tropical rain forest.
   E) tundra.

Answer: A
Topic: 34.13
Skill: Factual Recall

39) The factor(s) that help to perpetuate temperate grasslands, such as the American prairies, and prevent them from becoming woodlands include
   A) poor soil.
   B) seasonal drought and frequent fires.
   C) large numbers of cacti.
   D) mild winters with very little rain.
   E) overgrazing by cattle.

Answer: B
Topic: 34.13
Skill: Factual Recall

40) In which of the following biomes would you expect to find the highest abundance of large, grazing mammals?
   A) tropical rain forest
   B) chaparral
   C) temperate grassland
   D) desert
   E) temperate forest

Answer: C
Topic: 34.13
Skill: Factual Recall

41) Which of the following statements about temperate broadleaf forests is *true*?
   A) Temperate broadleaf forests have a narrow range of temperatures over the course of a year.
   B) Oak, hickory, birch, beech, and maple are common trees in temperate broadleaf forests.
   C) Trees in temperate broadleaf forests typically have a relatively short growing season of two to three months.
   D) Temperate broadleaf forests are less open than tropical rain forests.
   E) Before European settlement, the dominant biome in western North America was temperate broadleaf forest.

Answer: B
Topic: 34.14
Skill: Factual Recall

42) Which of the following biomes is dominated by coniferous trees adapted to surviving long, harsh winters and short, wet summers?
   A) coniferous forests
   B) tundra
   C) temperate broadleaf forest
   D) savanna
   E) chaparral

Answer: A
Topic: 34.15
Skill: Factual Recall

43) Which of the following statements about coniferous forests is *true*?
   A) Coniferous forests are the smallest terrestrial biome.
   B) Coniferous forests are characterized by long but mild winters and short, dry summers that are sometimes warm.
   C) Coniferous forests usually have nutrient–rich soils.
   D) Coniferous forests may experience considerable precipitation, but usually in the form of snow.
   E) Coniferous forests usually experience high rainfall, which keeps the soil saturated.

Answer: D
Topic: 34.15
Skill: Factual Recall

44) Which of the following tundra features would be found at the top of the Andes mountains in Ecuador?
   A) fierce winds and frigid nights
   B) areas of dry soil
   C) large, shallow–rooted vegetation
   D) a brief, bright growing season and a long, dark winter
   E) mostly sandy soil with a low pH

Answer: A
Topic: 34.16
Skill: Conceptual Understanding

45) Which of the following factors is fundamentally responsible for the character of arctic tundra soils?
    A) secretion of acid by lichens and plant roots
    B) high aluminum content due to a low rate of leaching
    C) permafrost
    D) summer aridity
    E) abundant winter snow

Answer: C
Topic: 34.16
Skill: Factual Recall

46) Which of the following has the greatest impact on the global water cycle?
    A) removing animals from their biome
    B) human destruction of forests
    C) connecting aquatic and terrestrial biomes
    D) cutting plants to prevent transpiration
    E) human overuse of water resources for large cities

Answer: B
Topic: 34.17
Skill: Conceptual Understanding

Art Questions

1)

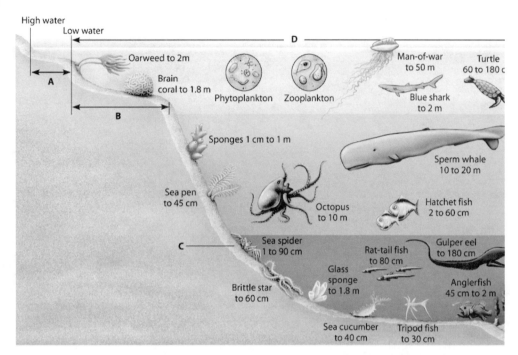

Which of the zones shown in this depiction of an aquatic biome is the photic zone?
A) zone A
B) zone B
C) zone C
D) zone D
E) zone E

Answer: E
Topic: 34.6
Skill: Factual Recall

2)

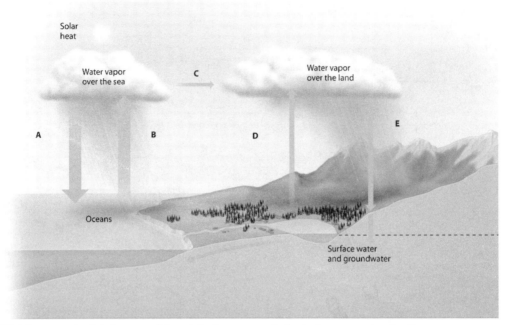

Which arrow in this image of the global water cycle includes transpiration?
    A) arrow A
    B) arrow B
    C) arrow C
    D) arrow D
    E) arrow E

Answer: D
Topic: 34.17
Skill: Factual Recall

Scenario Questions

After reading the following paragraph, answer the question(s) below.

The largest estuary in the United States is the Chesapeake Bay, which extends through six states, including Maryland, Virginia, and Pennsylvania. The bay is one of the most productive natural areas in the world. It's home to thousands of plants and animals, including many commercially important species.

The water of the bay is relatively shallow. Many areas are no more than 10 feet deep, with an average depth of 30 feet. Light penetrates the shallow water and supports the submerged plants that provide food and shelter for the many species living in the bay ecosystem. However, like many estuaries, the bay receives large amounts of fertilizer runoff from farms, lawns, and wastewater treatment facilities.

1) Which of the following is the most probable sequence of events when fertilizer runoff reaches the Bay?
   A) submerged vegetation increases, more food for fish and shellfish, fish and shellfish populations increase
   B) phytoplankton population increases, more food for fish and shellfish, fish and shellfish populations increase
   C) phytoplankton population increases, blocks sunlight to submerged vegetation, submerged vegetation dies, fish and shellfish populations decrease
   D) phytoplankton population decreases, increased sunlight to submerged vegetation, fish and shellfish populations increase
   E) submerged vegetation decreases, fish and shellfish feed on decaying plants, phytoplankton feed on fish and shellfish, commercial fisheries decline

Answer: C
Topic: 34.6, 34.7
Skill: Conceptual Understanding

2) Fertilizer runoff contains _____, which are the most important limiting factors for plant growth.
   A) carbon and hydrogen
   B) oxygen and carbon dioxide
   C) water and carbon dioxide
   D) nitrogen and phosphorus
   E) sulfur and magnesium

Answer: D
Topic: 34.6, 34.7
Skill: Factual Recall

Chapter 35 Behavioral Adaptations to the Environment

Multiple-Choice Questions

1) Relationships among mating individuals in which one mating partner of one sex mates with several individuals of the other sex are known as
   A) polygamy.
   B) monogamy.
   C) proximate.
   D) fixed action patterns.
   E) promiscuity.

   Answer: A
   Topic: Opening Essay
   Skill: Factual Recall

2) Answers to questions about the immediate mechanisms for a behavior are called
   A) conclusions.
   B) proximate causes.
   C) cognitive mapping.
   D) ultimate causes.
   E) habituation.

   Answer: B
   Topic: 35.1
   Skill: Factual Recall

3) The evolutionary explanations for behavior are called the
   A) evolutionary schematic.
   B) adaptive motivator.
   C) selected advantage.
   D) proximal causes.
   E) ultimate causes.

   Answer: E
   Topic: 35.1
   Skill: Factual Recall

4) When a nipple is placed in a newborn baby's mouth, the infant will immediately begin to suckle. This is an example of
   A) habituation.
   B) imprinted behavior.
   C) classical conditioning.
   D) innate behavior.
   E) imitation.

   Answer: D
   Topic: 35.2
   Skill: Factual Recall

5) Which of the following statements regarding behavior is *true*?
   A) Innate behaviors are performed the same way in all members of a genus.
   B) Fixed action patterns are learned behavior sequences.
   C) A learned behavior triggers a fixed action pattern.
   D) Innate behaviors are not related to genetics.
   E) A fixed action pattern is under strong genetic control.

Answer: E
Topic: 35.2
Skill: Conceptual Understanding

6) Five-year-old Jasmine was helping her mother bake cookies. She watched her mother carefully measure out the sugar, then heard her mother say, "Please open the oven door." When the cookies were placed into the oven, Jasmine knew to close the door. After an hour, when the cookies were done, the oven timer rang, and Jasmine knew that it was time to open the oven again. When the cookies came out, nobody had to tell Jasmine to eat the cookies. Her mouth was already watering! Which of the following is a sign stimulus from this story?
   A) Jasmine's mother asking her to open the oven door.
   B) Jasmine's mother watching when the measuring cup of sugar was full.
   C) Jasmine watching to see when the cookies were placed in the oven and when to close the oven door.
   D) The smell of the cookies making Jasmine's mouth water.
   E) The sound of the timer going off, signaling that it was time to remove the cookies from the oven.

Answer: D
Topic: 35.2
Skill: Application

7) When building a nest, a female Fisher's lovebird cuts long strips of vegetation and carries them to the nest site one at a time in her beak. The female peach-faced lovebird cuts short strips and carries them to the nest tucked under back feathers. Hybrid female offspring cut intermediate-sized strips and attempt to tuck them under back feathers before carrying them in their beak. What does this demonstrate about behavior?
   A) Behavior can be learned from parents.
   B) There is a genetic basis to behavior.
   C) Environment is important in forming behaviors.
   D) Lovebirds can be trained easily.
   E) The smaller the strip, the easier it is to carry.

Answer: B
Topic: 35.3
Skill: Conceptual Understanding

8) Many rats were tested for their ability to learn a maze. The average number of errors for a total of 14 trials was 64 per rat. The rats that made the fewest errors were bred to each other, and the offspring were tested in a similar way. This process was repeated for seven generations, at which point the average number of errors for 14 trials was 36. This experiment demonstrates that
    A) learned behavior cannot be inherited.
    B) maze–learning ability has a genetic basis.
    C) maze–learning ability depends mainly on early contact with adept parents.
    D) natural selection has a role in the evolution of fixed action patterns but not in the evolution of behavior involving learning.
    E) maze–learning ability increases with increasing homozygosity of the genome.

Answer: B
Topic: 35.3
Skill: Conceptual Understanding

9) The modification of behavior based upon specific experiences defines
    A) habituation.
    B) imprinting.
    C) associative learning.
    D) conditioning.
    E) learning.

Answer: E
Topic: 35.4
Skill: Application

10) When you successfully study with the stereo on in the background, you are demonstrating
    A) habituation.
    B) imprinting.
    C) associative learning.
    D) conditioning.
    E) imitation.

Answer: A
Topic: 35.4
Skill: Application

11) You are told that the song of males among a particular songbird species has an innate component but is also largely learned. Nestling males imprint on their father's song and then sing it themselves when they reach sexual maturity. Which of the following observations would lead you to doubt this information?
    A) A male chick reared in isolation grows up to sing a rudimentary version of his species' song.
    B) A male chick reared in isolation but introduced as an older juvenile into an aviary containing normal males of his species sings his species' song.
    C) A male chick who is reared in isolation but hears tape recordings of his species' song grows up to sing normally.
    D) A male chick who is reared in isolation but hears tape recordings of a different species' song grows up to sing that species' song.
    E) A male chick fostered in the nest of a different species grows up to sing the song of its foster species.

Answer: B
Topic: 35.5
Skill: Conceptual Understanding

12) Which of the following behaviors would be unlikely to involve imprinting?
    A) A nestling male sparrow learns the "dialect" of song that is used in his native district.
    B) A nestling male songbird raised in the nest of a different species grows up to sing the song of his foster species.
    C) A songbird that engages in solitary migration using star navigation returns each year to the district where it was hatched.
    D) A migrating mother gazelle leaves her calf hidden in grass while she feeds and always returns to the correct patch of grass.
    E) A migrating mother gazelle is always recognized by her calf when she calls to it.

Answer: D
Topic: 35.5
Skill: Conceptual Understanding

13) A male turkey that imprinted onto a human at hatching is transferred as an older juvenile to a flock of "normal" turkeys. When this turkey reaches sexual maturity, he will probably try to court
    A) male, female, or immature turkeys indiscriminately.
    B) immature male turkeys.
    C) mature female turkeys.
    D) humans.
    E) immature female turkeys.

Answer: D
Topic: 35.6
Skill: Conceptual Understanding

14) A grayling butterfly will normally fly toward the sun. This is an example of
   A) kinesis.
   B) migration.
   C) phototropism.
   D) taxis.
   E) instinct.

Answer: D
Topic: 35.7
Skill: Conceptual Understanding

15) After many hours of observation, Jennifer noticed that a squirrel in her backyard seemed to retreat up a certain tree every time it was frightened. At the base of that tree was a wheelbarrow. Jennifer wondered how the squirrel found the same tree each time. Perhaps it simply knew to use the tree with the wheelbarrow. That night, Jennifer moved the wheelbarrow a few feet over and placed it against another tree. The next day, the squirrel retreated up the new tree, with the wheelbarrow resting at its base. This experiment suggests that the squirrel was using
   A) kinesis.
   B) spatial learning.
   C) imprinting.
   D) habituation.
   E) social learning.

Answer: B
Topic: 35.7
Skill: Application

16) A blue jay hides hundreds of nuts throughout the fall and finds them throughout the winter and spring. The blue jay is most likely finding the stored food by using
   A) kinesis.
   B) a cognitive map.
   C) imprinting.
   D) habituation.
   E) social learning.

Answer: B
Topic: 35.8
Skill: Application

17) The most extensive study of cognitive maps have involved animals that
   A) migrate.
   B) burrow extensive tunnels into the ground.
   C) hibernate.
   D) engage in thermoregulation.
   E) build nests.

Answer: A
Topic: 35.8
Skill: Factual Recall

18) Squirrels on a bird feeder seem to be able to figure out how to steal seeds no matter what people do to prevent it. Yesterday, Jeremy hung out a new bird feeder design, and sure enough, by the end of the day the squirrels found a way to get to the seeds. The squirrels most likely figured out how to get the seeds through
    A) trial–and–error learning.
    B) habituation.
    C) the use of cognitive maps.
    D) imprinting.
    E) spatial learning.

Answer: A
Topic: 35.9
Skill: Application

19) In England, at a time when milk was still delivered to doorsteps each morning in foil–capped glass bottles, a songbird called the great tit started pecking through the caps and drinking the cream in the necks of the bottles. This behavior spread through the great tit population in a matter of years. The emergence and spread of this behavior probably depended on
    A) habituation.
    B) trial and error plus habituation.
    C) trial and error plus imitation.
    D) trial and error plus imprinting.
    E) habituation plus imitation.

Answer: C
Topic: 35.9, 35.10
Skill: Conceptual Understanding

20) The baby bobcats watched as their mother stalked a rabbit and pounced, catching a meal that was shared by all. The next day, two of the young bobcats were seen stalking a field mouse, which quickly escaped from the inexperienced hunters. The young bobcats were learning how to hunt by the process of
    A) social learning.
    B) imprinting.
    C) habituation.
    D) associative learning.
    E) cognitive map learning.

Answer: A
Topic: 35.10
Skill: Application

21) A big difference between imitation (social learning) and imprinting is that
    A) imprinting does not involve a reward.
    B) imprinting does not involve learning.
    C) imprinting can only take place among members of the same species.
    D) imitation has a primarily genetic basis.
    E) imitation is not limited to a sensitive period.

Answer: E
Topic: 35.10
Skill: Conceptual Understanding

22) Several primates have been taught to communicate with humans using sign language. This supports the view that animals other than humans can learn through the process of
    A) imitation.
    B) cognition.
    C) association.
    D) trial and error.
    E) classical conditioning.

Answer: B
Topic: 35.11
Skill: Conceptual Understanding

23) Behavior is an adaptation that enhances evolutionary fitness. Which type of learning behavior would be characteristic of the least specialized animals?
    A) associative learning
    B) imprinting
    C) problem solving
    D) imitation
    E) social learning

Answer: B
Topic: 35.4-35.11
Skill: Conceptual Understanding

24) You lose track of your friend in a store and start looking for her. Which of the following things that you could do represents the use of a search image?
    A) You ask a woman if she has seen anyone around this part of the store.
    B) You think about what color clothing she wore and look for that color.
    C) You go to the department in the store where your friend most likes to shop.
    D) You call your friend's name.
    E) You return to the last place you saw your friend.

Answer: B
Topic: 35.12
Skill: Application

25) An insectivorous bird has the choice of eating (1) meadow beetles, which are abundant and large but expose the bird to hawk predation; (2) under–a–rock beetles, which are large and fatty but hard to obtain; and (3) under–a–leaf beetles, which are easy to obtain but small. The bird has nestlings to feed. As an optimal forager, it will
    A) concentrate on meadow beetles and feed at dawn and dusk to avoid hawks.
    B) concentrate on under–a–leaf beetles because they are easy and safe.
    C) concentrate on under–a–rock beetles because they are energy–rich.
    D) eat one kind of beetle at a time (first under–a–leaf, then meadow, then under–a–rock), switching to a new kind when the old kind becomes scarce.
    E) eat all three kinds of beetles, balancing the energy spent obtaining each against the energy gained and the risks incurred.

Answer: E
Topic: 35.12
Skill: Conceptual Understanding

26) The sending of, reception of, and response to signals constitute animal
    A) foraging.
    B) cost–benefit factors.
    C) communication.
    D) problem–solving.
    E) associative learning.

Answer: C
Topic: 35.13
Skill: Factual Recall

27) Organisms that are nocturnal are more likely to communicate using
    A) sight and sound.
    B) sight and smell.
    C) smell and sound.
    D) touch and taste.
    E) touch, taste, sight, and sound.

Answer: C
Topic: 35.13
Skill: Factual Recall

28) Assuming that von Frisch's hypothesis about honeybee communication is correct, which
    of the following types of information will be communicated to other workers by a worker
    honeybee that returns to the nest after finding a good nectar source more than 50 meters
    from the hive?
    A) the concentration of nectar
    B) the direction of the nectar source
    C) the distance of the nectar source from the nearest water
    D) the color of the flowers producing the nectar
    E) the quality of the nectar

Answer: B
Topic: 35.13
Skill: Factual Recall

29) During the spring, male prairie chickens gather in open grassy areas and shuffle in a
    dance with their wings drooped, head erect, and tail feathers spread. The function of this
    dance is to
    A) frighten off smaller birds from the territory.
    B) select the showiest females and mate.
    C) attract the attention of females.
    D) imprint the younger male birds.
    E) teach courting behavior to younger male birds.

Answer: C
Topic: 35.14
Skill: Conceptual Understanding

30) Which of the following is communicated by courtship displays?
    A) The individuals are fertile and of the opposite sex.
    B) The males represent a threat to other males.
    C) The individuals are not interested in mating.
    D) The individuals intend to hurt each other.
    E) The individuals are of different species.

Answer: A
Topic: 35.14
Skill: Factual Recall

31) The need for intense parental care of offspring favors mating systems that are
    A) polygamous.
    B) lifelong.
    C) temporary.
    D) monogamous.
    E) promiscuous.

Answer: D
Topic: 35.15
Skill: Factual Recall

32) The certainty of paternity is greatest in organisms that
    A) are promiscuous.
    B) are polygamous.
    C) have extensive parental care.
    D) use internal fertilization.
    E) mate and lay eggs at the same time.

Answer: E
Topic: 35.15
Skill: Conceptual Understanding

33) Endocrine disruptors on reproductive behavior affect behavior by
    A) impairing the immune system.
    B) mimicking a hormone or enhancing hormone activity.
    C) increasing social behavior.
    D) interrupting food chain interactions.
    E) reinforcing mating rituals.

Answer: B
Topic: 35.16
Skill: Factual Recall

34) Which of the following terms broadly describes any kind of interaction between two or more animals?
    A) competition
    B) dominance hierarchy
    C) foraging behavior
    D) genetic programming
    E) social behavior

Answer: E
Topic: 35.17
Skill: Factual Recall

35) Territories are typically used for
    A) feeding.
    B) migration.
    C) identification of kin.
    D) topography.
    E) vegetation density.

Answer: A
Topic: 35.18
Skill: Factual Recall

36) Which of the following situations represents an example of territoriality?
    A) Males of an antelope species gather daily on a mating ground during the mating season. Each male defends a large segment of the ground.
    B) Male chipmunks occupy areas that contain ranges of several females. A male chipmunk defends his area against other males and females.
    C) Gannets breed in dense colonies. Each gannet defends the area within the beak's reach of its nest, but gannets feeding at sea are indifferent to each other.
    D) Troops of monkey species use well-defined, widely overlapping ranges. Troops avoid encountering each other and are aggressive if they meet.
    E) Male redwing blackbirds occupy and defend parcels of marsh. A dozen or more females nest in each parcel, which provides food and nesting sites.

Answer: C
Topic: 35.18
Skill: Conceptual Understanding

37) Which of the following would be an example of agonistic behavior?
    A) A dog raises its hackles, bares its teeth, and stands high to appear threatening.
    B) A honeybee does a waggle dance to indicate the direction of food.
    C) A male ruffed grouse spreads its tail and beats its wings to attract a female.
    D) Fireflies flash in a species-specific pattern.
    E) Ants mark their trails by releasing pheromones.

Answer: A
Topic: 35.19
Skill: Conceptual Understanding

38) Agonistic behavior
    A) usually causes serious injury to one or both of the combatants.
    B) increases the number of individuals who mate.
    C) is used to establish dominance hierarchies.
    D) is the result of habituation.
    E) is rare among vertebrates.

Answer: C
Topic: 35.19
Skill: Factual Recall

39) Pecking order in chickens is an example of
   A) dominance hierarchy.
   B) alpha order.
   C) agonistic behavior.
   D) social behavior.
   E) mating behavior.

Answer: A
Topic: 35.20
Skill: Factual Recall

40) Which of the following statements about chimpanzee behavior is *true*?
   A) The more frequent and vigorous the display by a male, the more likely it is that he will never attain a high social position.
   B) Male chimps do not have a hierarchy.
   C) Female chimps do not have a hierarchy.
   D) Social primates spend no time in reconciliation and pacification–type behavior.
   E) Social grooming is the single most important social activity in the chimp community.

Answer: E
Topic: 35.21
Skill: Factual Recall

41) Dominance hierarchies in chimpanzees support which of the following concepts of learning behavior for that species?
   A) reasoning and cognition
   B) imprinting and imitation
   C) conditioning and trial and error
   D) imitation and trial and error
   E) habituation and association

Answer: A
Topic: 35.21
Skill: Conceptual Understanding

42) An adult human jumps into a raging river to try to save a child who is drowning and is unrelated to the adult. This is an example of
   A) ingrained behavior.
   B) reciprocal altruism.
   C) imprinted behavior.
   D) kin selection.
   E) dominant behavior.

Answer: B
Topic: 35.22–Evolution Connection
Skill: Application

43) Which of the following situations could represent kin selection in action?
  A) You help your friend with linguistics, and your friend helps you with biology.
  B) You help your brother pay for his children's college tuition, even though he may
     not be able to pay you back.
  C) When your mother gets old, you help her pay her property taxes.
  D) You inexplicably forget to use birth control, and a child results.
  E) You need a loan to get a vasectomy, so you ask your brother.

Answer: B
Topic: 35.22–Evolution Connection
Skill: Conceptual Understanding

44) From a sociobiological perspective, altruism is a behavior that
  A) does not have a genetic basis.
  B) has the potential to enhance the altruist's fitness at a later point in time.
  C) will always be selected against.
  D) occurs only in the social insects.
  E) can be viewed as a type of mental illness.

Answer: B
Topic: 35.22–Evolution Connection
Skill: Factual Recall

45) Human social behavior appears to be
  A) a product of our genes.
  B) determined by the environment.
  C) a product of our genes, external influences, and environment.
  D) a result of many generations of intense competition.
  E) unrelated to genetics.

Answer: C
Topic: 35.23
Skill: Factual Recall

Art Questions

1)

What type of behavior is illustrated by the bird in this figure?
   A) imprinting
   B) territoriality
   C) mating behavior
   D) fixed action pattern
   E) foraging

Answer: D
Topic: 35.2
Skill: Application

2)

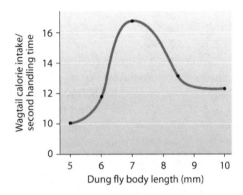

Graph from N. B. Davies. 1977. Prey selection and social behaviour in wagtails (Aves: Motacillidae). *Journal of Animal Ecology* 46: 37-57, fig. 9.

Which of the following conclusions is supported by this graph?

A) Prey size does not affect the number of calories per second of handling by wagtails.

B) Wagtails get more calories per second of handling with larger flies than with smaller ones.

C) Wagtails get more calories per second of handling with smaller flies than with larger ones.

D) Wagtails get more calories per second of handling with 7-mm flies than with either larger or smaller ones.

E) Wagtails get more calories per second from the largest and smallest flies than with the 7-mm flies.

Answer: D
Topic: 35.12
Skill: Application

Scenario Questions

After reading the following paragraph, answer the question(s) below.

A researcher is investigating the ability of salmon to migrate thousands of miles in the ocean yet return to the same location where they were hatched to spawn. Data from experiments suggest that more than one type of homing mechanism may be involved in this behavior. When salmon arrive at a river mouth from the open sea, they appear to use olfactory cues to find their home streams, but how do they find their way back to the correct spot along the coastline from the open ocean?

Several experiments are carried out to test the hypothesis that geomagnetic factors (the influence of Earth's magnetic field) play a key role in the ability of salmon to find the proper location along the coast. In one such experiment, salmon hatched in Ketchikan, Alaska, were subjected to the geomagnetic characteristics of a different location on the Alaska Peninsula, Cold Bay. The fish were then released to determine to which of the two locations they would return to spawn.

1) If the salmon return to spawn at Cold Bay, the behavior involved is primarily _____, but if they return to Ketchikan, the behavior is primarily _____.
   A) proximate . . . ultimate
   B) ultimate . . . proximate
   C) innate . . . learned
   D) learned . . . innate
   E) fixed . . . altruistic

Answer: D
Topic: 35.1, 35.2, 35.3, 35.5
Skill: Application

2) What type of behavior would explain the ability of the salmon to return to their home streams?
   A) imprinting
   B) spatial learning
   C) social learning
   D) habituation
   E) cognitive mapping

Answer: A
Topic: 35.1, 35.2, 35.3, 35.5
Skill: Conceptual Understanding

Chapter 36 Population Ecology

Multiple-Choice Questions

1) The decline of the Nile perch in Lake Victoria in east Africa and the reemergence of cichlids is an excellent situation for study by
   A) geologists.
   B) ecologists.
   C) population ecologists.
   D) geographers.
   E) population geneticists.

Answer: C
Topic: Opening Essay
Skill: Factual Recall

2) A group of individuals of a single species that occupy the same general area defines a
   A) population.
   B) community.
   C) species.
   D) subspecies.
   E) clone.

Answer: A
Topic: 36.1
Skill: Factual Recall

3) Which of the following is an example of a population? *One species & defined location*
   A) all of the microorganisms on your skin
   B) all of the species of cichlid fish in Lake Victoria
   C) all of the students in your classroom
   D) all students attending colleges and universities in your state
   E) the various plants found in prairies in the western United States

Answer: C
Topic: 36.1
Skill: Application

4) Assume that there are five alligators per acre in a swamp in northern Florida. This is a measure of the alligator population's
   A) dispersion.
   B) intrinsic rate of increase.
   C) range.
   D) equability.
   E) density.

Answer: E
Topic: 36.2
Skill: Application

5) The pattern of distribution for a certain species of kelp is clumped. We would expect that the pattern of distribution for a population of snails that live on the kelp would be
   A) absolute.
   B) clumped.
   C) homogeneous.
   D) random.
   E) uniform.

Answer: B
Topic: 36.2
Skill: Conceptual Understanding

6) You drive through Iowa in the spring and notice that along a stretch of several kilometers, every third fence post has a male redwing blackbird perched on it defending its nesting territory. This is an example of
   A) learned dispersion.
   B) clumped dispersion.
   C) random dispersion.
   D) uniform dispersion.
   E) artificial dispersion.

Answer: D
Topic: 36.2
Skill: Application

7) The density of Douglas firs in an old-growth forest is estimated by counting the Douglas firs in four sample plots of 1 hectare each. The number of fir trees in the plots is 10, 12, 7, and 11, respectively. What is the estimated density of firs in the forest?
   A) 2.5 trees per hectare
   B) 5 trees per hectare
   C) 10 trees per hectare
   D) 20 trees per hectare
   E) 25 trees per hectare

Answer: C
Topic: 36.2
Skill: Application

8) To obtain optimal production in a small garden, one should
   A) plant seeds in rows with minimal spacing between rows.
   B) plant seeds in clumps with large spaces between clumps.
   C) plant seeds in a uniform pattern throughout the garden.
   D) soak seeds overnight before planting in rows.
   E) sow seeds randomly throughout the garden.

Answer: C
Topic: 36.2
Skill: Application

9) A survivorship curve is a
A) graph that plots an individual's likelihood of reproducing as a function of age.
B) graph that plots an individual's likelihood of being alive as a function of age.
C) graph that shows the effect of predation on a prey population.
D) model for population growth that incorporates the concept of carrying capacity.
E) model for population growth that incorporates reproductive rates.

Answer: B
Topic: 36.3
Skill: Factual Recall

10) A Type I survivorship curve is the result of which of the following life history traits?
A) parents providing extended care for their young
B) large numbers of offspring being produced
C) infant mortality being much greater than adult mortality
D) death rates remaining constant over the life span
E) a short life span for most individuals

Answer: A
Topic: 36.3
Skill: Conceptual Understanding

11) A survivorship curve that involves producing very few offspring, each of which has a high probability of surviving to adulthood, is typical of
A) sea stars.
B) elephants.
C) oysters.
D) butterflies.
E) mice.

Answer: B
Topic: 36.3
Skill: Application

12) The maximum number of individuals a habitat can support is called its
A) reproductive potential.
B) carrying capacity.
C) community size.
D) density–dependent factor.
E) population growth.

Answer: B
Topic: 36.4
Skill: Factual Recall

13) Consider a stable frog population living at carrying capacity in a pond. If an average female produces 6,000 eggs during her lifetime and an average of 300 tadpoles hatch from these eggs, how many of these tadpoles will, on average, survive to reproduce?
   A) 0
   B) 2
   C) 10 to 20
   D) 100
   E) more than 100

Answer: B
Topic: 36.4
Skill: Conceptual Understanding

14) A population of fungi in a yard produces 10 mushrooms in year 1, 20 in year 2, and 40 in year 3. If this trend continues, by year 5 there will be _____ mushrooms.
   A) 20
   B) 40
   C) 80
   D) 160
   E) 320

Answer: D
Topic: 36.4
Skill: Conceptual Understanding

15) A newly mated queen ant establishes an ant nest in an unoccupied patch of suitable habitat. Assuming that no disasters strike the nest, which of the following types of equation will best describe its population growth?
   A) linear
   B) quadratic
   C) logarithmic
   D) logistic
   E) exponential

Answer: D
Topic: 36.4
Skill: Conceptual Understanding

16) A test tube is inoculated with 1×10^3 cells of a bacterial strain that has a generation time of 30 minutes. The carrying capacity of the test tube for this strain is 6×10^9 cells. What will the bacterial population be after 90 minutes of culturing?
   A) 3×10^3
   B) 8×10^3
   C) 9×10^3
   D) 1×10^9
   E) 1×10^{12}

Answer: B
Topic: 36.4
Skill: Conceptual Understanding

17) If an ecosystem has a carrying capacity of 1,000 individuals for a given species, and 2,000 individuals of that species are present, we can predict that the population
    A) size will remain at equilibrium.
    B) size will decrease.
    C) will show a clumped dispersion pattern.
    D) will show a uniform dispersion pattern.
    E) size will slowly increase.

Answer: B
Topic: 36.4
Skill: Conceptual Understanding

18) If a population has a birth rate of 40 individuals per 1,000 per year and a death rate of 30 individuals per 1,000 per year, how will the population change each year? (Assume that the population is below carrying capacity and that there is no immigration or emigration.)
    A) It will decrease by 70%.
    B) It will increase by 1%.
    C) It will increase by 5%.
    D) It will increase by 70%.
    E) It will increase by 100%.

Answer: B
Topic: 36.4
Skill: Conceptual Understanding

19) A human population will achieve zero population growth if
    A) no couple has more than two children.
    B) couples have an average of about 2.25 children each (to account for some children who do not survive to reproduce).
    C) no couple has more than one child.
    D) the birth rate equals the intrinsic rate of increase *r*.
    E) competition for limited resources increases.

Answer: B
Topic: 36.4
Skill: Conceptual Understanding

20) The death by bubonic plague of about one–third of Europe's population during the fourteenth century is a good example of
    A) abiotic factors limiting population size.
    B) a density-dependent effect.
    C) a time lag.
    D) a density-independent effect.
    E) carrying capacity.

Answer: B
Topic: 36.5
Skill: Application

21) A tidal wave wipes out the entire population of mice living on an island. This is an example of
   A) Type III survivorship.
   B) a density–dependent effect.
   C) the reason that most island forms have evolved mechanisms for rapid dispersal.
   D) the effects of abiotic factors.   *water*
   E) the interaction between density-dependent and abiotic factors.

Answer: D
Topic: 36.5
Skill: Application

22) In the logistic growth model, as population size increases, birth rates
   A) remain constant and death rates increase.
   B) decline but death rates remain steady.
   C) and death rates increase.
   D) and death rates remain steady.
   E) rates decline and/or death rates increase.

Answer: E
Topic: 36.5
Skill: Conceptual Understanding

23) Which of the following is most clearly a case of density–dependent population regulation?
   A) the summer drying of savanna grass for an insect that feeds on grass sap
   B) a dangerous new flu strain that is transmitted among humans by sneezing
   C) the first hard frost of fall for a population of annual morning glory vines
   D) the growth of shade trees over a population of sun–loving shrubs in an abandoned field
   E) the occurrence of rainstorms for an opportunistic desert annual

Answer: B
Topic: 36.5
Skill: Conceptual Understanding

24) In terms of population dynamics, what is "boom–and–bust" cycling?
   A) a situation in which the movement of limiting nutrients through an ecosystem is pulsatile rather than steady
   B) a situation in which a population oscillates around the carrying capacity of its environment
   C) a situation in which a growing population overshoots the carrying capacity of its environment and experiences a crash before stabilizing
   D) a situation in which sex ratios in a population exhibit reciprocal oscillations
   E) a situation in which the populations of a predator species and a prey species oscillate in unison

Answer: B
Topic: 36.6
Skill: Factual Recall

25) An ecologist hypothesizes that predation by a particular owl species is the major factor controlling the population of a particular rabbit species. The first step in testing this hypothesis would be to determine
    A) whether populations of the rabbit that live outside the range of the owl have higher population densities.
    B) whether the owls eat the rabbits.
    C) to which diseases the rabbit population is subject.
    D) what food the rabbits eat.
    E) what habitats the rabbits and the owls occupy.

Answer: B
Topic: 36.6
Skill: Conceptual Understanding

26) If the owl species in the question above is the major factor controlling rabbit populations, which of the following population effects could be expected in this rabbit–owl pair?
    A) A fall in the owl population should cause a fall in the rabbit population.
    B) A fall in the rabbit population should cause an increase in the owl population.
    C) An increase in the incidence of disease in the rabbit population should not change the owl population.
    D) An increase in the rabbits' food supply should not change the owl population.
    E) An increase in the owl population should cause a fall in the rabbit population.

Answer: E
Topic: 36.6
Skill: Conceptual Understanding

27) The life history strategy of an *r*–selected species is to
    A) overcome the influence of density–dependency.
    B) take advantage of human activity, such as clearing woodlots.
    C) become predators.
    D) limit population growth.
    E) increase the carrying capacity for the species.

Answer: B
Topic: 36.7–Evolution Connection
Skill: Factual Recall

28) Which of the following organisms best illustrates *K*–selection?
    A) the production of thousands of eggs every spring by frogs
    B) mice that produce three litters of 10–15 babies in the course of a summer
    C) a polar bear producing one or two cubs every three years
    D) a species of weed that quickly spreads into a region of cleared trees
    E) a dog that produces two litters of 8–12 puppies per year

Answer: C
Topic: 36.7–Evolution Connection
Skill: Application

29) Guppies from Trinidad form two distinct populations that differ in several life history traits that appear to relate to the local predator populations, pike–cichlids or killifish. Which of the following experiments would test the heritability of these traits?
    A) Raise both populations with cichlids to see if the population of smaller, faster–maturing guppies reproduces more quickly.
    B) Raise both populations without predators to see if they maintain their life history traits.
    C) Introduce cichlids into a habitat with killifish.
    D) Provide additional food to the guppies from cichlid habitats to see if they will grow to the same size as guppies from the killifish habitat.
    E) Grow both guppy populations together to see if they interbreed.

Answer: B
Topic: 36.7–Evolution Connection
Skill: Conceptual Understanding

30) Which of the following will likely decrease a population's size?
    A) improving the quality of its habitat
    B) increasing the size of its habitat
    C) practicing sustainable resource management in its habitat
    D) harvesting populations below their carrying capacity
    E) decreasing the food supply available to the population

Answer: E
Topic: 36.8
Skill: Factual Recall

31) Which of the following statements about insecticides is *true*?
    A) To control agricultural pests, pest management uses biological controls, chemicals, or cultural methods, but never a combination of these.
    B) Simply killing many individuals is often the best way to reduce the size of a pest population.
    C) Most insecticides kill the pest but not the pest's natural predators.
    D) Prey species often have a higher reproductive rate than do predators.
    E) Limiting and lowering the quality of an existing habitat usually raises the carrying capacity of a population.

Answer: D
Topic: 36.8
Skill: Conceptual Understanding

32) Which of the following statements about the human population is *true*?
    A) The human population on Earth today is more than 6.5 billion people.
    B) Human use of water has remained about the same over the last 50 years.
    C) Countries do not vary greatly in their available ecological capacity.
    D) To date, humans have not suffered from overpopulation and overconsumption.
    E) Humans living in the United States today use more than ten times their share of available ecological capacity.

Answer: A
Topic: 36.9
Skill: Factual Recall

33) A demographic tool used to predict a population's future growth is
   A) a hairline growth curve.
   B) demographic transition.
   C) age structures.
   D) maximum sustained growth.
   E) population momentum.

Answer: C
Topic: 36.9
Skill: Factual Recall

34) What is the age structure of a population?
   A) the curve that results when the likelihood of dying is plotted as a function of age
   B) the curve that results when the likelihood of being alive is plotted as a function of age
   C) the proportion of individuals in different age groups
   D) the difference in the age distribution of a population at two different points in time
   E) the structure of a population at different points on its growth curve

Answer: C
Topic: 36.9
Skill: Conceptual Understanding

35) The greatest crisis ever faced by humans is probably
   A) the ozone hole.
   B) global warming.
   C) hazardous waste disposal.
   D) air and water pollution.
   E) human population growth.

Answer: E
Topic: 36.9
Skill: Application

36) If most of the individuals of a human population are in their pre-reproductive years, you would expect the population size to _____ after 20 years.
   A) stay the same
   B) increase
   C) decrease
   D) decrease and then stabilize
   E) decrease and then decrease more sharply

Answer: B
Topic: 36.9
Skill: Application

37) Which of the following statements about human demographic trends is *true*?
   A) As women's status and education increase, they choose to have more children.
   B) After 1950, mortality rates increased rapidly in most developing countries.
   C) A human population in which women reproduce at an earlier age will experience slower population growth.
   D) About 10% of the world's population live in developing countries.
   E) The movement from high birth rates and high death rates to low birth rates and low death rates is called the demographic transition.

Answer: E
Topic: 36. 9
Skill: Factual Recall

38) The age structure diagram of a human population in a developed country like Sweden, which has a population growth rate near zero and in which neither the birth rate nor the death rate has changed much in the recent past, has the shape of
   A) an hourglass.
   B) a pyramid.
   C) a rectangle tapering near the top.
   D) a funnel.
   E) a triangle with the point at the bottom.

Answer: C
Topic: 36.10
Skill: Conceptual Understanding

39) A country whose age structure diagram has a base smaller than most of the next higher levels is experiencing
   A) a population explosion.
   B) near zero population growth.
   C) negative population growth.
   D) logistic growth.
   E) exponential growth.

Answer: C
Topic: 36.10
Skill: Application

40) During the nineteenth and early twentieth centuries, when the United States was still a developing nation, how did the introduction of public health improvements, such as sewage systems, milk pasteurization, and childhood vaccination, change the shape of the age structure diagram?
   A) All levels of the pyramid widened by an equal amount.
   B) The pyramid widened disproportionately at the base.
   C) The middle levels of the pyramid widened disproportionately.
   D) The upper levels of the pyramid widened disproportionately.
   E) The pyramid got taller as people lived to ages not previously attained.

Answer: C
Topic: 36.10
Skill: Application

41) The type of growth illustrated by the human race during the past 2,000 years is _____ growth.
    A) exponential
    B) logistic
    C) equilibrial
    D) Z-shaped
    E) linear

Answer: A
Topic: 36.11
Skill: Conceptual Understanding

42) The human population on Earth is expected to reach 9.5 billion people by
    A) 2015.
    B) 2050.
    C) 2093.
    D) 3150.
    E) 3300.

Answer: B
Topic: 36.11
Skill: Factual Recall

43) An ecological footprint
    A) is a means of determining increases in populations that lived in the past.
    B) is a means of understanding resource availability and usage.
    C) can be used to compare the needs of individuals living in the same neighborhood.
    D) measures dispersion and adaptability.
    E) will estimate population movements.

Answer: B
Topic: 36.11
Skill: Factual Recall

Art Questions

1)

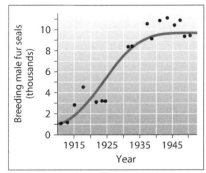

According to this graph of the population growth of fur seals, in what year did the population first reach its carrying capacity?
   A) 1915
   B) 1925
   C) 1930
   D) 1940
   E) 1950

Answer: D
Topic: 36.4
Skill: Application

2)

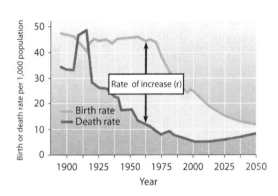

Data from Population Reference Bureau, 2000 and U. S. Census Bureau International Data Base, 2003.

According to this graph of population growth in Mexico, in what year was the rate of population increase in Mexico the greatest?
   A) 1912
   B) 1930
   C) 1965
   D) 1980
   E) 2000

Answer: C
Topic: 36.9
Skill: Application

Scenario Questions

After reading the following paragraph, answer the question(s) below.

You're a member of an influential African family that's been displaced from your home by civil war. You're trying to select a new country in which to settle to gain better economic opportunities. You know that Nigeria is a large country with rich natural resources and are considering it for your new home. You've learned some basic principles of population growth and did some research on the Internet. Among the data you found was the following diagram of the current age structure of the country.

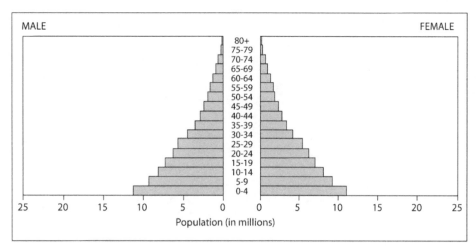

Populaion Pyramid for Nigeria, 2007

From U.S. Census Bureau International Data Base, 2007

1) The age structure data for Nigeria shows that the country has many more individuals under the age of 15 than over the age of 40. What does this imply about the future population of Nigeria?
   A) the population will probably remain stable
   B) the population will probably decrease
   C) the population will probably grow rapidly
   D) the population will probably increase, but slowly
   E) the number of older people will probably increase rapidly

Answer: C
Topic: 36.9, 36.10
Skill: Conceptual Understanding

2) Based on the age structure of the country, which of the following situations would be most likely over the next 20 years?
  A) strong economic gains stimulated by population growth
  B) an increased demand for resources based on population growth
  C) a decreased demand for medical services due to the small number of elderly citizens
  D) a decline in housing prices based on lack of demand
  E) a demographic shift to approximate zero population growth

Answer: B
Topic: 36.9, 36.10
Skill: Conceptual Understanding

Chapter 37 Communities and Ecosystems

Multiple-Choice Questions

1) A hippopotamus produces a significant amount of waste (dung) that nourishes a variety of life forms; this would not be possible if it were not for
   A) carp that scrape the skin of hippos for dead skin, parasites, and algae.
   B) an internal community of microorganisms that helps metabolize ingested plant material.
   C) the anatomy of the hippo's stomach.
   D) cichlids that clean the tail bristles of the hippo.
   E) water pears and fig trees that extract nutrients from the springwater through their roots.

Answer: B
Topic: Opening Essay
Skill: Factual Recall

2) A community is composed of
   A) potentially interacting populations of different kinds of organisms.
   B) one species of organism living in a specific environment on Earth.
   C) living organisms and their nonliving environment.
   D) several ecosystems on one continent.
   E) the factors that constitute an organism's niche.

Answer: A
Topic: 37.1
Skill: Factual Recall

3) One reason it is important to understand community ecology is
   A) to understand the life cycle of fish, such as cichlids.
   B) for identification of stomach microbes.
   C) to aid in conservation of endangered species.
   D) to provide a basis for farming protocols.
   E) to provide an enriched habitat for humans.

Answer: C
Topic: 37.1
Skill: Factual Recall

4) An owl and a hawk both eat mice. Which of these terms describes the relationship between a hawk and an owl?
   A) predation
   B) competition
   C) parasitism
   D) commensalism
   E) mutualism

Answer: B
Topic: 37.2
Skill: Factual Recall

5) When two different populations in a community benefit from their relationship with each other, the result is called
   A) predation.
   B) partnership.
   C) mutualism.
   D) herbivory.
   E) competition.

Answer: C
Topic: 37.2
Skill: Factual Recall

6) When a crocodile eats a fish, the interspecific interaction between the two could be expressed as _____ for the crocodile and _____ for the fish.
   A) − . . . −
   B) + . . . +
   C) + . . . −
   D) − . . . +
   E) − − . . . ++

Answer: C
Topic: 37.2
Skill: Application

7) Which of the following is an example of predation?
   A) a lizard's camouflage
   B) a hawk swooping down quickly to capture, kill, and eat a prairie king snake
   C) a goldfinch feeding on the seeds of a thistle plant
   D) the vivid colors of the poison–arrow frog in Costa Rica
   E) mechanical devices, such as quills in a porcupine

Answer: B
Topic: 37.2
Skill: Application

8) The sum total of a population's use of the biotic and abiotic resources of its habitat constitutes its
   A) environment.
   B) evolution.
   C) distribution.
   D) range.
   E) niche.

Answer: E
Topic: 37.3
Skill: Factual Recall

9) In an ecosystem, you would expect to find interspecific competition between
   A) males and females of a species in which both sexes occupy the same niche.
   B) populations of two species that occupy the same niche.
   C) males of a species during the breeding season.
   D) a prey species and its predator.
   E) two wasp species that mimic each other's appearance.

Answer: B
Topic: 37.3
Skill: Conceptual Understanding

10) If an overlap develops between the ranges of two closely related species, and if the species occupy the same niche in the zone of overlap, what will probably happen in the zone of overlap?
   A) A new species will arise by hybridization.
   B) Both species will coexist, provided the environment in the zone of overlap is different from that in either individual range.
   C) Both species will coexist, provided the environment in the zone of overlap is similar to that of one of the individual ranges.
   D) The species will partition the zone so that half of it is added to the range of each species and there is no overlap.
   E) One species will take over most or all of the zone of overlap.

Answer: E
Topic: 37.3
Skill: Conceptual Understanding

11) Dinoflagellates are important to coral and coral-dwelling animals because they
   A) produce energy that is used by coral animals through photosynthesis.
   B) provide shelter for the fast-growing seaweeds associated with coral.
   C) produce CO_2 and nitrogen for coral.
   D) are toxic to species that prey on reef-dwelling fish.
   E) maintain environmental conditions throughout the coral system.

Answer: A
Topic: 37.4
Skill: Factual Recall

12) A series of reciprocal adaptations in two species defines
   A) interspecific competition.
   B) niche compartmentalization.
   C) resource partitioning.
   D) coevolution.
   E) competitive exclusion.

Answer: D
Topic: 37.6–Evolution Connection
Skill: Factual Recall

13) One mechanism that prey populations evolve to avoid predation is
    A) increasing the number of offspring produced.
    B) camouflage.
    C) secretion of digestive enzymes that hydrolyze glucose.
    D) secretion of enzymes that break down toxic plant compounds.
    E) development of a short gestation period.

Answer: B
Topic: 37.6–Evolution Connection
Skill: Conceptual Understanding

14) Some herbivore–plant interactions evolved through a series of reciprocal evolutionary adaptations in both species. The process is called
    A) herbivory.
    B) coevolution.
    C) selection.
    D) trophism.
    E) diversity.

Answer: B
Topic: 37.6–Evolution Connection
Skill: Conceptual Understanding

15) Most plants have a variety of chemicals, spines, and thorns because the plants
    A) cannot run away from herbivores.   *plant eatr.*
    B) feed on the organisms that try to eat them.
    C) are camouflaged into their surroundings.
    D) are adapted to attract herbivores.
    E) are relying upon Batesian mimicry.

Answer: A
Topic: 37.6–Evolution Connection
Skill: Conceptual Understanding

16) The prokaryotes that cause tooth decay have a _____ relationship with humans.
    A) parasitic
    B) commensalistic
    C) mutualistic
    D) competitive
    E) ammensalistic

Answer: A
Topic: 37.7
Skill: Application

17) In addition to environmental factors, community composition of plants can be severely compromised by
    A) lack of soil nitrogen.
    B) parasites and pathogens.
    C) introduction of chestnut trees.
    D) non–native birds.
    E) rapid coevolution.

Answer: B
Topic: 37.7
Skill: Conceptual Understanding

18) Within an ecosystem, a tree is a
    A) secondary consumer.
    B) detritivore.
    C) tertiary consumer.
    D) primary consumer.
    E) producer.

Answer: E
Topic: 37.8
Skill: Factual Recall

19) On Earth, most organic molecules are produced by
    A) photorespiration.
    B) photosynthesis.
    C) glycolysis.
    D) hydrolysis.
    E) cellular respiration.

Answer: B
Topic: 37.8
Skill: Factual Recall

20) In a hypothetical food chain consisting of grass, grasshoppers, sparrows, and hawks, the grasshoppers are
    A) primary consumers.
    B) primary producers.
    C) secondary consumers.
    D) secondary producers.
    E) detritivores.

Answer: A
Topic: 37.8
Skill: Application

21) A hypothetical community on a barren mid-Atlantic island consists of two fish-eating seabirds (the booby and the noddy), the fungi and microorganisms that live on the birds' dung, a tick that feeds on these two birds, a cactus, a moth that feeds on cast-off feathers, a beetle that lives on dung organisms, and spiders that eat the other arthropods. There are no other plants and no lichens. Which of the following choices *incorrectly* pairs a member of this assemblage with its position in the trophic structure?
    A) spiders, secondary consumer
    B) booby and noddy birds, primary consumers
    C) fungi, detritivores
    D) moths, detritivores
    E) cactus, producer

Answer: B
Topic: 37.8
Skill: Application

22) In a food chain consisting of phytoplankton → zooplankton → fish → fishermen, the fishermen are
   A) primary consumers.
   B) secondary consumers.
   C) tertiary consumers.
   D) primary producers.
   E) secondary producers.

Answer: C
Topic: 37.8
Skill: Application

23) The primary decomposers of a community are called
   A) primary consumers.
   B) detritivores.
   C) primary producers.
   D) protozoa.
   E) herbivores.

Answer: B
Topic: 37.8
Skill: Factual Recall

24) In a certain ecosystem, field mice are preyed on by snakes and hawks. The entry of wild dogs into the system adds another predator of the mice. Of the following, the most likely short–term result of this addition is
   A) an increase in snake population.
   B) a tendency for hawks to prey on the dogs.
   C) extinction of the hawks.
   D) a reduction in numbers of mice.
   E) migration of the hawks to another ecosystem.

Answer: D
Topic: 37.8
Skill: Application

25) Which of the following statements regarding food webs is *true*?
   A) A consumer may eat only one type of producer.
   B) Detritivores consume dead organic matter from a specific trophic level.
   C) Several species of primary consumers may feed on the same species of producer.
   D) Nutrient transfer moves from producer to consumer and back.
   E) A hawk at the top of the food web is only a quaternary producer.

Answer: C
Topic: 37.9
Skill: Conceptual Understanding

26) The number of species in a community is called the
    A) species diversity.
    B) community.
    C) species richness.
    D) species population.
    E) species index.

Answer: C
Topic: 37.10
Skill: Factual Recall

27) We expect that a keystone species that is a predator will
    A) maintain the species diversity in a community.
    B) harvest prey species down to extinction.
    C) help many of its prey reproduce.
    D) be a parasite.
    E) reduce the diversity of the community.

Answer: A
Topic: 37.11
Skill: Conceptual Understanding

28) During ecological succession, the species composition of a plant community generally
    A) changes from a diverse community in which many plants are common to one in which a few species are numerically dominant.
    B) simplifies until most of the plants originally present have disappeared.
    C) remains stable as long as major environmental factors (climate, human interference) remain constant.
    D) changes gradually because each species responds differently to the changing environment.
    E) changes until climax forest is established and a single species remains.

Answer: D
Topic: 37.12
Skill: Conceptual Understanding

29) When a New England farm is abandoned, its formerly plowed fields first become weedy meadows, then shrubby areas, and finally forest. This sequence of plant communities is an example of
    A) evolution.
    B) a phylogenetic trend.
    C) a trophic chain.
    D) secondary succession.
    E) genetic drift.

Answer: D
Topic: 37.12
Skill: Application

30) Which of the following statements about the role of fire in ecosystems is *true*?
   A) Forest fires did not occur in the times before human settlement.
   B) Fires decrease the number of animal communities in ecosystems by destroying habitat.
   C) Forest fires are extremely destructive to ecosystems and should be put out as quickly as possible.
   D) Fire is essential to maintaining some ecosystems.
   E) Fire is not an important factor in developing and maintaining ecosystems.

Answer: D
Topic: 37.12
Skill: Conceptual Understanding

31) Non-native species that are introduced in new environments, spread far beyond the original point of introduction, and cause damage are called
   A) destructive species.
   B) enemy species.
   C) invasive species.
   D) predatory species.
   E) proprietary species.

Answer: C
Topic: 37.13
Skill: Factual Recall

32) Biological control is defined as
   A) the use of chemicals, such as pesticides, to control pests.
   B) the intentional release of a natural enemy of a pest population.
   C) the exploitation of coevolutionary principles to produce pesticides.
   D) a mechanism for encouraging growth of an invasive plant or animal.
   E) an intentional attempt to increase the numbers of specific prey populations.

Answer: B
Topic: 37.13
Skill: Factual Recall

33) The flow of _____ into ecosystems occurs in one direction only, while _____ are recycled within the ecosystem itself.
   A) minerals . . . energy compounds
   B) genetic information . . . genotypes
   C) organic compounds . . . minerals
   D) energy . . . chemicals
   E) food . . . energy

Answer: D
Topic: 37.14
Skill: Factual Recall

34) Which of the following processes does *not* occur in ecosystems?
   A) Energy flows through the system.
   B) Carbon is cycled between biotic and abiotic forms.
   C) Nitrogen is cycled between biotic and abiotic forms.
   D) Producers convert light energy to chemical energy.
   E) The energy source that powers the system is used by consumers to make organic compounds.

Answer: E
Topic: 37.14
Skill: Conceptual Understanding

35) For a given area and time period, the amount of solar energy converted to chemical energy is called
   A) primary succession.
   B) secondary succession.
   C) primary production.
   D) secondary production.
   E) primary photosynthesis.

Answer: C
Topic: 37.15
Skill: Factual Recall

36) A biology teacher takes fish, algae, pond weed, invertebrates, and bottom muck from a local pond and establishes them in an aquarium. When the system is stable, the teacher seals it into a large, airtight glass box and leaves the box in a sunny location. After three months, the organisms in the aquarium appear alive and healthy. Which of the following statements about the experiment is *true*?
   A) No energy has entered or left the glass box during the three months.
   B) Some of the energy in the system has moved from one organism to another during the three months.
   C) Some oxygen from water molecules has become part of organic molecules.
   D) The air in the glass box contains no carbon dioxide.
   E) During the three months, the biomass of animal life was greater than the biomass of plant life.

Answer: B
Topic: 37.15
Skill: Conceptual Understanding

37) In an average ecosystem, about how much energy is present in the organisms at a given trophic level compared to the organisms at the next higher trophic level?
   A) a tenth as much
   B) half as much
   C) twice as much
   D) ten times as much
   E) the amounts vary, depending on trophic level

Answer: D
Topic: 37.16
Skill: Factual Recall

38) If there are 1,000 metric tons of producers in an ecosystem, about how much of the energy in those producers will be available to secondary consumers in this ecosystem?
   A) 100%
   B) 50%
   C) about 10%
   D) about 1%
   E) about 0.1%

Answer: D
Topic: 37.16
Skill: Application

39) You want to do all that you can to safeguard the environment by preserving energy. One simple thing that you can do is to eat a diet consisting only of organisms that are
   A) producers.
   B) primary consumers.
   C) secondary consumers.
   D) tertiary consumers.
   E) a mix of producers and consumers.

Answer: A
Topic: 37.17
Skill: Application

40) Which of the following substances is cycled between organic matter and abiotic reservoirs?
   A) fat
   B) carbon
   C) protein
   D) enzymes
   E) nucleic acid

Answer: B
Topic: 37.18
Skill: Factual Recall

41) Given that CO_2 is produced by respiration, why does the amount of CO_2 in the atmosphere remain relatively constant? (When answering this question, exclude the impact of human activities on atmospheric CO_2.)
   A) CO_2 is converted in photosynthesis to carbohydrates.
   B) CO_2 is split apart during photosynthesis.
   C) CO_2 mostly forms carbonate rocks.
   D) CO_2 is trapped in dead organisms' bodies.
   E) CO_2 is a buffer.

Answer: A
Topic: 37.19
Skill: Conceptual Understanding

42) Carbon mainly cycles between the biotic and abiotic worlds through the processes of
    A) respiration and transpiration.
    B) transpiration and photosynthesis.
    C) evaporation and photosynthesis.
    D) respiration and photosynthesis.
    E) respiration and evaporation.

Answer: D
Topic: 37.19
Skill: Conceptual Understanding

43) Which of the following ecological problems might result from fertilizing a golf course with phosphorus–rich fertilizer?
    A) poisoning of the grass caused by excess phosphorus
    B) weed growth promoted by excess phosphorus
    C) heavy growth of algae and cyanobacteria in lakes and rivers caused by phosphorus runoff
    D) accumulation of toxic levels of phosphorus in animals in the vicinity, especially those higher on the food chain
    E) a slowdown in the weathering of rock that releases phosphates into the soil under natural conditions

Answer: C
Topic: 37.20
Skill: Conceptual Understanding

44) Which of the following statements about the phosphorus cycle is *true*?
    A) Consumers obtain phosphorus in organic form from meats.
    B) Phosphorus has its main abiotic reservoir in water.
    C) Plants release dissolved phosphorus ions in the soil.
    D) Phosphorus that drains from soils into the sea becomes part of new rock and will cycle back into living organisms.
    E) Sewage is a major source of phosphates.

Answer: E
Topic: 37.20
Skill: Factual Recall

45) Which of the following statements about the nitrogen cycle is *true*?
    A) The nitrogen cycle requires different types of bacteria.
    B) Nitrogen gas is converted to nitrates in plant leaves.
    C) Nitrogen cannot be cycled through living organisms.
    D) When plants and animals die, nitrogen is removed from the nitrogen cycle.
    E) Nitrogen is a component of all fats.

Answer: A
Topic: 37.21
Skill: Factual Recall

46) Which of the following represents a step in the nitrogen cycle?
    A) atmospheric nitrogen converted to nitrates
    B) conversion of nitrates to atmospheric nitrogen in the presence of oxygen
    C) nitrites binding to soil particles
    D) nitrogen–fixing bacteria convert atmospheric nitrogen to ammonia
    E) ammonium converted to atmospheric nitrogen

Answer: D
Topic: 37.21
Skill: Factual Recall

47) Denitrifying bacteria convert _____ to _____.
    A) ammonium . . . nitrogen gas
    B) nitrates . . . nitrogen gas
    C) nitrogen gas . . . nitrates
    D) nitrogen gas . . . ammonium
    E) nitrogen gas . . . nitrites

Answer: B
Topic: 37.21
Skill: Factual Recall

48) In experimental studies conducted at the Hubbard Brook Experimental Forest, it was found that
    A) water runoff stayed about the same in deforested areas.
    B) nitrogen loss was about double in deforested areas.
    C) most nutrients flowed into and then out of nondisturbed forests.
    D) water runoff increased in the deforested areas.
    E) water runoff decreased in the deforested areas.

Answer: D
Topic: 37.22
Skill: Factual Recall

49) It appears that forest plant growth at Hubbard Brook halted because of acid rain and snow that caused
    A) a warming of the ecosystem.
    B) a shortage of calcium in the soil.
    C) the addition of sulfur to the soil.
    D) too much soil erosion.
    E) a recent fire.

Answer: B
Topic: 37.22
Skill: Conceptual Understanding

50) Eutrophication of a lake could occur if
    A) phosphate–rich detergents were dumped into the lake.
    B) fertilizers were applied in an insoluble form.
    C) sewage was treated before being dumped into the lake.
    D) runoff from overfertilized lawns was prevented from reaching the lake.
    E) fish were removed.

Answer: A
Topic: 37.23
Skill: Factual Recall

Art Questions

1)

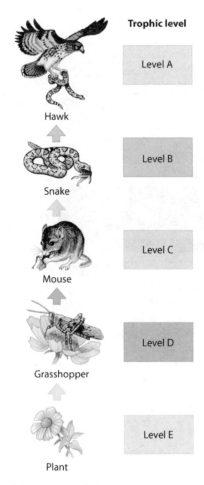

Trophic level

Level A

Hawk

Level B

Snake

Level C

Mouse

Level D

Grasshopper

Level E

Plant

A terrestrial food chain

Which trophic level in this food chain represents the producer?
   A) trophic level A
   B) trophic level B
   C) trophic level C
   D) trophic level D
   E) trophic level E

Answer: E
Topic: 37.8
Skill: Application

2)

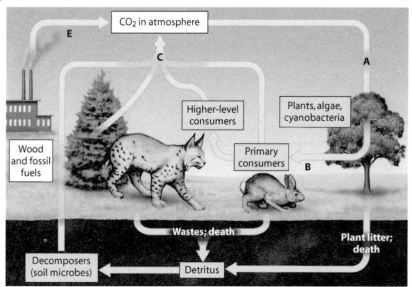

Which arrow shows CO_2 released as a product of cellular respiration?

   A) arrow A
   B) arrow B
   C) arrow C
   D) arrow D
   E) arrow E

Answer: C
Topic: 37.19
Skill: Application

3)

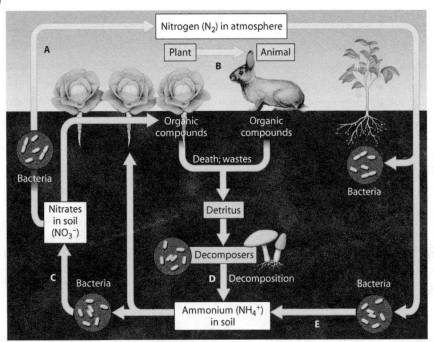

Which arrow shows nitrogen fixation?
  A) arrow A
  B) arrow B
  C) arrow C
  D) arrow D
  E) arrow E

Answer: E
Topic: 37.21
Skill: Application

Scenario Questions

After reading the following paragraph, answer the question(s) below.

Biosphere II is a huge dome-covered self-contained structure located outside Tucson, Arizona. Biosphere II was built to try to duplicate Earth's biosphere and ecosystems in miniature and to use the information gained from the experiment to help design similar habitats on the Moon and Mars. The habitat contained small versions of many of Earth's ecosystems, including an ocean with a coral reef, mangrove wetlands, a grassland, a desert, an agricultural system, and a human habitat. Eight men and women were sealed inside the habitat for a proposed two-year stay. The air, water, and food for the "biospherians" all came from inside the sealed habitat, and their only contact with the outside was through computers and telephones.

Before the two years were up, however, the experiment failed. Supplemental oxygen was pumped into the facility and food supplies were provided through the airlocks. What caused the failure of the experiment? It was traced to nutrient pollution. The soil in some of the biosphere ecosystems was unusually rich in nutrients. These excess nutrients caused a huge population explosion in decomposer bacteria, which led to oxygen depletion.

1) How could a population explosion of bacteria lead to oxygen depletion?
    A) The excess consumers used the oxygen for cell respiration.
    B) The excess producers used the oxygen to complete photosynthesis.
    C) The excess decomposers removed all the nutrients from the habitat.
    D) The excess decomposers prevented plants from performing photosynthesis.
    E) The excess bacteria caused sickness in the human and animal residents.

Answer: A
Topic: 37.8, 37.14, 37.19, 37.21, 37.23
Skill: Conceptual Understanding

2) To stabilize the environment in the habitat and enable it to become self-sufficient again, it would be helpful to
    A) add nitrates and phosphates to the terrestrial and aquatic ecosystems.
    B) add producers to absorb excess carbon dioxide and produce oxygen.
    C) add consumers to absorb carbon dioxide and produce oxygen.
    D) add decomposers to recycle nutrients in the soil and water.
    E) add carbon dioxide to restart the carbon cycle.

Answer: B
Topic: 37.8, 37.14, 37.21, 37.23
Skill: Conceptual Understanding

Chapter 38 Conservation Biology

Multiple-Choice Questions

1) The primary goal of conservation biology is to
   A) estimate the total number of species that exist.
   B) catalogue species.
   C) maximize the land set aside for wildlife.
   D) integrate human culture back into nature.
   E) counter the loss of biodiversity.

   Answer: E
   Topic: Opening Essay
   Skill: Factual Recall

2) Approximately _____ living species have been named and described.
   A) 750,000
   B) 80 million
   C) 30 million
   D) 1.8 million
   E) 10 million

   Answer: D
   Topic: 38.1
   Skill: Factual Recall

3) The current rate of extinction may be as much as _____ times higher than at any other time in the past 100,000 years.
   A) 10
   B) 100
   C) 1,000
   D) 10,000
   E) 5,000,000

   Answer: C
   Topic: 38.1
   Skill: Factual Recall

4) Biodiversity considers
   A) the genetic diversity within and between populations of a species.
   B) the fate of water in the ecosystem.
   C) commensal relationships between species.
   D) mutualistic associations between fungi and algae.
   E) the relationships of individuals to a food chain.

   Answer: A
   Topic: 38.1
   Skill: Factual Recall

5) Approximately _____ of the prescriptions dispensed by U.S. pharmacies contain substances derived from plants.
    A) 10%
    B) 25%
    C) 30%
    D) 50%
    E) 75%

Answer: B
Topic: 38.1
Skill: Factual Recall

6) In the 2,000 years that humans have lived on Madagascar, the island has lost approximately _____ of its native species.
    A) 10%
    B) 25%
    C) 30%
    D) 50%
    E) 75%

Answer: D
Topic: 38.1
Skill: Factual Recall

7) The U.S. Endangered Species Act oversees
    A) natural waterways in the United States.
    B) threatened species.
    C) mammals, but not invertebrates, that are losing their range.
    D) approximately 20% of endangered species.
    E) the health of off–shore species.

Answer: B
Topic: 38.2
Skill: Factual Recall

8) Habitat destruction by humans has been implicated in the decline of _____ of the species in modern history.
    A) 17%
    B) 22%
    C) 49%
    D) 73%
    E) 87%

Answer: D
Topic: 38.3
Skill: Factual Recall

9) Currently, the single greatest threat to biodiversity is
   A) global warming.
   B) habitat destruction due to humans.
   C) the introduction of exotic species.
   D) overpopulation.
   E) overexploitation of populations for food.

Answer: B
Topic: 38.3
Skill: Factual Recall

10) You arrive back in the United States after having visited a foreign country located on another continent. The customs agent stops the person in front of you and confiscates the fruit basket this person is bringing home. Being the knowledgeable person you are, you calmly explain to your enraged fellow traveler that the reason for the detainment is that the fruit basket may be
   A) carrying endangered fruit.
   B) carrying an exotic species that could damage North American ecosystems.
   C) contaminated with CFCs that will damage the ozone layer above North America.
   D) contaminated with sufficient DDT to cause serious harm to anyone who eats the fruit.
   E) made of materials that are toxic to humans.

Answer: B
Topic: 38.3
Skill: Application

11) The three greatest current threats to biodiversity, in order starting with the greatest, are
   A) habitat destruction, overexploitation, and the introduction of invasive species.
   B) habitat destruction, the introduction of invasive species, and overexploitation.
   C) overexploitation, habitat destruction, and the introduction of invasive species.
   D) the introduction of invasive species, habitat destruction, and overexploitation.
   E) the introduction of invasive species, overexploitation, and habitat destruction.

Answer: B
Topic: 38.3
Skill: Factual Recall

12) Which of the following is an introduced species in the United States?
   A) African green monkey
   B) mallard duck
   C) fire ants
   D) elephant
   E) carrier pigeon

Answer: C
Topic: 38.3
Skill: Conceptual Understanding

13) To decrease pollution from sulfur, your local power plant built very tall smokestacks. The ultimate consequence of this would most likely be
A) the reaction of the sulfur with ozone, resulting in a breakdown of the ozone.
B) biological magnification.
C) to dilute the sulfur pollutants in the atmosphere and thus reduce their effects on the environment.
D) to create an environmental problem at a distance from the power plant.
E) a decrease in the pH of local lakes.

Answer: D
Topic: 38.4
Skill: Application

14) Chlorofluorocarbons (CFCs)
A) were once used as pesticides.
B) were once used as an energy source.
C) contribute to acid precipitation.
D) accumulate in the tissues of organisms.
E) deplete the ozone layer.

Answer: E
Topic: 38.4
Skill: Conceptual Understanding

15) Which of the following is a likely consequence of the thinning of the ozone layer?
A) increases in lethal and nonlethal skin cancer
B) increases in escape of heat from Earth
C) global warming
D) harm to the oceans
E) elimination of flying insects

Answer: A
Topic: 38.4
Skill: Factual Recall

16) You spray your lawn with a pesticide, such that the concentration of the pesticide in the tissues of the grass on your lawn is 10^{-6} parts per million (ppm). Grasshoppers eat the grass and are in turn eaten by rats, which are then eaten by owls. Keeping in mind that roughly 10% of the energy at a trophic level is transferred to the next highest trophic level, what do you estimate to be the concentration of the pesticide in the tissues of the owls?
A) 10^{-2} ppm
B) 10^{-3} ppm
C) 10^{-4} ppm
D) 10^{-5} ppm
E) 10^{-6} ppm

Answer: B
Topic: 38.4
Skill: Application

17) Large coastal dead zones depleted of oxygen are primarily caused by
    A) CFCs released into the environment.
    B) DDT released into the environment.
    C) PCBs released into the environment.
    D) nutrient pollution.
    E) acid precipitation.

Answer: D
Topic: 38.4
Skill: Factual Recall

18) The increase in the concentration of a substance in the tissues of organisms as it is passed up a food chain is called
    A) concentration of toxins.
    B) biological magnification.
    C) maximization.
    D) incrementalization.
    E) predatory accumulation.

Answer: B
Topic: 38.4
Skill: Factual Recall

19) Carbon dioxide traps heat and warms the atmosphere. This is known as the _____ effect.
    A) warming
    B) summer
    C) carbon
    D) carbon dioxide
    E) greenhouse

Answer: E
Topic: 38.5
Skill: Conceptual Understanding

20) Global warming is the result of
    A) rises in ocean levels.
    B) species extinction.
    C) rising concentration of greenhouse gases.
    D) increasing occurrence of heat waves.
    E) pollution.

Answer: C
Topic: 38.5
Skill: Factual Recall

21) Average global temperature has risen _____ over the past 100 years.
    A) 1°F
    B) 10°C
    C) 100°F
    D) 10°F
    E) 0.8°C

Answer: E
Topic: 38.5
Skill: Factual Recall

22) The increase in global temperature resulting from the greenhouse effect is primarily due to
    A) CO_2 allowing more solar radiation to penetrate to the Earth's surface.
    B) CFCs slowing the escape of heat from Earth.
    C) the loss of ozone that trapped cooling UV radiation in the atmosphere.
    D) CO_2 slowing the escape of heat from Earth.
    E) CO_2 slowing the escape of UV radiation from Earth.

Answer: D
Topic: 38.5
Skill: Conceptual Understanding

23) CO_2 flooding into the atmosphere is absorbed by _____ and converted into biomass.
    A) the ozone layer
    B) other atmosphere gases
    C) photosynthetic organisms
    D) large land masses
    E) the sun

Answer: C
Topic: 38.6
Skill: Factual Recall

24) An important change in populations and species in response to climate change is
    A) coat color.
    B) distribution.
    C) metabolism.
    D) genetic makeup.
    E) mode of reproduction.

Answer: B
Topic: 38.7
Skill: Factual Recall

25) An organism's responses to climate change that result in phenotypic variation is called
    A) genetic drift.
    B) mutation.
    C) alteration of generation.
    D) phenotypic plasticity.
    E) population fragmentation.

Answer: D
Topic: 38.8–Evolution Connection
Skill: Factual Recall

26) Some populations may avoid extinction as the climate changes, especially those with high genetic variability and short life spans, through
    A) genetic shift.
    B) genetic modification.
    C) feedback inhibition.
    D) distribution of populations.
    E) evolutionary adaptation.

Answer: E
Topic: 38.8–Evolution Connection
Skill: Factual Recall

27) Fragmented populations
    A) result from the introduction of endemic species.
    B) are composed of endemic species.
    C) are at little risk of extinction.
    D) are likely to exhibit low levels of genetic diversity.
    E) are more vulnerable to the greenhouse effect than are populations that are not fragmented.

Answer: D
Topic: 38.9
Skill: Conceptual Understanding

28) Once population size is reduced by habitat fragmentation, the key factor driving the species toward extinction is
    A) loss of genetic variation.
    B) too many animals migrating away from small populations.
    C) loss of food.
    D) increased risk of predation.
    E) too many animals migrating between populations.

Answer: A
Topic: 38.9
Skill: Factual Recall

29) A proactive conservation strategy
    A) is no longer considered valid, as populations are already too small.
    B) seeks to merge small populations into larger populations.
    C) seeks to detect, diagnose, and halt population declines.
    D) tries to boost declining populations through captive breeding.
    E) uses bioengineering to increase genetic diversity in populations.

Answer: C
Topic: 38.9
Skill: Factual Recall

30) The red-cockaded woodpecker is dependent upon _____ for maintenance of its source habitat.
   A) thick vegetation
   B) fire
   C) open water
   D) floods
   E) corn snakes

Answer: B
Topic: 38.9
Skill: Factual Recall

31) Which of the following improved the population of red-cockaded woodpeckers?
   A) providing food at bird feeders
   B) introducing exotic species
   C) allowing controlled fires to reduce forest undergrowth
   D) planting more shortleaf pines
   E) relocating food plots

Answer: C
Topic: 38.9
Skill: Factual Recall

32) An assemblage of interacting ecosystems is a
   A) biome.
   B) landscape.
   C) PVA.
   D) gap.
   E) hot spot.

Answer: B
Topic: 38.10
Skill: Factual Recall

33) Movement corridors
   A) increase inbreeding.
   B) reduce dispersal.
   C) can be harmful because they allow for the spread of disease.
   D) can be harmful because they allow for gene flow.
   E) generally increase the mutation rate of connected populations.

Answer: C
Topic: 38.10
Skill: Factual Recall

34) Which of the following statements about movement corridors is *true*?
   A) Movement corridors can connect otherwise isolated habitat patches.
   B) Movement corridors are most important to humans.
   C) Movement corridors can promote inbreeding in declining populations.
   D) Movement corridors are detrimental to species that migrate between habitats seasonally.
   E) Movement corridors can prevent the spread of disease.

Answer: A
Topic: 38.10
Skill: Factual Recall

35) Habitat fragmentation
  A) results from natural disasters.
  B) favors animals that prefer large, open ranges.
  C) often results from human activities.
  D) results in a significant increase in diversity.
  E) favors parasites.

Answer: C
Topic: 38.10
Skill: Conceptual Understanding

36) Small areas that exhibit exceptionally high species diversity are referred to as
  A) biologically magnified.
  B) endemic environments.
  C) biodiverse environments.
  D) biodiversity hot spots.
  E) exotic hot spots.

Answer: D
Topic: 38.11
Skill: Factual Recall

37) Species found in only one place on Earth are called _____ species.
  A) hot spot
  B) native
  C) exotic
  D) keystone
  E) endemic

Answer: E
Topic: 38.11
Skill: Factual Recall

38) Most biodiversity hot spots are found in _____ regions.
  A) western
  B) tropical
  C) temperate
  D) tundra
  E) taiga

Answer: B
Topic: 38.11
Skill: Application

39) About one-third of all animal and plant species are concentrated on _____ of Earth's land.
  A) 50%
  B) 20%
  C) 10%
  D) 5%
  E) 1.5%

Answer: E
Topic: 38.11
Skill: Factual Recall

40) The greatest challenge facing the zoned reserve systems of Costa Rica is
    A) high predation by jaguars.
    B) forest fires.
    C) soil erosion.
    D) poaching and illegal mining.
    E) the growing human population.

Answer: E
Topic: 38.12
Skill: Conceptual Understanding

41) Which of the following statements about zoned reserves is *false*?
    A) Costa Rica is a world leader in establishing zoned reserves.
    B) An extensive region of land that includes one or more areas undisturbed by humans is called a zoned reserve.
    C) Few, if any, ecosystems remain undisturbed by humans.
    D) The areas surrounding a zoned reserve are not to be used to support human populations.
    E) Costa Rica hopes to maintain at least 80% of its native species by using zoned reserves.

Answer: D
Topic: 38.12
Skill: Factual Recall

42) The introduction of wolves into Yellowstone National Park in 1991 resulted in
    A) nearly 20 human deaths.
    B) a general decline in overall habitat as death spread like wildfire.
    C) ecological changes involving about 25 species.
    D) the migration of most of these wolves out of the park and back to Canada.
    E) the death of all of the wolves, likely due to an insufficient amount of available prey.

Answer: C
Topic: 38.13
Skill: Conceptual Understanding

43) The Yukon to Yellowstone Initiative is a plan to
    A) connect all of the national parks in the western United States.
    B) connect all of the national parks in the United States.
    C) connect all of the national parks in the United States to the provincial parks in Canada.
    D) connect parks in the United States and Canada with protected corridors where wildlife can travel safely.
    E) create a giant, fenced, private land area between the national parks in the United States to create a protected zone for wildlife.

Answer: D
Topic: 38.13
Skill: Conceptual Understanding

44) If wolves were now removed from Yellowstone National Park, we would expect that
   A) elk populations would increase.
   B) deer populations would decrease.
   C) insect diversity would increase.
   D) the vegetation would remain unchanged.
   E) vegetation would increase, providing shelter for smaller animals.

Answer: A
Topic: 38.13
Skill: Application

45) The aspect of conservation ecology concerned with returning degraded ecosystems (as nearly as possible) to their predegraded state is
   A) ecosystem augmentation ecology.
   B) bioremediation.
   C) sustainable development.
   D) restoration ecology.
   E) landscape ecology.

Answer: D
Topic: 38.14
Skill: Factual Recall

46) Using living organisms to clean up polluted ecosystems is known as
   A) biological demagnification.
   B) PVA.
   C) bioremediation.
   D) landscaping.
   E) augmentation.

Answer: C
Topic: 38.14
Skill: Factual Recall

47) The Kissimmee River Project is an
   A) excellent example of large–scale bioremediation to clean up a horrible mercury spill.
   B) excellent example of a dam that has interrupted the breeding of salmon and other species.
   C) attempt to restore the natural wetlands associated with the Kissimmee River.
   D) effort to join two previously unconnected lakes to permit better drainage.
   E) effort to provide loggers and miners with better access to natural resources in forests of Puerto Rico.

Answer: C
Topic: 38.14
Skill: Conceptual Understanding

48) The Kissimmee River Project is intended to
    A) drain natural wetlands into the central Florida region.
    B) increase biodiversity of the region.
    C) restrict ecotourism and other recreational usage in the impacted region.
    D) route migrating birds down the Atlantic coast.
    E) provide areas for homes and businesses.

Answer: B
Topic: 38.14
Skill: Conceptual Understanding

49) Sustainable development
    A) will require making difficult decisions regarding travel to other planets.
    B) will require many people to contribute financially.
    C) will speed up evolution.
    D) will require global, multinational cooperation.
    E) cannot be achieved.

Answer: D
Topic: 38.15
Skill: Conceptual Understanding

Art Questions

1)

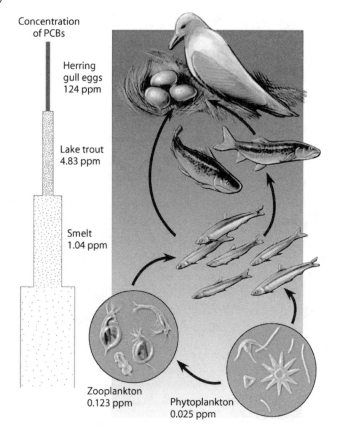

Concentration of PCBs

Herring gull eggs 124 ppm

Lake trout 4.83 ppm

Smelt 1.04 ppm

Zooplankton 0.123 ppm

Phytoplankton 0.025 ppm

According to this figure, which organisms have the highest concentration of PCBs, and why?
A) phytoplankton, because they are at the bottom of the food chain
B) phytoplankton, because they are at the top of the food chain
C) herring gulls, because they are at the bottom of the food chain
D) herring gulls, because they are at the top of the food chain
E) smelt, because they are in the middle of the food chain

Answer: D
Topic: 38.4
Skill: Application

2)

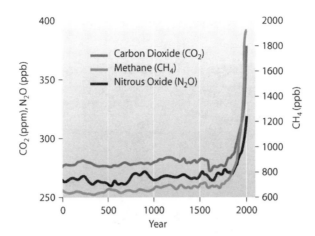

Graph from IPCC 2007. In *Climate change 2007: The physical science basis.* Contribution of Working Group 1 to the Fourth Assessment Report of the Intergovermental Panel on Climate Change. S. Solomon et al. (eds.) Cambridge University Press, Cambridge, UK and New York, NY, FAQ 2.1, fig. 1. Used with permissio

According to this graph of changes in Earth's atmosphere, which of the following took place between 1800 and 2000?
   A) Nitrous oxide levels increased from 270 ppb to 390 ppb.
   B) Nitrous oxide levels increased from 800 ppb to over 1,200 ppb.
   C) Carbon dioxide levels increased from 950 ppb to 1,800 ppb.
   D) Carbon dioxide levels increased from 290 ppm to 380 ppm.
   E) Methane levels increased from 800 ppm to almost 2,000 ppm.

Answer: D
Topic: 38.6
Skill: Application

Scenario Questions

After reading the following paragraph, answer the question(s) below.

Introduced species are a problem all over the world, and there are many examples in the United States. Several years ago, a fisherman caught a northern snakehead fish in a pond in Crofton, Maryland (a suburb of Washington, DC). Snakeheads are a favorite food of immigrants from China, and live fish can frequently be found in Asian markets. It's suspected that the fish in the Crofton pond were purchased locally and then intentionally released.

Snakeheads are top predators, and 90% of the northern snakeheads' diet consists of other fishes. The northern snakehead can breathe out of water and travel short distances (about 100 feet) across land. They also breed rapidly. Females can lay more than 100,000 eggs per year. Juveniles have also been identified in the Potomac River and other rivers in Pennsylvania.

1) When snakeheads enter aquatic ecosystems, biodiversity in these ecosystems would most likely
   A) increase, since another species has been added to the environment.
   B) decrease, since the snakehead will prey on native species.
   C) remain the same, since local species will prey on the snakeheads and remove them.
   D) increase, because they will crossbreed with other types of fish, producing new species.
   E) remain the same, because the snakeheads will merge without problems into established communities.

Answer: B
Topic: 38.1, 38.3
Skill: Conceptual Understanding

2) Based on the characteristics of the snakehead described above, which of the following is most likely to be a productive strategy to reduce the spread of this species?
   A) fencing the river banks to prevent the snakeheads from "walking" to other bodies of water
   B) extending the fishing season for prey fishes
   C) introducing a natural predator to feed on juvenile snakeheads
   D) introducing a fungus that prevents fish eggs from hatching
   E) introducing algae and photosynthetic bacteria to reduce nutrient levels in the water

Answer: C
Topic: 38.3
Skill: Application